BRAINQUAKE

In the Grip of Epilepsy

Amy S. Morris

Copyright © 2003 by Amy S. Morris.
Library of Congress Number: 2002093934
ISBN: Hardcover 1-4010-7145-7
Softcover 1-4010-7144-9

All rights reserved. No part of this book may be reproduced or transmitted in any form or by any means, electronic or mechanical, including photocopying, recording, or by any information storage and retrieval system, without permission in writing from the copyright owner.

This book was printed in the United States of America.

To order additional copies of this book, contact:
Xlibris Corporation
1-888-795-4274
www.Xlibris.com
Orders@Xlibris.com

16232

Contents

Prologue 8

1 The Grip 13
(Thanksgiving, 1992) My first *gran mal* seizure and the history of earlier warnings.

2 The Label 30
(Dec '92-Jan '93) The official diagnosis and its immediate consequences. The directly related aspects of my contract job. Issue of public knowledge. Protection of privacy of diagnosis.

3 The Search for Control 40
(Jan '93-Jan 17 '94) My partner's immediate abandonment. The loss of driver's license. Serious depression. Dangerous side-effects. Job-related travel to Germany. Plunging white blood cell count: bone-marrow biopsy. New Year's Eve: cardiac infarction.

4 More Dominos 74
(Jan '94-July '95) Loma Prieta earthquake: forced move. Cardiology. Contract job promotion. Medication changes and serious side-effects. Effects on my job. Travel to Italy. Horrible depression. Began to consider brain surgery. Spoke of suicide.

5 Catch-22 111
(July '95-Jan 1 '98) Told boss—his personal support. Promotion. Week-long in-patient EEG. Job travel to Rome.

Considered surgery. Dilemma: requisite six weeks absence and several months recovery from surgery (in addition to costs) versus performance of contract job projects in support of it becoming permanent. Decision for status quo. Mother's health problems. Continued side-effects—changes in medications.

6 Hitting the Wall 165
(Jan 1 '98-Sept 2 '98) Mother's health deteriorates. Contract job *not* made permanent—terminated after six years of promotions. Insurance will end. Decision for surgery. Pre-operative in-patient EEG. Mother's death.

7 Into the Storm 206
(Sept 2 '98-Nov 3 '98) Grief. Decision to go on. Emotional numbness as defense.

8 Brain Surgery 238
(Nov 3 '98) Asleep-Awake-Asleep brain surgery. Map *three* spoken languages—only 3-language surgery done at UCLA so far. 14 hrs. total. Physical recovery.

9 The Aftermath 274
(Nov '98-May '99) End of job. Insurance paperwork blizzard. Public "discovery." Physical recovery and resurfacing grief.

10 The View from 14,000 Feet 307
(Jun '99-Oct '99) To Colorado to sell my parents former home. Memories of mother. Mountain climbing. Decision to write book. The "larger view."

11 The View from Sea Level 324
(Nov '99) Return home. The Big Picture. My insurance mess. My drug wars. My "third choice."

12 On the Beach 351
(Nov '99) Emotional "recovery." Language "recovery." Depression.

13 The First Draft 370
   (Dec '99 . . . .) The original ending. Return of the seizures. New medication—new side-effects. Emotional morass: How to finish this book?

Resources 383
   My medical reference source. Sources for the layperson. Other helpful information.

I thank:

My father, who has helped me: all my life, with epilepsy and its consequences—and with this book. He showed me how hard it is for a parent to watch his child suffer.

My friends, who demonstrate the deep love that some can give no matter what pain you suffer or, worse yet, you cause.

My brothers, who support me and my parents—both endeavors are priceless.

Dr. Antonio Delgado-Escueta. He keeps me on the cutting edge—literally—of treatment for epilepsy.

My mother, whose awesome, fearless, loving kindness never wavered.

She gave her family her all.

On a seismograph, this is what an earthquake looks like:

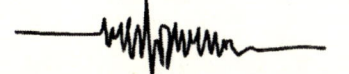

On an EEG, this is what a seizure looks like:

I'm having a *brainquake*.

Prologue

Why write this book?

Why is this book on epilepsy in the form of an extended personal account? I am a case of information which applies to other kinds of disorders, but this is a personal account of my disorder itself. That is important because it provides information about what it feels like to have a problem like this. For one of the major aspects of this problem—and other problems like it—is how it makes the patient *feel*.

I have copies—patients legally have access to copies—of my official medical files, so I have lots of information about the history of my problems. The history of my problems—with "intractable" seizures—is, in a sense, also a case study of cutting-edge medical treatment for epilepsy. I've tried to make sure that I stay close to the medical realities of my experiences. But even though I have my records, I'm not claiming to be qualified to give a scientific or medical account of this disorder. I have also stayed close to a recent and extensive textbook on epilepsy—Engel and Pedley—when the larger picture—or my perception of that picture—was crucial to this personal account. I have provided information on that source in the list of resources at the end of this book. You might want to ask your doctor for recommendations about resources of interest to you. I don't want to be understood as claiming that kind of authority. But the medical problem itself, and questions, both about treatment and about larger social issues of it, are directly related to the personal experience of any patient. Epilepsy isn't in your arm, or your toes, or your liver—it's in your brain. It's in your *self*.

I get embarrassed sometimes about a number of things. I worry sometimes about how egotistical this book is—as though I expect everybody to be deeply interested in what I do, how I do it, and how I feel about it. I'm embarrassed about seeming to be so self-involved and to think that everybody else should know all of this about me— should hear the whole story. I don't think that. But I have come to think and feel over the past ten years that there are some issues about epilepsy—especially my kind of epilepsy—that can be considered only in the perspective of a personal account. The consequences of these issues—personal and medical and social—are complicated and intertwined. One of the major effects of disorders like these is that they will in all probability affect all aspects of your life and for the rest of your life. Furthermore, they will affect everyone who loves you. And so part of the length of this account is to present a case of those facts.

I get embarrassed about some of the things that I have experienced, and how I felt about them. I get embarrassed about the very idea of making that stuff—which embarrassed me to begin with—public. But I also want to make the point that one of the major effects of medical problems like mine is that they involve the most personal and private aspects of the patient's life. One of the issues of treatment of these disorders is that your doctors and your loved ones must address those very personal issues. We know from long experience that one of the problems with epilepsy is *exactly* that public knowledge of it has some serious consequences. But I have gone public—and I'll tell you about that. Now that I have, I may as well just tell the whole story.

So I stand here in a kind of paradox. I don't want you to think that I think you want to know absolutely everything about me. But I do want to give a record of the complicated aspects of this problem. And I think that it might be better to show you what those aspects are, rather than just say that "there are complicated aspects of this problem" and then go to the next topic. (Some medical textbooks do that.) I want to give the evidence, even though the evidence is, in part, that I *am* the evidence.

So let me ask for your forgiveness if you get bored with this story. Skip some pages. And let me tell you that I am still embarrassed. But I'll do it anyway.

This story is personal—it simply has to be personal—but it is about the medical issues and their consequences, not about other aspects of my life. For that reason, I've referred to most people in this book by shorthand letter names. But it's important to provide more information about the medical professionals involved in my case because their professional background is crucial to this story. All of them have reviewed portions of my book and given me permission to use the material they have reviewed.

Here they are:

> **Antonio V. Delgado-Escueta**, M.D., Professor of Neurology, Comprehensive Epilepsy Program, UCLA. Director, VA Southwest Regional Epilepsy Center, West Los Angeles VA Medical Center
>
> *aka—in my account—Dr. D-E*

> **Itzhak Fried**, M.D., Ph.D., F.A.C.S., Associate Professor and Director of Epilepsy Surgery, Division of Neurosurgery, and Co-Director, Seizure Disorder Center; Head, Neurobiology of Human Memory Program, Department of Psychiatry and Biobehavioral Sciences, UCLA
>
> *aka Dr. F*

> **Susan Y. Bookheimer**, Ph.D., Associate Professor of Psychiatry and Biobehavioral Sciences, Director of Brain Mapping Center, UCLA
>
> *aka Dr. B*

Barbara M. Van de Wiele, M.D., Associate Clinical Professor, Director, Division of Neurosurgical Anesthesiology, UCLA Medical Center
aka Dr. V

Dr. Van de Wiele invited me to submit an account of my neurosurgery for publication in the *UCLA Department of Anesthesiology News*, Winter 2001, UCLA School of Medicine ("My Experience of the Asleep-Awake-Asleep Procedure," p. 3).

Jon A. Kobashigawa, M.D., F.A.C.C., Clinical Professor of Medicine, UCLA School of Medicine; Co-Chief Division of the Clinical Faculty of Medicine, Department of Medicine; Medical Director, UCLA Heart Transplant Program
aka Dr. K_1

Katherine Kahn, M.D., Professor of Medicine at UCLA; Associate Division Chief for Research, Division of General Internal Medicine and Health Services Research, Senior Natural Scientist at the Rand Corporation
aka Dr. K_2

Ms. Liz Carter, Patient Coordinator, UCLA Neurological Services
aka Ms. C

Ms. Sandy Dewar, R.N., M.S., Clinical Director and Patient Care Coordinator, Seizure Disorder Center, UCLA
aka Ms. D

Ms. Irene Wainwright, Administrative Assistant, Department of Neurosurgery, UCLA
aka Ms. W

@ @ @ @ @ @

So, here are the rules of this game:

- Epilepsy is a disorder, not a disease.
- In the United States, 5 people out of 1,000 have epilepsy.
- Social prejudice—and the fear of it—is an ongoing problem.
- Medication control is the first defense.
- When that fails, neurosurgery is considered.
- *Epilepsy changes a person's life . . .*

Here we go.

1 The Grip

Thanksgiving Day, 1992

On Thanksgiving Day I sat at the dinner table with three of my best and oldest friends, remembering the past, joking about the present, and hoping for the future. Things were looking up, because I had finished my Ph.D. in the Humanities, and had taught for a year (at UCLA) in a job which only ever lasts one year. I had spent the summer unemployed, looking for the next interesting job in a university, and having to consider whether I could find something that might work in tandem with my partner's law school studies up in Berkeley. I was thinking that our three-years of living together would determine any choices about the next job I would look for. So I was pleased to tell them about the exciting job I had only just gotten, in late September, at a research institute in the Humanities. I could do some exciting work with a unique institute. It was not a permanent job, but I was a contract employee, so I had some security and most (but not all) of the benefits of a permanent job, not just a temporary teaching job. I could stay there and make some money while my partner finished law school, and then we would have to make some decisions about the future. The future was looking good.

It had been a rather odd day for me, though. Since early morning, I had felt a little strange. I seemed to be "tuning" in and out of the situation, the conversation, the interactions. I had had this feeling occasionally in the past few years, so I knew it had nothing to do with the occasion, the turkey, the potatoes, or the stuffing. I somehow knew it might be some medical problem. Now, because I got the job with health insurance, I could try to find out what was going on. But on that day, I celebrated and enjoyed my friends. I missed my partner, who was in law school up in Berkeley, and enjoyed the fact that, indeed, the future was looking good.

The odd feeling I had suddenly intensified. I remember, now, still, very clearly: I sat at the dining table talking—feeling odd and feeling strangely cold. I was tuning in and out of the conversation, talking some, but hitting moments in which I didn't talk at all. I could hear my friends, but I felt like I was suddenly very far away from them. I went to the microwave to heat up some coffee, but somehow I couldn't seem to make my arm put the cup down—I just stood there holding it. One of my friends just took it from my hand, not realizing anything was wrong, and put it in the microwave, talking away. I sat back down at the table, feeling very, very strange—as though something terrifying was about to happen. Then I turned my head to the right and looked up behind my shoulder, at the ceiling. I remember looking at the corner of the ceiling, but I don't remember why. The next moment I remember I was lying with my head on the dining-room table, eyes closed, feeling like I was just waking up. I heard the voices of my friends from what seemed far away, saying: "she's waking up, let's get her to the bed." I had a brutal headache, and I was no longer exactly sure where I was. They helped me to the bed, because I felt shaky. My closest friend—M—sat with me there, holding my hand, and said, "Amy, you're here at J's house. You just had a seizure."

My god.

But there had been earlier episodes, some so subtle that I hardly recognized them until they were past. Long, long before, nearly seven years before that Thanksgiving Day, I was in my gym, doing my aerobics class, doing fine, enjoying the workout and enjoying the music. And then, abruptly, I felt like my sense of the music and of the people around me seemed to telescope, so that I felt like I was stepping back, perceiving the world around me as though it were from a backwards telescope. The music seemed buffered, somehow, by the distance between the others and me. I felt just a moment of fear—visceral fear—rise up from my belly, and then pass on. But there was nothing to *be* afraid of. I kept doing the workout to the music that I heard, in synch with the rest of the people in the room, and soon I slipped back into place, back to normal, back to reality. I wondered at the time what kind of experience that was. I thought it was a reaction to the effects of the aerobic exercise, so I eased off a little, wondering if that would happen again. It didn't happen again that day, or in months to come. Life went on.

In the years between that day in the gym and that Thanksgiving Day, I spent a lot of time in graduate school, working on the foreign language skills required, doing research for my own work and for my professors in graduate-student support jobs. Of course my life was very rich, and full of experiences which were positive, and so I was decisive about how to plan the future. I do remember somewhat vaguely that this weird thing happened to me again a *few* times. I didn't know what it was, but I always worried that maybe I was exercising too hard, or being too strict on a diet. This wasn't a long-lasting thing, so I didn't worry much about it. Certainly I didn't *want* to worry about it. I didn't want to talk about it. Indeed, I had trouble actually remembering the way that it felt, and I would have had great difficulty describing the experience, so it would have been hard even to describe it to anybody else. But I had the perception that the episodes were getting more frequent, and although the experience that felt weird was very short—a few minutes—I had a bad headache afterwards. But when it happened, I took some ibuprofen, and that helped. And I would go to bed early, and feel better the next day, or have a slight headache, but that happens to lots of people all the time. So all was well, and so I went on with my life. In short, I was denying to myself that this could be a serious problem.

The Student Health maze

On the other hand, I couldn't deny that I was having some medical problems. My closest friend and I decided to spend the summer of 1988 travelling in Europe, since she was between jobs, and I was between semesters of graduate school. I had as much fun that summer as at any other time in my life, but I came home in the early fall, with a rash on my arms (that resembled insect bites) and an ugly memory of a bout with the flu during the weeks abroad (or something like the flu). Being a registered student, I went to UCLA Student Health to get those bug-bites looked at and maybe some salve or something to treat them. When you start those medical procedures, you get an interview about your past history, so that the doctors can make informed decisions about what might be your problems and how to treat you. So I sat there, doing that interview, understanding all those reasons and approving of the motives for it.

I gave the explanation of where I had been that summer in case that was pertinent to what the little red bumps were. I told them about the "flu." Eventually they asked—and I answered—about other little things about my physical health that I knew about. Those little things included that I had had some unusual episodes of fever at a younger age—wondering if that meant that I was susceptible to some kinds of disease. And, for the first time, I ended up also explaining these strange little personal experiences: I sometimes felt odd, and a little removed from what I was doing at those moments. I sometimes felt chilled, and I got a headache, but it didn't seem serious because it went away. I thought that maybe, because of my childhood fevers, and these odd feelings as a adult, I might have some kind of sensitivity to some kind of influenza. I thought it might somehow be related to the seeming "bug-bites" which hadn't healed in the last week or two.

I considered that all these "problems" might be related to each other, so I gave all this information to the physician at Student Health this information. All of that stuff got written down into my file. Because of my travel and my history of fever, that doctor decided to test me for a very unlikely but possible disease from my travel, malaria. I got some antibiotics for the rash, was told to be attentive to whether I had an allergic response to those, and went home, thinking that the problem was probably solved. But, the next morning, those little bumps had swollen-up into big red ones, so I trotted back to Student Health.

The suspicion was that perhaps I was allergic to the particular antibiotic they had given. That happens to people, so they took me off that one, and put me on another antibiotic. And when my blood tests had all come back, an interesting thing had appeared. Because I had given them some information about my family's medical history, they knew that my mother had rheumatoid arthritis. So they had given me a blood test to check for, among a number of things, possible information on whether my condition had anything to do with an "auto-immune disorder." There is a test for "ANA"—antinuclear antibodies—not commonly done as part of a routine workup. My ANA was "positive," but no trace of anything like malaria had shown up, and so the doctors thought I should be checked out by an immunologist.

So, I got referred to the Student Health doctor working on immunological conditions to check whether, because my mother had an immunological disease—arthritis—the bumps had to do with my condition or with my response to the medication, or both. I went to see that doctor. That doctor looked at my bumps, looked at my fingernails, read my file, asked about the information that I had given about strange fevers and experiences plus my mother's arthritis, and diagnosed me with "lupus." *Jeez!* I had showed up in Student Health with some bumps! They had given me antibiotics, and the bumps had gone away. So, I no longer had the problem for which I had gone to Student Health in the first place, but now I had this strange diagnosis of something much more serious. I called my dad on the phone. He was at that time, a professor of speech pathology and part of a medical team at a major university hospital. I wanted him to think about this diagnosis, find out some information, and tell me what I should do next. He said: get another opinion.

I hear the words for the first time

Of course, I didn't want that diagnosis of lupus to be true. I felt that it wasn't fully supported by the information I had given (based on the information about lupus I read and my dad told me about). In any event, back I went to Student Health for a second opinion. That second physician read my file, listened to my story, looked at my features and my fingernails, considered my accounts of those little odd episodes, and *disagreed* with the diagnosis of lupus. He thought that the strange little episodes were more important than the other items, and so he referred me to yet another Student Health doctor, for those other little episodes. That one read the file, listened to the stories, ignored the bumps, disagreed with the lupus diagnosis, asked some questions about the notes on those little odd mental episodes, and, in twenty minutes, diagnosed "seizure disorder." *Jesus Christ!*

This was in the fall of 1988.

The bumps—the reason I had gone to Student Health in the first place—by now had gone away. I hadn't believed the lupus guy. I disliked the seizure guy from the moment he opened his mouth and for the fact that he paid no attention to the bumps, but made a diagnosis like that in twenty minutes. Besides which, nobody had *any* opinion about the odd fevers I had had as a teenager, so I felt no satisfaction from these diagnoses. I felt, furthermore, that the doctors in Student Health all disagreed with each other and were too quick to be any good at diagnosis. I was doing well on my own work, and my bumps had gone away. I no longer had "symptoms" of that possible disease, and so I didn't pursue that. And I had met this delightful man.

I had begun a lovely relationship with a man teaching at UCLA. I met him right after I had returned from Italy and begun the Student Health maze. We got to know each other well, and I moved in with him the following summer, in 1989. We talked about our work, we talked about his career, we talked about the unknown future. But I still had some intermittent fevers, and *I* still thought that they might have something to do with my history of fevers. Plus, if I had actually gotten some disease the previous fall, I still wanted to try to get that cured. So, back to Student Health.

I had another blood test for any problems. I was tested for Lyme disease, but that came back negative. I had another "positive ANA"—1:320. But the main problem was that then, that summer, I had fevers and a sore throat. So my doctors then were specifically looking for causes of that fever, and began a series of tests for other information and other possibilities. After several of *those* tests, I gave a positive result in one of them, and so was diagnosed in July with "Mono" (Mononucleosis). It's not all that unusual for women my age, working at a university. There is no actual "cure" for that, but if you follow the recommendations of the doctors to take care of yourself, you recover. And I did that. This was yet another case of fever, but not exactly like the ones I had had before. For this fever, though, there is a blood test, and so the doctors had no doubts that mono was the cause of this fever and this sore throat.

As follow-up, I went again to see the doctor who had, the preceding fall, tested me for possible malaria. She was following my medical history in Student Health. Her diagnosis again confirmed that my consistent fevers indicated that I must have some germ or virus illness. My series of illnesses then, and her blood tests for them, indicated that this could not be *just* an auto-immune condition and could not be *just* some effect of a possible neurological problem. But, her diagnosis was that perhaps my symptoms were somehow related to the results of my tests for ANA. She still wanted to test for some neurological disorders, though, and so she scheduled one of the major tests for that.

One of those tests was my first "MRI." The technique uses some "magnetic resonance imaging" to measure what is happening in your body. For me, they wanted to do the test on my brain processes. You have to lie down on a sort of cot, and then they slide you into a little cave-like opening in a big machine. Then they measure some of the structures in your brain. Some people are kind of claustrophobic, so they have to deal with the fact that this machine—like a tunnel—might make them feel that way. I have never had that problem, so it didn't bother me. The machine makes loud, clicking noises. They give you some earplugs, and you have to lie still for about a half-hour. That can be a little uncomfortable, but the test is not at all painful. It gives your doctors some "pictures" of the structure of your brain.

That first MRI test was done in early August, 1989. The results were sent back to my doctor. In my medical files for that test (I have a copy), my doctor's notes concluded "no abnormalities." So this experience gave me some confidence that any diagnosis having to do with my brain seemed to be mistaken. However, she indicated clearly that the MRI findings did not rule out that I had neurological problems, and she also suggested that I had a seizure disorder. Once again, that diagnosis seemed to have absolutely nothing to do with my fevers, and so I decided, again, that I would want to have a second opinion. She respected that. But, at that point in time, I didn't really want another scary medical opinion. My "mono" was cured.

Then there was yet another medical problem. I had this strange vaginal discharge. I continued to think that I might be having some kind of contagious germ or virus disease. So in to Student Health I went, one more time, but this time to the Women's Clinic. They weren't sure what was causing this problem, but the doctor there didn't think that this would have anything to do with the questions about neurological problems. So, I found myself downstairs in the lower depths of the UCLA hospital, getting a technically complicated urological test (a "Cystourethrogram") to see what *that* problem might be. (As it happened, there was some technical problem with that test, and so I had to go back two days later and have another Cystourethrogram.) That second test (noted in my file) came back: "benign atypia." That means I had some kind of slightly abnormal cyst, but it wasn't at all dangerous, and it didn't really indicate anything which ought to cause concern.

You might be able to understand why I felt the way I did. I had come into Student Health the previous fall with some funny bumps. Two weeks later, they were gone. But the doctors there began this complicated series of tests, appointments, diagnoses and referrals. I got a bunch of complicated, inconsistent, and seemingly unrelated tests for a bunch of strange, abnormal diseases. They all came back "normal" or "benign." The only one which wasn't "normal" was that ANA test, and nobody said that that test directly and specifically proved anything.

And every now and then I would have some truly weird experiences. I would just feel strange for a little while—for no apparent reason—and feel this "wave" of cold. I would feel a little withdrawn from my surroundings. My heart would race. I would have this sense of fear, even though I didn't think there was anything I should actually be afraid of. Sometimes I would wake up in bed and lie there, in the dark, compulsively swallowing again and again and again—that felt so strange! I couldn't imagine why I was doing that. It didn't last long. But while things like these were happening to me, I couldn't really talk about them. I couldn't talk very easily. I would just be silent.

Sometimes I would have a moderately high fever again, but it would never last longer than a few hours. Then I would break into a sweat, and my temperature would return to normal. I would be able to sleep, and feel close to normal the next day. Sometimes I would have both of those experiences together. The fever was what Student Health had never figured out, so I didn't want to go back and deal with that problem all over again. But I started to make a little note to myself. I circled the dates of the fevers on my little pocket calendar. And I started to circle the dates of those odd experiences, too. I didn't know what to call them, so I just put a little question mark next to the circled date. I didn't know what they were, but I thought maybe they were related to the fevers. I didn't talk about them.

At the end of that summer (1989)—in fact, the day before my birthday—I remember waking up alone, since my partner had gone off to teach. I had a brutal headache. That happens sometimes, of course, to many people. I had a friend who had migraines, and who had told me her story, and so I hoped that this was just the regular occasional headache. I took some ibuprofen, and went back to bed. I slept some that morning. My partner came back about noon, and asked me how I felt. I told him. He told me about the night before: he had woken up because I was making some small noises, and moving a little bit strangely. It didn't last long, and I hadn't woken up from it, but he didn't know what it was. He had thought that it might be best to let me rest that morning. But I knew that his description of what I had done resembled the symptoms which had made some of the doctors suspect that I had some kind of seizure disorder. I knew that I had to go back and find out what the medical explanation for that might be.

I waited until the trimester began, and in October, I saw another neurologist in Student Health. I have a copy of his notes from that examination. I will try to include some quotes from my record so that I don't misstate what the doctors were telling me. The notes describe the complexity of a diagnosis. He notes the ANA test which seems to indicate something might be wrong with my immunosuppression system. He notes the "nocturnal fevers" as well. He describes my strange experience at the end of August and wrote about my account of that: "no muscular aches-pains, no bitten tongue or evidence of incontinence." But, although he reports that I seemed to have three types of seizure events ("partial sensory, partial complex & tonic-clonic"), he notes that there is not a "clear etiology," and that my (or my partner's) description of those events indicated that they were "atypical in all three cases."

Here we go: another case of something being "atypical"—that is, not typical symptoms for a typical diagnosis. He advised me to go to the Emergency Room within 24 hours of the next experience like that last one, because if I get a blood test within 24 hours, that would provide information about a possible seizure. He recommended that I should have an EEG test after sleep deprivation. That's a test in which you sleep-deprive yourself the night before. When you go for the test, they put electrodes on your scalp, which can measure some of the electrical activity in your brain. Then you lie down for about an hour, quietly, while they measure your brain waves. If you have some kinds of neurological problems, and if you were sleep-deprived before the test, you are more likely to have those events while they are monitoring your brain activity. And then the physician did the most important thing—he referred me to a specialist. Not another Student Health doctor, but Dr. Antonio Delgado-Escueta, who is a Professor of Neurology, and in charge of the Comprehensive Epilepsy Program at UCLA. I refer to him as Dr. D-E.

Some dark clouds move in

I didn't want to mess with Student Health again. I wanted to get serious, and get a highly-trained, trusted medical opinion on this stuff, so I got an appointment with that specialist, Dr. D-E. That was my first appointment with him (fall, 1989). He began by saying that no one should make the diagnosis of epilepsy without sufficient evidence. It should never be made with only a little information which *might be* related to seizures, but might be something else. He wasn't blaming any of the doctors I had seen, but he was letting me know that this diagnosis—seizures—was not clear to him. And if it isn't clear to a major-league specialist, I didn't think it should be considered to be clear. He also told me that the consequences of a diagnosis are serious. That confirmed what I had felt about the doctors who had made that "quickie" diagnosis in Student Health.

He was impressively interested in all the details, though. He asked my permission to speak to my partner, who had seen those strange actions that night in August. I gave it, and he called on the phone, and they talked. I remember that he asked my partner some of the same questions that he had asked me, for instance, whether I had wet the bed! I had said no. I remember wondering whether the fact that he asked my partner implied that he didn't believe me, and I wondered why he might think that I would lie. But, wetting your bed would be embarrassing, so maybe people don't want to talk about it. My partner also said that I had not. That was a prelude, though, to one of the strangest aspects of a diagnosis like this. It took me a while to learn it, and I will tell you all about that one in a little while.

So, he said he didn't think there was enough evidence to make the diagnosis, because he didn't have sufficient information, and because the consequences of making it are life-altering. But he warned me carefully that if I should have any further episodes like that one in August, I should let him know, because I would need to get treatment as soon as possible. I left that appointment grateful that the specialist had *not* made the diagnosis of seizures. So I could carry on with my life.

I had arrived at the point in graduate study for a Ph.D. at which the student stops taking classes to work seriously on writing the dissertation. I went to Europe to do some necessary research and to seriously write. My partner got a teaching job in northern California, and so moved up there. But when I came back in the summer of 1990, I went north to live with him while I kept writing my dissertation. I'm grateful for his support, since I wasn't employed then. And since I was not employed, I had no health insurance. Furthermore, UCLA student insurance was not available to me because of my advanced-Ph.D.-study status and because I was not in Los Angeles. Everything went relatively well. I finished my dissertation, was awarded the Ph.D. in 1991, and got a job as lecturer in the Humanities program at UCLA.

The good side of that job is that I got to teach, and to earn some money. The bad side is that I had to go back to UCLA, whereas my partner stayed up north. He had decided to leave the uncertain job market of teaching in the humanities and go to law school to prepare for a better future career. We continued, though, to be with each other, talking about what might be possible after he got his degree. My job at UCLA was only a lectureship, not a "tenure-track" position. I knew that it would be temporary, and that I would stay in the market for jobs elsewhere, hoping that I could find one close to where my partner would look for a job in a law firm.

I truly enjoyed the teaching. I was giving lectures on humanities and literature to a huge lecture hall full of all kinds of students. I worked hard at writing lecture material in order to present the most interesting and important aspects of literature in western culture. I worked on rewriting my dissertation with the idea of publishing it. All jobs, of course, have some bad times as well as the good times, but things were, in my opinion, going well.

One day, toward midterm, I stood there at the podium giving a lecture to 200 people. I've always been comfortable with a large audience of students, and so I wasn't actually reading my own notes out loud, but organizing my presentation "on the fly." I remember that day well. I was giving a presentation on Roman literature. In the middle of my talk, I got this very strange sensation, as though I were moving backwards in space, farther away from this auditorium full of people. I suddenly felt icy cold. And I felt that odd little wave of fear—odd because I knew there wasn't any reason for it. I just stopped talking, and stood there, waiting for it to pass, feeling like there was a wave of air conditioning sweeping by. I seemed to be hearing some people talk—I felt like I had heard that conversation before. And yet, I knew that neither my TAs nor my students were talking out loud to me. I just stood there, and that cold wind did pass. Some moments later, though I didn't know exactly how long that had lasted, I "came back." I didn't exactly remember what I had been talking about, so I looked at my notes, and made some decisions about what to move on to. It took me a little while to look at my notes and actually remember exactly what I was talking about. I looked out at this sea of people, and wondered whether they had thought it strange that I had stopped talking. It was not the time to worry about that, so I carried on with my lecture. Later on, I casually asked my teaching assistants, who were at the lecture, whether anybody thought it strange that I had been silent for a moment in the middle of my lecture. They laughed, and said that it was odd for me, but that everybody thought that I was just looking at my notes. People giving lectures do that sometimes. So I got some comfort from the fact that nobody seemed to have thought it was strange, and therefore it hadn't interrupted my performance of my job. That was in the fall of 1991.

By the end of 1991, I began to realize that these events were, in fact, something serious, and that they seemed to be occurring more often as time went on. In fact, they seemed to be occurring close to once a month. But every now and then I would have a fever, too. And I was afraid—looking back now I know that I was afraid—that this experience was something dangerous. One afternoon I was driving with my friends when that odd, cold wave hit me. I could hear one friend talking to me, asking me questions, but I couldn't answer them. I was just looking straight ahead, driving. I felt that sense of fear, but I knew that there was no reason to be afraid. I couldn't talk, but I could drive. I didn't freeze up. I could steer, and brake. But now, looking back, I have to ask myself whether I was really driving "normally" just because I didn't have an accident. And, once again, my friend thought I was just lost in my own contemplation of something, for I have been known to do that.

I was also afraid that anything having to do with medical decisions would alter my life and my options, and I wanted to keep my options. I thought about what Dr. D-E had said: the diagnosis would have some serious, life-altering effects. And the career possibilities for people with a Ph.D. degree in the humanities are slim at best. You have to work hard to get a job at all in your field, much less a "good" job, and you have to be committed to the fact that you may have to move in order to get one. It isn't just that you have to move to choose the best offer, it means that since there are very few positions at all, you might have to move in order to get any career-oriented teaching position. So, I was also considering the fact that those were the main problems. I was turning away from whatever that medical problem might be. After all, it didn't affect anything about my job, and it didn't happen often, and I didn't want to deal with those complicated factors that the diagnosis would cause.

Significantly, the other thing that I did *not* do was talk to anybody else about this. One of the factors for that was just my personality. I don't talk to lots of people about how I feel about everything in my life. And I had trouble talking about this because I didn't really remember everything which happened when that was happening to me, and so my description of it, even to myself, was not very clear. It frustrated me that I couldn't really describe these experiences even to myself.

And then, of course, there was the issue of the word "seizure." When I heard the word "seizure," I thought of a highly visible, major seizure. I thought of TV shows or movies I had seen. When people have "seizures," they all of a sudden start to jerk their arms or twist their bodies in some kind of rhythm. Their bodies get rigid, and they just drop to the ground. They seem to pass out, to not know that anything is happening to them. I had the idea that people who see someone having a seizure knew immediately what was happening. Also, I had the feeling that the observers don't want to deal with it, and they don't know exactly what to do. They are embarrassed, or even "freaked out." Only a few people "know" what to do: to try to hold a person down to avoid physical injury, and maybe try to put something hard in the mouth to keep them from biting their tongue. I understood that people having a seizure are unconscious afterwards, and then they sleep a while. When they wake up, they don't remember anything about that experience.

None of this had ever happened to me. I had never had a seizure! If I had ever done that, somebody would have noticed. So I shouldn't be diagnosed as having a "seizure." More denial.

I knew something, but nothing personal, about those seizures—called *gran mals*. I didn't know anything about the other, much less-famous kinds of seizures that you never see or hear about. Indeed, even if you are in real life looking directly at a person having this kind of seizure, you might not notice anything unusual. I had never heard of the ones diagnosed as *partial-complex*. It took me a while to learn about them.

So life went on. My partner moved ahead in law school. I made the "short list" for several academic jobs, and I had several interviews just after Christmas. I came close to a couple of jobs, and I talked to my partner about what the future might bring. He was supportive of my possible jobs, but we talked a little about the fact that he might not get a good job in the same city as those possible jobs. But he still had graduate work to do for the law degree, so we didn't make any big decisions. We just carried on to see what the future might bring. I didn't get the offer of those academic jobs in other parts of the country, but the lectureship I had at UCLA was for a full year. So I had a lovely summer (1992) celebrating that accomplishment, and travelling with my partner for vacation with his family. Sometimes I would get that slightly odd feeling, and I knew that I was about to have those moments when I couldn't talk very easily. Usually I would get up and wander off for a minute or two—I would go into the kitchen or the bathroom, or I would go looking for a book on the bookcase. And then I would go find my ibuprofen for the headache I knew was on the way. As time went by, I started to get more than one—a series of them. So when one arrived, I knew that I had to be ready for the next ones. I didn't want other people to see them. I didn't want to be asked to explain them, because I didn't have an answer to that question. Lots of times they would happen to me in the early hours of the morning, and so I could just lie there—awake—until the series went "through me." I would be exhausted that following day.

I told you before about that satisfying job teaching, but that kind of job never lasts more than one year. I applied for another job, a position at a very prestigious research institution. That institution needed people with my kind of academic background to do research for their work and to help to produce conferences on extremely interesting cross-discipline topics in the humanities and art history. In September, 1992, I got that exciting job. I called my partner up north and was warmly congratulated, even though that job was still down south. I called my parents and they were very pleased that things were working out for me. I started my exciting new job, and two months later I went to spend a long weekend with my dearest, oldest friends and tell them about the bright future.

That was Thanksgiving, 1992.

2 The Label

Putting a Name to it

When I got home from that Thanksgiving with my friends, I knew that, finally, I had to cope with this problem and face the consequences. My friends had told me that I had had a *seizure*, and as is always the case for that kind of seizure, I didn't remember most of it. One of my friends is a nurse, and while she never claimed to know a lot about this, she knew that what she had seen was a *gran mal* seizure. I called the office of Dr. D-E, whom I had seen three years before, to make the appointment. I knew that big changes were coming, but had as yet no idea just how pervasive they would be. My partner was, in the middle of December, in the throes of preparing for his exams, so I decided to hold off telling him about the episode. We had been invited to fly to his parents' home for Christmas, so I had to decide soon as well whether to tell them what the situation was. I was afraid to tell anybody. I was afraid to tell my partner that I had that awful disorder, and to tell his parents that their son was involved with a woman who had an awful disorder.

The appointment played out: Dr. D-E heard my account of the experience and I told him what my friends had said to me about what they had seen. He looked at the records of my previous visit and asked me many detailed questions about what had happened. Then he made that official diagnosis he had been very careful about making. *Epilepsy.* There was no hiding the fact, and there was no way to avoid the consequences. He told me that I had to start treatment right away, because seizures do damage to the brain. They frequently get worse, and sometimes even kill. I had never before heard that this illness could be fatal. I should take the issue very seriously because I had now had, in addition to the other strange but conscious experiences, the famous, scary, undeniable event: the *gran mal*.

The dominos began to fall.

He told me again that he would legally have to file with the State of California that the diagnosis had been made, and that I would lose my driving privileges until my seizures could be effectively and consistently controlled by medication. Because of that, he gave me strong advice: go down to the DMV and voluntarily turn in my driver's license. His report to the state would be dated that day—a Friday—so I should turn in my license the following Monday.

In the state of California, your driver's license will be legally suspended by the Department of Motor Vehicles (DMV) when the diagnosis is made. It will be reinstated only with the physician's recommendation that seizures are under control. There are serious reasons for that: if you have a seizure while you are driving, you might lose control and crash. If you have a *gran mal* seizure, you will pass out and your body will have those strange, rhythmic convulsions, so you will certainly lose control. You might injure yourself. Even worse, you might injure some innocent other person. You might slam into another car. You might slam into some children on a sidewalk. *Don't drive*. My doctor told me the serious truth: this is both a moral and a legal issue. You have no right to risk others.

This is one of the most devastating effects of the diagnosis, but I knew that it was the right thing to do. I didn't even care, sitting there listening to this catastrophic diagnosis, about whether I would crash my car and hurt myself. In fact I remembered, looking back, that I had had my weird experience once when I was driving, but it didn't affect my ability to watch out for traffic, to put on the brakes, to change lanes, to drive as carefully as I would always drive. But I sat there and dealt with *this* fact: maybe my sense that I could drive normally was inaccurate. The fact that I didn't have an accident that time doesn't mean that I drove entirely "normally." It only means that luck was on my side then. As we all know, sometimes accidents happen to people who do nothing wrong.

And there is more to this legal aspect of this problem. The diagnosis becomes semi-public state documentation. That means that if I were to be involved in any accident, even if it had not been my fault, even if I had had no seizures at the time of the accident, other parties could legally find out that I had been diagnosed with seizures. They could claim that my seizures were the cause of the accident. It wouldn't matter, he said, if in fact you were not having seizures. You could never prove that you had *not* had them—there is no proof for that. You could never prove that your seizures had not caused the accident. Some patients have their license "revoked" by the state because they did not voluntarily surrender it, and some patients decide to drive anyway without a license, illegally and dangerously. He spoke from professional experience. *Turn in your license, and don't drive.*

He said that my volunteering to turn in my license might be a positive factor: when he decided that my medications were controlling the seizures well enough, he could advise the DMV that they give me back my license. But he would have to be confident that the medication controlled the seizures in order to recommend that. And, indeed, it is still the DMV which makes the decision whether to reissue that license.

One of the worst effects of this disorder is that it might cause personal catastrophe, especially while driving. One of the worst effects of this diagnosis is that it causes you to lose control over many of life's most important activities. I learned about this one right away. And it seriously affects other aspects as well.

"How long will it be before I can get my license back?" I asked.

He was careful. "We'll see."

"Are we talking a month?" I said with fear. I felt the need to know the general ballpark.

"More. Maybe six. We'll see how the medication works."

I was stunned when I left Dr. D-E's office. *Six months without driving?* I have to take buses everywhere. I can't drive to work, I can't drive to the grocery store, I can't drive to go see a movie, I can't drive up into the mountains. I can't drive a friend to the airport, or to a doctor's appointment. I can't drive to a party, or home from a party when I'm tired. For some people, in some cities, this would not be so bad. I have a good friend who doesn't drive anyway, and it took her a while to understand why that was such a loss to me. But she lives in the Bay area, where public transportation is much better. And she never had a car there, so she had never gotten into the habit of using one. I had. I had always organized my adult life with the implicit fact that I had a car and could drive.

But, in addition to the personal catastrophe of not being able to go where you like and when you like, there can also be serious problems with your local transportation systems. In Los Angeles, with its huge urban sprawl and its less than satisfying public transportation, that consequence of the diagnosis is torture all by itself. My choices about where to live had in the past had nothing to do with access to public transportation. Now, public transportation had everything to do with my life. It changed nearly everything about my life.

That weekend was one of the worst of my life. I tried to make some logical list of things I should do, and to do as many as possible for which I needed my car. I tried to follow the list, and do all the errands I could think of. I went to the grocery store to stock up on anything you can stock up on. What I ended up doing, though, was just driving around, with the logical intention of making sure that I did everything I could do that weekend. But I lost control, not of the car, but of my intentions to accomplish things, and I ended up just driving up the coast, knowing it would be the last opportunity for a long time to do that myself. I walked down to the beach, looking at the sea, crying about the consequences still to come.

On Monday I gritted my teeth. I took a bus to the DMV, stood in line, and then voluntarily turned-in my license. I got on a bus to the Palisades looking over the ocean, and stood there, gritting my teeth, trying not to cry.

In addition to telling me about the medical consequences of the disorder itself, Dr. D-E told me also about, in his experience, the *personal, psychological* consequences of having the disorder diagnosed. Looking back, I came to understand that he is a very good doctor in part because he knows about and will tell his patients about more than just the strictly physical effects of this disorder. He said that clearly some people close to me will need to know the diagnosis, because they may have to help me with my responses to the medication and the consequences of having the disorder. But his advice was that I should think carefully about telling others, because we know from experience that there are lots of people who respond strongly and negatively to that word: *epilepsy*. They may literally be afraid of or at least disturbed at continuing to know you. This is an old, old problem.

He told me about some of his other patients and the negative social reactions they have experienced. (Of course, he never told me the names of any of his other patients or any other personal details about them.) He wasn't telling me to tell no one, indeed, he wasn't telling me what I should do. He was advising me to consider carefully who to tell. The clouds were moving in.

Some of the people I did tell thought that it was the right thing to be careful about who might know this fact. But others, including my father, disagreed with that point of view. They certainly thought that I should be open and candid about the diagnosis and its effects. The choice was mine (or so I thought), and at the time, I couldn't face going public. I didn't want to deal with how other people felt. And indeed, I wasn't ready to talk about how I felt. I felt like I had been hit by a bomb. It wasn't clear what part of me had survived the blast.

The fear of epilepsy is another one of the worst aspects of this disorder. History tells us that some people have a strong negative response to the very idea, to the very word itself: *epilepsy*. Some are afraid of being anywhere near a person having a seizure. I understood that in some ways when my doctor told me. I had never been the kind of person anyway to tell others everything about myself. I would have to cope with the enormous depression that knowing this thing about myself began to produce in me. But I had to tell some people. Telling others about this diagnosis is a classic example of finding out who your friends *really* are. I am here to tell you that I paid the price.

My father and my mother have always been among my closest friends to me. I had told them before this diagnosis was made some things about my experiences and about the complicated diagnoses made in Student Health. But I had no fear that they would react negatively, and I knew that they would personally support me no matter what happened. I have been grateful about that all my life. Dr. D-E told me in the course of time that some of his patients had enormous trouble with that. Some people don't want their parents to know anything about the diagnosis. Some parents seem to deny that their children suffer from this. Some seem to be unable to encourage their children to accept the consequences, and try to adjust and carry on with their normal life. My doctor knew that, and of course he would never compromise the privacy of his patients. In fact, because I never had a moment's fear about my parents' possible responses, I failed to specifically tell my doctor that I would tell my parents everything about this diagnosis.

There came a point in which my father wanted to talk to my doctor to ask some questions related to his own attempts to find out about this disorder. Dad asked me whether that would be okay with me—and it was. In fact, over time I had realized that it was actually a good thing to have some people who know you well to be able to find out some information. That is precisely because while you react personally and emotionally, they can ask questions and get some answers on some aspects that might not even occur to you. Indeed, they can sometimes find out about things that you don't want to hear about or to deal with.

My parents visited me in Los Angeles, and my dad called my doctor's office to see if he could speak to him for a few minutes about some of these issues. He called and left the message with my doctor's office. They didn't call back. He called again, and left another message, being familiar with the fact that sometimes doctors will have an extremely busy day, and might not get to all their messages. Sometimes it happens that messages get lost under a pile of other messages. The doctor did not return his call. My dad wondered why a doctor would not return a call to a parent needing to know about this serious diagnosis, and said he was puzzled by that. I called my doctor's office to see if I could find out, and told the assistant who spoke to me that I would like my doctor to try to answer whatever serious questions my father had. She said she would give him the message.

A short time later, the phone rang: it was Dr. D-E. Then I tumbled to the situation: he wouldn't talk to his patients' parents, or to anybody, about his patient without specific permission. I was lucky that I didn't need him to decline to talk to my parents about me, but I realized that some patients might need that and want that. I respected it even though it wasn't a problem for me. So my father spoke to my doctor about my case.

That first two months

The diagnosis was officially made on December 11, 1992, two weeks after that *gran mal* on Thanksgiving Day. Some ten days later I got on the plane to the east coast. My partner's parents had very graciously invited me to spend Christmas with their family. In addition, I had several academic job interviews at the big yearly conference in my field, which happens the week after Christmas. But I had to fly up the coast to do them. They had been fortunately scheduled on the same day, so I decided to fly up there from my "family's" house, early in the morning. I could do the interviews and then fly back the same day to spend as much time as possible with my "family."

I knew that I had to tell my partner, but I didn't know if I should tell his parents. They had always been kind to me. It isn't that I suspected that they would react negatively, but I didn't want to even take the *chance* that they would react that way, not then. Not until I knew more about the consequences. Not until I told my partner, and not until I knew how *he* felt about my telling his parents. I was afraid to tell anybody, but I needed his support—God, how I needed that. Now that he had finished the semester and done his exams, and could relax a little for the Christmas holidays, I felt that I could tell him about all of this.

We were walking along the ocean shore, and I was trying to figure out how to say it, how to break the news, and how to deal with my fear that this would frighten him about the future. Finally, I simply told him the story, from the beginning: the horrible experience at Thanksgiving, my appointment with the doctor two weeks ago, and the diagnosis of epilepsy. And I told him about my fears. He gave me a hug, and asked me some questions about what the doctor had told me, and about how I was feeling. We walked for a long time along the beach. I told him who I had told, and that I was scared to tell anybody else. I trusted him, though, entirely. He was quiet, and I was sure that he was still trying to process the effects of that diagnosis. I had told him about the suspension of my driving privileges, and about my fears, and about my doctor's advice to be careful about who knew. It was no surprise to me that he might be a little overwhelmed with considering all the consequences. There are lots of consequences.

We talked a little bit about the future. He wasn't at that point in law school yet where he could know what the job market would be. If I received a job offer from one of the universities with which I had interviewed, we would have to consider the question of location. We talked a little about that. We knew that some aspects of the future were still not clear. I didn't know whether my medical issues would affect my job performance, which in the academic world requires not only that you teach, but that you start right away to do research and to get your work published. I was deeply concerned with the issue of letting anybody know that the diagnosis had been made, and of being afraid that the knowledge of that condition might affect whether I was offered a position.

My feelings during those conversations were colored by the fact that I hadn't told anybody at work. And I didn't want anybody to know that about me. I didn't want anybody to be afraid of being around me. I wondered if my very new friends at work would pull away because of that. I wondered if some would spread rumors about that. I wouldn't know who knew, but I would have to cope with their responses.

I was also afraid for my job itself. I was a contract employee. I had been hired in September 1992, with a six-month contract. That contract would expire March 23, 1993. With my present job, I had some health insurance, but I had to consider what would happen if I lost that job. Since I was not a permanent employee, they wouldn't have to "fire me" to end my job. All they would have to do was not renew my contract. I had to work at realizing the magnitude of the effects of having this diagnosis, and realizing that made me more afraid and more withdrawn and more paralyzed about how to deal with it. Looking back, I think I was literally frozen by considering the complicated consequences of this one, simple diagnosis.

Before I had come to Florida to see my "other family" at Christmas, I had begun the medication Dr. D-E had prescribed Tegretol©. Now, over Christmas, I felt very, very fatigued. Emotional response to a diagnosis like this one can do that. I felt like I was coming down with a cold. Plus, though I didn't know it then, the fatigue was a side effect to this medication. Adding to the emotional strain and physical fatigue was a job interview. It was my very first, for an academic job, in New York state at a highly prestigious university. I wasn't sure that I wanted a job in New York, when my partner was in California. Nor was I sure that it wold be wise to eave Los Angeles now that I had just started my treatment program at UCLA. But being invited to interview at this university was an honor, and I felt that I must do it. So up and back I went, on the same day. And came back to Florida utterly exhausted. (The interview went well, but I didn't get a job offer.)

All the errands that I had had to do, both in my now totally re-organized life and for my new job in Los Angeles, took a lot of energy. So I was glad to relax with my partner's family, whom I have always enjoyed. I was glad to be with my partner again. He wasn't sleeping well, but he was a little worried about his exams; after all, they were the first ones he had taken in law school. I knew that he was suffering from stress as well, for one night I woke up because he was tossing and turning, having a bad dream. He certainly apologized, but I couldn't fall back asleep. I wandered out to the living room, sat on the couch, and wondered about the future.

When I went back home a week later I found out that my first blood test had shown that my new medication had, as a Christmas present to me, made the white-cell count in my blood literally plummet. That was bad news.

But there was worse to come.

3 The Search for Control

On the night of January 12, 1993, ten days after I came back from Christmas vacation, I opened a letter from my lover, telling me that he had left me.

I sat there stunned, reading it again and again to be sure that I had understood it. I was *so* tired. I was responding strongly to the side effects of the drug I had started one month before. I didn't know this yet, but the blood test I had done right before Christmas demonstrated one of the ominous effects of the medication I was on: my white and red blood cell counts—the measure of the effects of the drugs on my health in general—had plummeted. I was suffering from the fatigue that that causes, as well as the psychological effects of the diagnosis. So there I sat, so tired, so terrified of my diagnosis, so worried about the future, reading a brief handwritten page from my lover and partner of the last three and a half years telling me it was over.

I called him in shock. I began to cry even before I could speak. I managed to ask what on earth he meant. I asked why he hadn't talked to me about wanting to leave or needing to leave. I couldn't understand why he would leave me like *that*. He said he was sorry but he was involved with somebody else. Just like that.

Like every other serious personal relationship, ours had involved lots of aspects of being deeply connected with another human being. Decisions about things in our life had been made for that goal—at least mine had been. I won't speak for him. My decisions about career choices had been affected by their possible requirements and, especially, their locations, for we would have to make career choices to stay in the same general area. I "knew" that his career choices after law school would also be affected by that (but it seems that they were not). I had confidence in our future, but maybe I had been deluded.

If this book were a personal account of other aspects of my life, I would feel the need to discuss how complicated his decision might have been. I would feel the need to describe how tangled our conversations—such as they then were—became. But that's not the point of this book. I don't expect readers to cope with that. I will never be able to say whether he would have left me anyway, independently of this medical diagnosis. But the *fact* is that he left me two weeks after I told him about it. So the fact is that I was standing there, already devastated by the diagnosis and the side-effects of the medications, when he turned and walked away. Can you imagine how that would make somebody feel?

My neurologist, Dr. D-E, found out about that in my next appointment (1993) with him. He was sympathetic, but not surprised. He told me that it happens a lot. Sometimes it happens when another person sees that you are having seizures, and sometimes it happens when another person understands the effects of the diagnosis, or deals with the effects of the medications. I am not saying that that is a factor in whether a physician makes this diagnosis or not, because of course the major factors for him (or her) are judgments about the disorder itself and the treatment of it. But Dr. D-E was then and still is sensitive to the social effects, so he knows the consequences of both the disorder and the diagnosis.

I remember, mainly, in that first appointment with him—back in 1989—that he had said that the effects of the actual, legal diagnosis could be serious. And when he made the diagnosis—1992—he had told me about some of the negative social reactions people have both to the episodes themselves and to the official diagnosis. In many cases, like mine, personal relationships are radically changed by the diagnosis and the treatment. Lovers and spouses and friends had left patients with diagnosed epilepsy. But my doctor was careful, as he is always careful, not to make assumptions about what all of the causes of a relationship break-up are. He just told me that it's not uncommon with a diagnosis of epilepsy.

This is one of the reasons that epilepsy stands out from other medical problems, because the diagnosis itself doesn't make everything better. It directly addresses your physical defense against the seizures, but it also changes your life. It reflects one or more of the possible emotional, social and life-changing effects of the both the disorder itself *and* the diagnosis.

The Search Begins

When I had come back from Christmas break with my partner's—my *ex*-partner's—family I developed an odd and annoying vaginal discharge. My family practitioner had checked me out right after I got back from Christmas vacation, and done some tests. I made an appointment to come back a week later to see what the results were. That was right before I had gotten that January 12 letter from my partner. When I came back to find out what the problem was, I ended up in her office, weeping, almost unable to speak. She was a very considerate person, and eventually I could tell her why I was so distraught. She was very thoughtful. She knew about my diagnosis of epilepsy, and she had seen my blood tests. The white blood cell count of "4.5-10" is considered normal—my most recent test revealed another drop in my count: my "3.7" had gone down to "3.2" in two weeks. She was a little concerned about my vaginal discharge in part because my white blood cell count was so low. She asked me about whether my partner and I had made love in the last month, and we certainly had. She was concerned that maybe I was responding to some known problems that sexual relations can cause. And, in addition, because my low white and red blood cell count would make me more susceptible to infections than normally, she wanted to do some tests for those possibilities. She knew that it would be hard, but said it would be helpful if I could talk to my ex-lover to find out what I might have been exposed to.

So I had to go home that evening and call him. I had to call and I had to have one of the most painful conversations that human beings might have. I had to tell him that this phone call was not about our relationship and it was not about blame or other issues. It was simply and rationally about medical concerns. It was about stuff which is always very personal, but I had to know about it to tell my doctor. And that I didn't want to discuss anything else.

I had to ask him whether he had any symptoms of sexually-transmitted diseases, and I had to ask him, essentially, whether this "someone else" had any sexually-transmitted diseases. I had to ask him, too, whether he had had sex with additional people as well. So I had to ask him for details about all the things I really didn't want to know. I had to tell him that I hadn't had sex with anybody but him, so if I had *any* sexually-transmittable diseases, they had to come from him.

He was of course embarrassed and, I think, felt sympathy for my situation. He was extremely reluctant to talk about the present situation, but he told me that his partner, his only present sexual partner—that is, aside from me—had, in fact, been diagnosed with herpes simplex. He wasn't personally worried about it because she had said it was at the present time dormant, and it wasn't transmittable while inactive. He didn't know of any other problems he might have with sexually-transmittable diseases. We said good-bye. I sat there, in yet another explosion of emotional shock, and thought about the possibility: *herpes*.

My family doctor was still concerned. She said to me that it is very seldom the case that dormant herpes simplex will be transmittable to partners, but there are in fact some cases. It is hard to know whether there might be a very few virus cells present, which might be transmittable. And, because it wasn't clear what my infection might be, and because it *was* clear that I had a low blood cell count (which means a weak defense system), she thought it best to treat me right away, and to test a few times more whether I had gotten herpes. Of course, as we know, herpes doesn't always show up immediately. But it can show up later.

I went to the pharmacy with that prescription in shock and got some medication for *that* medical problem. I went home in shock. I will remember that day all my life. It was raining—it had literally poured for several hours. I had to take the bus, because, of course, I could no longer drive my car. I had to stand at the bus stop in the pouring rain, with water pouring down my back and literally flowing through my shoes, crying. But no one could have noticed my tears in the rain.

And I had to do another blood test for the seizure medication I had begun to take in December, Tegretol©. The blood test measures both how much medication you are absorbing and the other chemical factors of your blood which have directly to do with your health and with your response to medications. So those blood tests are important—they will be constantly monitored when you are first on a medication to follow the possible side effects of damage to your body. There are of course some other, less threatening side effects. This medication was giving me a sense of "vertigo"—a slight dizziness—and some uncoordinated movement. I would bump into things, and I would stumble sometimes. For the first time in my life, I would actually have trouble just walking down the hallway. My sense of balance was affected. I would bump into doorframes at work and at home which had never before caused me any problems. I went to the Sav-On and bought $10 worth of gas and acid tablets, knowing my insurance wouldn't cover that stuff. And this medication, like many others for epilepsy, is known to cause fatigue. I was so tired. I was so fatigued and so depressed by the diagnosis and the effects and the personal catastrophe which had just happened. I was weak and dizzy and in shock and depressed.

1993: Happy New Year.

I woke up the in the early hours one morning, feeling a blast like cold winter wind, and some wave of frigid water splashing up my belly towards my head. *God, here it comes!* It was so strong! My heart beat would race—I had this wild wave of fear and the gruesome bitter taste of burnt metal. I would be swallow, again and again and again, even though there was nothing for me to swallow. I heard those familiar muffled background voices, and had that strange, powerful, eerie sense of *déjà vu.* I knew what was coming: a seizure.

There would be more than one. I would lie in bed, dead tired but awake, feeling fear, feeling the headache coming on, and knowing for a certainty that the drugs wouldn't stop the seizures.

And this was only the first month of this diagnosis and this medication. It was only the beginning . . . .

I had to go to work every day and try to do my job without telling my colleagues about this horrible mess. I had to do the laboratory tests and go to the medical office so that my progress with the medication could be monitored. The blood test on February 11, 1993: white cell count 3.0—going down. Dr. D-E, who had made the diagnosis and prescribed the medication had put me in the care of one of his colleagues, another neurologist, Dr. L. Because of the fact that my red and white counts had gone down in a series of blood tests, so far and so fast, they decided that they ought to take me off that first drug, Tegretol©.

Many patients do very well on Tegretol©, and it is considered one of the "first line" medications for some types of epilepsy. But there are some instances of the medication causing "aplastic anemia"—a dangerous reduction of blood cells—which can have serious health consequences. So Dr. L was keeping very close watch on both my red and my white blood cell counts.

So, because my blood tests were revealing not only negative, but dangerous effects, Dr. D-E and Dr. L decided to put me on the next major seizure medication, Dilantin©. They also did another EEG—the electroencephalogram—on me, in their continued attempt to determine where my seizures were starting. My records show that that EEG showed some abnormal activities in my left temporal lobe. They began to decrease the Tegretol©—carefully and slowly—and increase the Dilantin©—carefully and slowly—so that I wouldn't have a strong response to the reduction of Tegretol©. When you take this kind of medication, you have to be very careful because reducing the medication too fast can cause seizures. So I started down on drug #1 and up on drug #2. I got to the point where I was spending about $35 a month on that medication. (Let me start to tell you about the costs of my treatment and my medications.)

As a result of the diagnosis of epilepsy, I got referred to a psychiatrist as well. This is part of the treatment of the *diagnosis* as well as of the disease. I vaguely remember that first appointment with him. I remember that my doctor had told me about the common emotional effects of the diagnosis, and I remember that the psychiatrist asked me some questions about how I felt about the diagnosis itself. I could hardly even arrive at what I thought about the diagnosis itself, because I was still in shock from my lover leaving me, in shock from the effects of the drug which made me exhausted and dizzy all the time, in shock from the constant stomach upset, and in shock about the possibility of herpes.

I remember that he seemed to want to investigate some more complicated aspects of how I responded to the diagnosis, but I couldn't respond. I didn't want to talk about it. I didn't know yet what I even thought about it. I didn't know how much I wanted to make public (even to a doctor). I hadn't chosen to go to a psychiatrist—I had been told to do it as part of the medical treatment. It was part of the compulsory effects of the diagnosis itself. I didn't want to be analyzed. I didn't want anything more medical to be done to me. I didn't want to have to react. I don't remember much more about it (because I tried to forget it immediately), but I went home thinking that a doctor's interest in my more complicated, and maybe not yet recognized, to say nothing of expressed, emotional response to the diagnosis was ridiculous! I had gotten a life-changing diagnosis, I had responded poorly to the drugs, I was physically weak, my partner had exposed me to herpes and then walked away. Was it some hidden, psychological mystery *why* I was upset and depressed?

I slept a lot. I cried a lot. I popped my little triangular pills. I went to and from the bus stop—to work—in the rain.

I woke up very early one morning with a blast of cold, freezing fear. *Here they come* . . . Then the awful, brutal headache.

I got to know the staff at the blood labs. I would get on the bus and go there every other week or so to keep track of the level of the drugs. My neurologist needed to track the "trough" level of the medication—as well as my red and white blood cell count—and so I had to do the blood tests early in the morning, before I took the morning meds or ate any breakfast. And there was the trouble of having blood withdrawn on a repeated basis. I remember some gruesomely painful blood tests there, including two where they couldn't find the vein and so pulled blood from the dinky little veins in my skin, which produced a nasty, painful bruise three inches in diameter. These frequent blood tests were difficult to arrange, expensive, and sometimes painful, but I knew they were necessary. Blood test February 11: white blood cell count down. Blood test February 24: white count the same, red count down.

I went to the dentist for a routine teeth-cleaning, and got asked the routine questions: on any medications? I told my dentist about the meds, and he told me that he was glad he knew, because one of them, Dilantin©, was well-known to cause some gum problems. He would keep an eye out for that. I washed my hands a lot, to try to protect myself against ordinary germs—my low white count put me in the risk category there.

March 7: about 5am I woke up instantly, with a wave of fear . . . . But those seizures weren't as bad as they had been. The drug was taking effect. In March, thank god, my job contract was renewed. But, the new contract informed me that my "appointment" would "end no later that March 23, *1994*." I looked at that. I signed that, and I sat there, nervous. *No later than*. Would it end *before* March 23, 1994? I sat there and wondered about the legal aspect of that contract. At least I hadn't lost that job. But the contract also said that that appointment "may be renewable for an additional one year term." *May be*. Not "will be" renewable. I sat there and thought about that position. It might—or might not—be renewable. It might or might not be offered to *me*. An afterthought also occurred to me: I can still do my job, well enough to be offered the renewal. The good side was that I would still have that job for a while, maybe for another year. But the bad side was that I had no guarantee, even for that year, much less for future years. *A reason to stay silent about this diagnosis.*

I would have to be careful walking down the hallway at work. I had to be very careful walking anywhere. I would find myself leaning against walls for no particular reason. I would be so tired that I would lie down, but when I tried to get up, I would sit there on the bed, right on the edge between dizzy and nauseous. I didn't *want* to eat. When I did eat, I ate antacids as well. I started to lose weight. I started to hang on to railings.

One day, at work, in the elevator, I felt weak and dizzy— more even than what was "normal" for me on that medication. I stopped in mid-sentence, reaching for the railing, and just passed out. When I recovered consciousness, the security guard there— a very kind man—helped me up. He asked if I knew why I had fainted, and I lied. The next day I looked at my bruises—I looked like I had rolled down a cliff. I didn't know why I was so bruised— but I had to deal with it. I wrote a letter that night to my mother:

> *I wish I could just write you and say that I'm better, but I don't think it would be the truth. The immediate*

shock of everything is past, but the deeper implications of everything are only now starting to surface, and they hurt.

I went back to my neurologist and told him about the fact that my seizures were "breaking through"—through the medications. And I had to travel for my job, so I had to make sure that I slept well enough to function. So I got prescription #3: Ativan©. It is a strong depressant. Because it acts much faster than the other medications, you can take it in addition to your other meds, but only for stressful situations. You don't take it all the time. It technically "relaxes" you. It "helps you to sleep." What it does is *knock you out*. From my official medical records on that visit:

> "Due to the fact that the white blood cell count has continued in the low range, we have suggested to the patient that she pursue a hematology evaluation to be scheduled by her primary physician with the purpose being to determine what etiologies may be most likely to explain the continued low white blood cell count. . . . Pending the results of the hematology workup we will postpone increasing the Dilantin© at this time. . . . Because of the herpes infection being transmitted from a previous partner we have suggested the patient also undergo an HIV test to rule out the possibility of a concomitant infection from this source."

So I went back to my family doctor—Dr. B—in April to keep track of the problem with vaginal infection, for it did not heal. I was trying to keep from feeling naked fear that what looked like it might be herpes was, actually, AIDS. She told me, though, that she didn't think we needed to worry about that yet. *Thank God.* She would keep an eye on my condition. I left her office trying for some rational response—herpes is the lesser evil—but failing to rise above the grip of fear. I got more prescription medicine for the vaginal infection which might be herpes. I had gone years without any prescription medications, but this one was the *fourth* medication prescribed for me in five months.

April 11: I woke up in the early hours of the morning, with a blast of cold air and a sense of fear, swallowing again and again . . . .

I did some other blood tests and got my bill for all those tests (not including the purchase of the medication itself) in the month of April: $440.40. Of course, this was the bill stating the charges that the providers had billed my insurance company, so I wasn't personally expected to pay this amount just yet. But if I hadn't been insured . . . ! Processing of bills for all of this medical stuff—including the reduction of certain charges for services by "preferred providers"—always takes a few months, and dealing with that is another effect of a complicated medical diagnosis. (This bill was settled in June, and I paid my portion of adjusted April blood test charges, $28.60.) And that was just the tests. The bills for the doctor's appointments themselves were extremely complicated, owing to the fact that there are different kinds of appointments—and therefore charges—for each physician. In addition, any medical procedures which involve both a physician and medical tests will be broken down, billed, and then processed separately. I can give you some account of the cost of my treatment, but I don't dare to try to keep track of the cost of my physicians' appointments themselves.

May 1: more seizures. Milder than the ones I had had before this medication, but still "break-through" seizures.

I had gone years without blood tests, but by June of 1993 I had done eight of them. They don't measure any of the effects of the seizures—they measure aspects of the effects of the medications themselves. The negative effects of the ones I had so far taken had simply increased in the last six months, and they were severe. In fact, the results of the blood tests were scary enough that the doctors, both the neurologist and my family health doctor, suspected that my white blood cell counts might have plummeted to a seriously threatening level. It also seems to be the case that one of the rarer side effects of Dilantin© affects the condition of bone structure as well. So in early June, less than six months after the diagnosis and the start of the medications, they made an appointment for me to have another test for the dangerous affects of my medications: a bone marrow biopsy.

A bone marrow biopsy is one of the most painful medical procedures known to us. There is no way to anesthetize the nerve layer on the surface of pelvic bone. All you can do is get *ready* for the pain. My family doctor warned me about that, and, indeed, she even came with me for the biopsy. (I thought at the time, and I still think, that that was an incredible kindness on her part.) She held my hand as they slid the needle in. In fact, "slid" is the not entirely the right verb. They "slide" it in through your skin and your muscle, but then they have to push hard to "force" it—literally—through your pelvic bone into the marrow. I will remember it all my life. I thought I was ready for the pain, but you can't *be* ready for that. It was a kind of pain I had never felt before and I have never felt since: the weight of heavy pressure on your lower back, a deep slow puncture into the nerves, and a grinding crunch of bone.

A few days after that was done, I had to fly out of state to visit my ill grandmother, and I will also remember all my life the pain of that bouncing shuttle ride to and from the airport. When I came back home, I found out that the biopsy revealed my doctors' suspicions: my blood cell count in my bone marrow—where it originates in the body—was suppressed. My family doctor put me on iron supplements. I bought some more bottles of pills. Dr. L had paid careful attention to my blood cell count all along, but now he immediately reduced the medications I was on—you can't just stop taking these medications, for that would cause a seizure all by itself. I had to start that day to taper down one of the two I was taking—on Dilantin©—and taper up on a new drug, the *fourth* epilepsy medication I had been on in the last six months, Mysoline©. May 8: breakthrough seizures.

Mysoline© is a powerful depressant for seizures, because it functions, essentially, as a "downer." It is a kind of drug closely—and directly—associated with depression itself. It is an anti-epileptic medication used *only* after other medications have been tried. The first two I had been on were in the "first line of defense"—and not only had they not suppressed the seizures, but they had also had—for me—dangerous side effects. I needed to do yet more blood tests to keep track of my multiple drug levels (the initial bill for one of those tests: $219.60). So, in the summer of 1993, I started to take those square yellow pills and began to live a life on 24-hour major league depressant downers. I continued to feel weak from my low white blood-cell count (continuously since December 1992). And since my blood-cell count had dropped so low, and because I had to stay on some seizure medication, it hadn't ever recovered to "normal."

I was constantly sleepy—major league sleepy—from the side effects of Mysoline©. Indeed, this kind of fatigue isn't, technically, a "side effect." The main reason to prescribe this medication is that it suppresses the brain activity which is directly related to having seizures. It is a stronger depressant than the other medications I had been taken off of. So I began to drink more and more coffee just to try to stay awake at my job. And I would go—on the bus—to the pharmacy to get my meds, and then to a drug store to get $10 worth of antacids and stomach bloat tabs.

Three weeks after the bone marrow biopsy, I had to go to Germany for my job. Dr. L told me that it was not a good idea to do this in the condition I was in, but I went anyway. It was part of the nature of my job. So I put four bottles of different prescription medications and my passport in my purse, packed, and got on the plane. While I flew, I had to make sure I had drug #3—Ativan©—to make sure that I would "fall asleep" soon, and then I get out my notes on when to take meds #1, #2 and #4. I had to pay careful attention to when exactly to take x amount of each in order to taper carefully *down* on the first two and *up* on the third. I would look at my notes, sort the meds, toss down the powerful little white pills of Ativan©, and pass out.

I had planned a while back to take some vacation in Italy before I started that job assignment in Germany. I took my backpack full of hiking stuff and four big bottles of medicine and the instructions on how and when to take them and walked along the coast of a gorgeous part of Italy, exhausted, afraid and depressed. I couldn't manage to appreciate the beauty of where I was, and the pleasure of such a vacation. I hiked from one little coastal town to another, and tried to merely enjoy the beauty of the day, pushing away thoughts about the painful parts of my life. I had to carefully plan my meal times around the medications, not around my hunger, for they upset my stomach if I took them without food. I took lots of pills. I slept a lot. I ended up standing high on the coastal ridges, looking out to sea, remembering standing on the beach in December after the diagnosis had been made, staring out to sea, in pain.

I fought back memories of the previous summer on another coast with my lover's family, looking out to sea. I had talked to him many times in the past about his visiting Italy with me so that I could show him the beauty of it, but it had never happened. I stood there on the gorgeous coast, feeling despair and horrible fatigue, wishing I had the strength to forget the past, and just crying.

I had planned to stay on the Ligurian coast of Italy for a week, and then go north to Germany for my work project. Three days into that first week, though, I picked up a phone and called my mother just to feel her presence over the long-distance telephone line. She knew how and what I felt, and told me that if I wanted to I should get on the train directly to the airport and get on the next plane home—home to her. Don't worry about that at all, she said. We can put you back on a plane to get to Berlin whenever you think you need to be there. *Come home if you want to, nothing else is important right now*. She stayed with me a long time on that long-distance line when I couldn't even talk anymore, all I could do was hold the warmth of that phone against my cheek and cry.

But I didn't go back home. I knew that it would cause nothing but problems in getting back to Berlin, and I knew that it might cause me more health problems as well. One of the serious dangers of my epilepsy is that a lack of sleep can induce seizures. The paradox is that my seizures would usually occur at night or very early in the morning, while I was sleeping, and so would wake me up. I hadn't had any seizures there in Italy, so I decided not to fly home, but to try to push the pain away, go do my job and not think about everything else. That part of Italy will always remind me that I felt that way. I walked once more along the sea, said goodbye, and then headed north to Germany.

That afternoon I arrived in Berlin. I went to the Checkpoint Charlie monument—the former checkpoint gate through the now-destroyed Berlin Wall to East Germany. I was dead tired, but I went to the museum there, to look at photos from the recent post-war history. There are some truly moving photographs there, one of a sign put up by the West Berliners thanking the east Berlin soldiers on the wall for the "inaccuracy" of their shooting as people escaped over the wall. I went through the Brandenburg Gate—formerly in the Berlin Wall—to the Pergamon Museum, which has some of the finest art in the world. You can stand in the exhibition rooms, looking at the remains of the Pergamon altar, or the model of the Babylonian Processional castle, and *see* some of the achievements of classical Greek and Byzantine culture while standing in a monument of the awesome nature of 20th century culture. Then I stood out in the Marx-Engels-Platz and thought some more about the bigger human picture.

That first night in Berlin I went to bed early and then woke up in the wee hours of the next morning with a long series of six seizures: waves of deadly fear and icy shivers and the bitter taste and pervasive smell of burning metal. I had this sense that I had felt this—and heard these strange voices—*exactly this way* in the past: *déjà vu*. Similar seizures had happened in the past, but that's not the same as that powerful feeling of exact repetition. I couldn't sleep, even though I was unbelievably tired, and I had a brutal, imploding headache. I was taking that complicated set of medications, but they didn't prevent the seizures. All I could do was to jam down some ibuprofen for the headache, but that doesn't ever get rid of that kind of headache—it takes hours before it will go away.

So I sat up in my hotel room, just after 3:00 am, staring out the window at street lights, having scary seizures, being deadly tired, and being afraid, afraid, afraid—feeling the sense of fear which was part of the seizure, *and* being afraid of having more. I had to go to work that day, and all I could do was to hope that I didn't have seizures while I was taking charge of that project, in the middle of the group I would work with. In fact, I had several that day. Once, because I knew they would happen a few moments before they did happen, I managed to excuse myself to go to the bathroom. I made it to the stairwell before the seizure happened. I had to stop climbing the stairs, grip onto the railing, and let it pass. Fortunately, nobody saw me there gripped onto the stairwell. I had several very rough days, with not enough sleep and bad headaches and fear that I could not do my job and fear that other people would see this happen. But I did my job.

We were working on producing an interesting conference on some connections between the brilliant 19th-century philosopher Nietzsche and some aspects of art and architecture in the 20th century. Because I had the background in literature and philosophy, I enjoyed working on trying to consider what those connections might be. I also spent a little time reflecting on the irony of our interest in this particular philosopher, who had very serious medical problems himself, and who ended up going mentally insane for some parts of his life. He was a brilliant intellect, and I spent some of my professional time, and some of my personal time, reading his complicated work on the big issues in western civilization and in the personal dimensions of life.

We went from Berlin to Weimar, Germany. It is nearly a perfect location for a conference like the one we were producing, because it is a major German center of historical culture. World-class German intellectuals—Nietzsche is one of them—and crucial European political developments in the past three centuries are related to this part of Germany. Some of the highest achievements of European culture are directly linked with Weimar. And yet, just outside the edge of the city is Buchenwald—an infamous concentration camp in World War II. One of the German scholars involved in our conference plans took me and a colleague to visit Buchenwald. I felt that I should go there.

It's a terrifying place. I had studied the details of the war, and I knew some things about the camps, but—like most Americans—I had never actually been to one. I tried to be intellectual about the history of it, so as to try to "understand" it, but I couldn't sustain that. When I stood by the ovens, in the doorway of the gas chambers, I broke down. I stood there, knowing that I was crying for the thousands of people who had died in that room, but also for my own sense of suffering and loss. And I felt ashamed of that—of my selfishness. I pushed myself into looking at the deeper, historical reality. My life was full of pain and depression, but it had never been anywhere near this level. When we left, we went through the gate which has an epigraph on it: *Jedem das Seine* (To each his own). I walked away thinking about the horrible irony of that, since it seems to say that all the people inside the camp got what they had deserved, and that people do not all deserve the same. I walked away thinking in my own philosophical way, that lots of people get what nobody deserves. I was one of them, but I hadn't died in a gas chamber. I hadn't lived in a concentration camp. I was a *hostage to fortune*, but I had the strength to deal with what was happening to me. I suffered—and there was no clear end in sight—but I gritted my emotional teeth and carried on.

My job included a lot of long-distance flights, and I had to be very careful to try to deal with the jet lag dangers. Dr. L indeed told me several times that I shouldn't do that kind of work precisely because it might directly cause seizures. I had to face the dilemma of doing my job as well as possible—doing the very kinds of tasks for which I was hired—and risking seizures *because* I was doing them. So I began to have to deal with yet another medical issue. I had to get some prescribed sedatives and take them regularly when I was travelling, or in any situation in which my ability to sleep was threatened. And of course there are lots of situations in life which affect your sleep patterns: personal relationships, job tasks, parties, or even dinner with friends. I had to try to avoid events which would deprive me of sleep, and so I found myself avoiding lots of social events with coworkers and even with friends. Both my professional and my personal life required that I be sure to sleep enough.

When I got back from Europe, I got the first bill—not yet processed by the insurance company—for the bone marrow biopsy: $1176.50 (not including the bills for the doctor's appointments themselves.)

I began, too, to be very much afraid that I couldn't hold out all day long. I asked my boss if I could come early in the morning so that I could finish my normal work day at midafternoon. One of the best aspects of my job was that my boss permitted me to set that kind of schedule so long as I got everything done on time and so long as I would stay late on those days which actually required it. I hadn't told him—I hadn't told anyone at work—about my medical situation. So his decision to let me organize my own schedule had to do with the nature of my job and my performance of it, and his willingness to be flexible.

I changed my normal schedule. I arrived at work long before anybody else. In the early morning, before I took the breakfast dose, I was at the lowest blood level possible for that medication. I went to lunch, alone, long before anybody else wanted to eat, and I had to take some more meds and some more antacids at lunch. I felt more and more withdrawn. I worked in my own office with the door closed anyway, because part of my job was to carefully read scholarly work in several foreign languages. It was lucky that I could keep my door closed, so that nobody would notice if I had a seizure. I remember, however, having one in a staff meeting. But since I didn't have to talk, and since I was having a nearly invisible partial-complex seizure, not a recognizable *gran mal*, nobody noticed. When the meeting was over, I went back to my office and swallowed some more ibuprofen for the headache.

    I always got tired—so tired—early in the day, and I left the office at 3:00 or 3:30. I started going to work seven days a week—I should say seven mornings a week—to prove to my boss that I could do this job I that had held less than a year. I made myself go to the gym close to everyday, even though I felt physically exhausted. That physical exercise at the gym was actually a kind of antidote to that depressant medication. I would burn up a little bit of the drug and feel better, maybe actually close to normal, by dinner time. So I went to the gym religiously. I had started going to a gym long before the diagnosis to try to control my weight, and I had always enjoyed it. But I got to the point where going to the gym every day, alone, in the afternoon, and doing some serious cardio-vascular exercise made me feel as good as I could possibly feel (on that medication)—for about an hour and a half. But at dinner I would have to take some more downers. I would start to fall asleep again an hour after dinner.

    I didn't want to have to try to have "fun" in the evenings with friends, or go out to a late dinner, or, God forbid, a movie or a concert. I couldn't really socialize very well in part because I suffered from the physical fatigue of a low blood cell count, and the depressant effects of the medication itself. And I couldn't deal—with social reality—well at all. I think I had a shorter fuse. I think I knew that, somehow. But I also couldn't do it because I didn't want to be asked why I was always so tired. I know, from much later conversations, that some people simply assumed that I was on drugs because I was acting like that. I had more social problems because others interpreted my behavior that way. And the bottom line is that I *was* on drugs: a major league downer. The only difference was that I was on a prescription downer, and I took them every day and every night, taking the exact amount prescribed by my doctor. So, in the evenings I would try to watch TV because I was so tired and so sleepy that I couldn't really do anything very complicated. I would go to bed early, and try to read a novel. I would fall asleep early. My book would drop to the floor, and I would slip into unconsciousness for close to nine hours a night. Every night.

And there continued to be money problems about medical charges. For example, in early August, I got a letter from "Special Accounts—UCLA Hospital," telling me that charges for their medical services were OVERDUE!!! But which charges? I had learned fast that it often takes months and months for the insurance agency and the medical agencies to process the bills. So it was a little ridiculous to tell me that it was my fault they hadn't been paid. I called to try to find out the situation, but couldn't speak to a person in that department. I left a message. No response. I called again—I left a message. No response. I called again . . . When I got through to that department, they told me to "disregard" that notice. I hung up, furious at that. And it was only the beginning . . . .

August 29: 4: 46 am: I woke up, startled, in the warm summer, feeling a wave of cold . . . .

By September I was off Tegretol©, still on both Dilantin© and Mysoline©. I did my routine blood test for those levels: $219.60. A year after I had taken that job, I could stay awake only long enough to work hard at my job, and no longer. I couldn't manage to read any more complicated scholarly stuff on my own time, and I didn't have the physical strength to spend extra time in the library reading on my own research topics. Late in the day, after work, in my fatigue, I couldn't process what I was reading. I had stopped trying to rewrite my dissertation to try to publish it. I had not tried to keep contact with my former professors because I didn't want to have to explain all of this to anyone, and certainly not to professors who expected me to be publishing articles.

I didn't want to try to talk to those graduate school friends and teachers who knew my ex-lover. They would ask me why he left, and I wouldn't want to give the answer. I wouldn't want to discuss the issues. I didn't want to go public with this disorder, and I didn't want to try to have conversations about what I was—and was not—doing. I didn't want this information to go into the hands of people making decisions about prospective employees, because I had all the confidence in the world that, once out, it would certainly make its way to the small, almost incestuous academic job market. Indeed, I knew from experience that, because of the current market, there would almost always be many equally qualified candidates for an academic job. The decisions about who to hire would certainly focus on any negative aspects which might rule a candidate out. So the reality is that even if prospective employers had no personal negative response to epilepsy, they would very likely consider all the available factors to a job offer.

Because I felt all of that so strongly, both personally and professionally, any conversation with my graduate school colleagues would require one of two very painful acts: either tell people about this medical catastrophe and pay the price, or lie. Some people would be much better than I ever was at having a congenial but not blatantly revealing conversation, but I don't think I could possibly have achieved "congenial" (much less congenial on downers). I had trouble answering the most ordinary question: Hey, Amy, how are you? So I tried to avoid it. I slid deeper into seclusion and so deep into the biological and emotional effects of the depressants that I couldn't even manage to *care* that I couldn't do it.

I don't want to give the impression that I think that all those academic colleagues were or would have been critical of or rude to me. It is hard to judge that, because it is hard to know ahead of time who will react negatively to hearing about this diagnosis, and who will react with sympathy and support. I carried with me the fact that the person I had trusted the most—my lover—had just walked away right after hearing the news. I have dealt with both of those cases. But I'm telling you now about how *I* felt—not how *they* felt—and about the effects of feeling that way. Fear that other people would respond negatively can cause you to decide not to tell anybody. Sometimes you will never know how this friend or that friend would respond. You have to make some choices, though. Will you try to talk about this hoping that you would get some support, or will you try to not talk about this, hoping that you can at least preserve the friendship or acquaintanceship that you have? The lady, or the tiger?

I remember especially one night in October. I woke up from even that phenobarbitol-induced oblivion in the early hours of the morning with a brutal grip of fear—terrifying fear!—and of the glacial winter wind. Burning metal seared my mouth. And then a huge wave of freezing water surged up my body heading for my head. My heart was pounding. I heard the voices. The seizing tidal wave was about to hit! *Oh God! Oh God! Oh God!*

I didn't go back to sleep—in the next few hours I got hit by four more huge waves.

I was going down on the Dilantin©. I had to go down very slowly.

November 4, 1993: another series of seizures. On November 12, I did another blood test: low white blood cell count. The initial bill was $173.20. After insurance reimbursement, I eventually paid $13.86. The next day I got another refill of Ativan©, and got on the plane for a trip to New Zealand, taking two big beige downers and one little white downer with some food, and then politely passing out. I don't even remember the twelve and a half-hour flight because I was unconscious for most of it. Not just dozing—major league unconscious. In New Zealand I shared some vacation time with my parents, grateful for the fact that they *knew* about what was happening to me. I didn't have to pretend that all was well, and I didn't have to avoid any questions or lie with any answers. To this day I don't know how I could have coped with life if I had had to hide all of that from my parents.

In early December, I had another neurology appointment. My neurologist—Dr. L—had referred me back to see the specialist, Dr. D-E, who had made my diagnosis the year before.

My white blood cell count "remained low." I spoke to him about how exhausted I felt all the time. How bad I felt about the entire past year. How gruesome life had become. How many sets of seizures I had had in the past year. He *increased* my level of Mysoline©—to see if that would suppress the seizures—and made a new appointment in the following April.

In December I went back to my family home for Christmas. I tried hard to keep from remembering the previous Christmas at my ex-lover's family home. I had trouble staying up evenings. I had trouble staying awake afternoons. I had seizures on Christmas Eve. Christmas morning was awful because the memories of the previous Christmas stayed constantly with me. On the 28th I went down—by another 50 mg—on the Dilantin©. I had trouble doing anything. That entire year felt like punishment—though I had no idea what I had ever done to "deserve" it. I remember standing out on the back porch, in the cold winter wind, in the throes of fear, staring out at the barren backyard, crying. But I lived through Christmas, and I made it, finally, unbelievably, to the final day of that horrible year, 1993.

But not quite.

I was sitting on my bed the morning of New Year's Eve, talking with my dad, when I suddenly felt a horrible crushing pain in my chest.

My father couldn't understand what was happening to me, but he knew that it must be something totally abnormal and maybe dangerous. I laid down on my back, staring at the ceiling, feeling the pain, remembering with a flash the pain of the bone marrow biopsy. This pain was a little different, though. This one was not the sensation of a seizure. This one was not a searing, crunching stab into my spine. It was a brutal vice-grip on my heart.

It didn't go away. It got worse.

My brother picked me up in his arms and took me out to the back seat of the car. He drove us to the Emergency Room at the University Hospital ten blocks away. I know that there were a bunch of doctors and nurses there, putting me on a gurney. I know that they started some tests, because I could feel their touch. I know they talked to me, but I don't remember talking back. I know they unbuttoned my blouse and pushed up my bra to use the stethoscope, but I don't remember feeling embarrassed by that. What I remember is *the pain*.

What I remember is my father's face, standing there, with his mouth open, astonished, not believing that I was having what I looked like I was having: a heart attack.

I remember vaguely hearing some noises and some voices in the emergency room around me, but I paid no attention. I was just trying to breathe and to put some slight sense of distance between my brain and my heart. I was wondering whether I was having some kind of seizure again. I remember being puzzled that I didn't feel anything that I usually felt with a seizure. I remember having the wild thought that maybe this was the beginning of a *grand mal*. But Jesus, my heart *hurt*. My brain knew that it wasn't having a seizure. My brain knew that some other catastrophic thing was happening.

I think I remember the doctors asking me some questions, but I'm not sure that I remember actual reality, because my brain was trying to float up towards the ceiling to get away from the pain. I think I remember my dad's voice telling the doctors the name of my neurologist, and I think I remember him telling them the names of my medications, but I'm not sure that I remember when that happened, or how, or with whom. It all feels like a detached illusion.

I remember that they put a huge moist patch on my chest, and that they told me that would ease the pain, and I think I remember being pushed on a gurney through the grey-ceilinged hospital corridor into a dim room. I think I remember the voices of my parents. I know I remember the pain.

That huge patch has nitroglycerin in it. I somehow knew that—maybe I had heard them tell my parents. I had this wild thought that what was happening was some kind of explosion. I had this wild urge to correct that: it was some kind of *implosion*.

I remember—my body remembers—the pain. I remember another implosion: brutal headache, a side effect of the nitro. I think I asked them to stop with the nitro because of the headache. I think they said it was better to have the headache than the heart attack. I think my parents were there, holding my hand, stroking my face, watching me deal with the contest of pain in my heart and in my head. At some point, finally, mercifully, I passed out.

Happy New Year, 1994.

January, 1994 . . .

My mother never left my hospital room that night. She was the kind of person who could respond to any crisis with unwavering personal strength and support. My father had stood there in shock, barely able to move, staring at this totally unbelievable event, wanting to know what in the hell was happening to me. My mother didn't feel the need to stop and ask what was technically, medically happening. She knew that the doctors would get right on that question. She needed to be right there letting me feel her touch and letting me know that she would never leave me alone. And that was what I needed.

We were at the University Hospital in Iowa City. I will never be grateful that this thing happened to me, but I will always be grateful that it happened *there*. I was with my family, including two brothers. My family's home was a short distance from the University Hospital, so the transport time was minimal. My father had been on the faculty there for some 35 years and knew how the place worked. The cardiology program there has a good reputation. But we weren't thinking about that, we were trying to make some sense of the episode. Here I was, a young woman, in peak cardiovascular condition, with a *heart attack*! How could that be?

I remember some fear, too, seeping in. I was worried—again—

about the entire insurance issue. I wasn't sure exactly what the insurance company might pay for, but, more importantly, I was worried about the effects of those issues on my contract job. One of the aspects, of course, of having a medical diagnosis of epilepsy, or of anything as complicated and life-altering as epilepsy, is the knowledge that you will be an expensive employee from the medical insurance point of view. It isn't just the case that you will have an emergency, it's the case that you will require treatment and medication *for the rest of your life*. Whatever company that insures you will be looking at your medical expenses for the rest of your life.

Unless, of course, you are a contract employee. I got my job in September of 1992. I got the diagnosis three months later. I started getting constant blood tests and constant medications as well as a few major-league medical tests. I started being an expensive employee a few months into that job. So I remember lying there, contemplating what one night in an Emergency unit and an unknown number of nights in intensive care would cost. I lay there wondering whether asking for the insurance carrier to pay for *this* event would affect any possibility that my contract be renewed. I was a couple of months from its "renewal" date.

I lay there in intensive care, staring out the window at the light snowfall, wondering what, exactly, my employer would know about all that medical stuff from the last year. I had heard some rumors about the institution I worked for. I had heard that one of the aspects of it being a non-public trust was that it paid for the medical treatment of its employees, having hired the insurance company only to administer all the complex paperwork of medical insurance. So, I lay there wondering whether my employer would know about this hospitalization, and would pay the costs. I seriously wondered whether it would be smarter *not* to ask for coverage of this catastrophe. I remember talking to my dad about it, and he understood the issues entirely. But we decided that it was better to immediately report it, and hope for the best, rather than to delay so long that the insurance company might very well refuse to cover it *because* we had delayed. So my father did the deed. That is, he called the insurance office at my place of employment, and told them the story.

I know that the chief cardiologist on my case provided information about my admission and the current treatment to my insurance company. That official letter of notification is in my medical history files, and so I have seen it. I have also seen the initial response from my insurance company to that doctor's report, saying that it would agree to "cover" six days in the hospital for me, but, as this company always states in any preliminary documents, this decision would "not guarantee that any benefits will be paid." This is one of the constant concerns with medical insurance. This company (and possibly many others) will paradoxically tell you they will cover it while at the same time telling you that saying they will cover it doesn't legally mean that they will in fact cover it. So, this notification tells you that they haven't said "no" but they don't want to be understood as having said "yes." This is an official "maybe." You need to have that Official Maybe in your file.

The week of observation following the chest pain episode is important. Apparently there are clear indications that many heart attack patients have a second attack with that week. I did not.

Even though I spent the entire time there in astonishment that I was there at all, I remember how fantastic the nurses were. They were in many cases like my mother—not needing to know why on earth I was there, just taking care of me because I was there. They paid attention, of course, to my medical records, in order to make sure they took good care. One or two of them, though, were perceptive to my curiosity about all that machinery around my bed, strapped on and stuck in and beeping away, and they spent some time explaining what it was and what it did. So, as a kind of defense against lying there in shock, I got a little crash course on having a relationship, up close and personal, with metal boxes and tubes.

My extended family had come to spend the holidays together. I wasn't keeping track of the days, so I was slightly surprised when they showed up in my room to say good-bye. But it isn't the case that I spent 24 hours in bed, either. After a cardiac event, the nurses need to slowly and carefully give you some physical "exercise"—that means just getting out of bed and walking around a little. I had a portable EKG (electrocardiogram) strapped onto me—or perhaps I should say that I was strapped onto it. So, after a day or two there, I could get up and walk around a little, finally getting a look at the "outside," that is, just the corridors around my room. I had to be careful, though. They told me not to raise my arms above the level of my heart. They pulled off the electrodes a few times so that I could take a shower—I had to sit under the shower head in a plastic chair. If you should feel the need for an odd experience, try that one for the first time. The nurses caught my sense of the ridiculousness of that, and laughed with me: "Look at the bright side. You get the very top of your head extremely clean this way!"

And then there were the doctors. In a university hospital, the experienced doctors will take a group of younger doctors on rounds, both to look at the patients and to discuss the cases. You will usually—but not always—be asked by the supervising doctors some questions about your experiences and about how you feel. But you will also sometimes sit there like a packet of meat. Sometimes they will be looking at some part of you, and sometimes they will be reading some cryptic description of you on that little clipboard file outside your room. They will usually be talking only to each other, and sometimes one will be giving pop quizzes, and the others answering test questions.

I have to say that I was not totally surprised at that because of my father's experiences in the university health care system. One of the reasons that you end up being grateful to your nurses is that they will almost always be talking directly to *you*. Some people have told me how angry they were at that pack of MDs bolting in, talking about you in the third person, and then bolting out. I can understand the frustration, but I didn't take it personally. At that kind of hospital, the physicians are trying to treat you as well as they can, but they are also trying to teach other, younger doctors about all the medical complexities of diagnosis and treatment. And, in my case, they were standing there looking at a patient who had had a cardiac infarction for, literally, no known reason. So I'm sure my case and my files were interesting from a teaching point of view.

And, once again, I would always admit that you want to have a very personal and friendly GP for your normal medical stuff, but I would always insist that you want to have a highly-trained specialist for anything as complicated as this. More importantly, you want that highly-trained specialist to pay a lot of attention to training new highly-trained specialists. So I noticed that I seemed to be an odd cut of meat on a tray for them, but I was hoping to God that they were specialized enough that they might come up with a reason why I was there at all.

I also did—or had done to me—a *bunch* of blood tests measuring my physical reactions to the event and to the medication. They were testing to see if my bloodstream could show something which had caused that event. Of course my father had been sure to tell them about the medications I was on by prescription, so that they could know in advance that I would turn up positive on whatever actual chemistry those medications would cause in my blood. They asked me, too, just to be sure that they knew about everything. I gave them all the information, of course. Indeed, I ended up spelling the name of one drug—only recently made legal—because even a young resident in a major teaching hospital had never heard of it.

On night number three, I think, after dinner, I was sitting there talking to my parents about something pleasant—I think we had talked about my nephew playing in the snow in the backyard. One of the doctors who had been part of the group analyzing me came in and asked if he could speak to me personally:

"Of course." I thought: *Whoa! One of these doctors wants to speak to me **personally**. That's a new twist.*

"Could I speak to her privately?" he said to my parents.

They looked at each other, raised their eyebrows, and said okay. I suggested that they feel free to walk around or whatever.

The doctor sat down in a chair next to my bed. He pulled the chair up a little closer to my bed. He hugged the clipboard and smiled. He looked down. He looked back at me. He hesitated.

I waited patiently.

He said, "We'd like to do another test." Pause.

I raised my eyebrows, waiting for whatever else he had come in here to sit next to my bed and say. I mean, jeez, they had already done bunches of tests. Why start asking me *now*? And it's not like I'm going to know which ones they should or shouldn't do. I want them to be looking for what crazy thing might have caused this. I said, encouragingly, "Yeah?"

"We want to test," he said, "for cocaine." He sat there, gauging my response.

I said the first thing that occurred to me: "Well yeah! Test for any bloody thing you guys can think of!"

He was a little surprised at that. But he collected his thoughts and asked, "Have you used cocaine?"

I sat there, surprised by the possibility. "Not that I know of, but hey, my life has been a medical catastrophe for a year now. Test me for *anything* you think might have caused *this* one."

I had warmed up to him. It seems that the cardiologists thought that I had probably taken cocaine, or some other recreational drug, which might have produced the infarction. So he had come to me, not to my parents, and asked a sympathetic question. He stayed on my case while I was in intensive care, and I remember thinking that he would be a valuable highly-trained doctor because he could also be a sympathetic one.

They ran the blood test for cocaine. It came back negative.

They gave me the print-out of the present file on drug-testing they had done for me. All of them—except my known medications—were negative.

Round about day five, as I recall, they scheduled me for the cardio-vascular stress test—the treadmill thing. You get all gooped up, then you get all electroded-up, then you get all strapped up, and then you take a stroll on the box. They want to measure exactly what your heart is doing. It is amazing that, with the sonic technology we now have, they can actually "see" what is going on, as well as measure the heart beats with the electrodes. So I got on the treadmill and felt some actual pleasure, since it had been weeks since I had been to the gym doing my therapeutic exercise. That happens to people who exercise a lot—you get addicted, and when you go for a while not exercising, you start to feel deprived.

So, they start you out slowly. You can, of course, tell them that you don't feel good at any moment, and they'll stop the test. What they normally do is speed up gently. Then they start to put the treadmill at an angle, so that you are going "uphill." They are measuring everything your heart is doing during all of this. Then, while you are going uphill, they speed up a little. After a little while, you have to start to jog to keep up with the moving belt. The technician kept looking at me: "Okay?" "Sure?" "No pain?"

I was fine. No pain. After a while they speed up the machine, so that you have to actually run uphill to stay with the spinning belt. "Tell me, now," she said again, "whenever you start to feel bad, or you don't think you can keep this up." I nodded okay.

Running uphill makes your heart get pumping. But I had spent nearly every afternoon for the past year running uphill for an hour and a half. So the rest of my body said: "Oh, okay. We're doing that now. Got it." I jogged uphill for a while. She looked surprised. "You are okay? You sure?" I was fine. She pushed the knobs on her machine to the limit. A normal treadmill can go only so fast up this kind of slope. I was breathing hard, because I never spent my time running at such a sharp angle. And, of course, the machine controls how fast you have to run. I arrived at what I thought was my limit, but before I said that, she said: "That's it. We slow down and go back down now. When I tell you, step off the machine and lie down over here. We need to measure everything while it's still pumping away." You lie there breathing hard and sweating. It's not generally a good idea to stop running and lie down, but that's exactly what gives them the information they want. So, there you are, sweating, and then you get gooped up some more. They can use this sonographic machine to see what's going on in there. So you lie there and the technician slides this funny flat-ended pistol-looking thing up and down and around the gook on your chest. It's weird, but it doesn't hurt at all. She smiled.

The supervising doctor came in to evaluate my exams. I remember that he looked at the records, then he looked at the sonogram, then he looked at me, then he looked back at the records, then he looked at me, and then he looked at the sonogram. I read that expression very well: *this is the treadmill info on this person lying here?* He and the technician talked a while about the technical test information, and he signed some papers, and he smiled, and he went on down the hall. The technician smiled at me. "You know, the only other test I've ever done here that showed up in better cardiac shape than yours was on a 17-year old hockey player!"

So, six days after the attack and one day after the hockey player test, the head physician for my case came to tell me that the tests had all come back indicating that I had no known cardiac disease. My family records indicated that I had no known family history of cardiac problems. It remained unclear whether some particular event might have caused that infarction, since there was a witness to it—my father—and he could give no information which might suggest a cause. "Idiopathic" is the word. It means that your case doesn't match *any* known causes. So the official diagnosis was a case of "Prinzmetal's Angina," which means "heart pain with no known reason why." The cardiologist gave me a photocopied article on the terms, told me to take an aspirin a day, shook my hand, wished me well, and signed me off. The discharge document showed that they had done the following: electrocardiogram, assay blood LDH enzymes, radiology of chest, ECG [EKG] analysis + inpatient consulting, internal med ECG report, Echo exam—heart, Doppler exam—heart, cardiovascular stress test. The bill for those services: $2,236. The initial bill for that stay in intensive care: $4,870.41. Most of the doctors who treated me were not in my PPO—so my insurance company would cover only 80% of their service charges. The notice I received from my insurance company stated that they had received the necessary information from my head cardiologist. They stated that while they agree to cover six days in intensive care, this does "not guarantee that any benefits will be paid." In the end I paid $220.87. (Think what this experience would have been if I had not been covered by a good insurance plan!)

And, of course, I maxed out on my deductible for that year pretty quickly.

So, I had gone a week in intensive care with no further cardiac problems, but they still had no clear idea what caused the cardiac problem I had clearly had. For their records of my medical treatment indicated that "something" had happened. (It isn't that I just somehow made that stuff up.) I was to take it physically easy for the next month. My father had called my boss's office to explain what had happened, and so they didn't expect me to return to work until the middle of January. I needed to get back to Los Angeles in time to get a refill of my meds as well. The cardiologist had been insistent, though, that I should not under any circumstances fly home. The altitude and low-pressure apparently can be dangerous to someone in this condition.

My father had only just retired, and so my parents planned the trip necessary to drive me back home from the midwest. I remember that "trip"—I couldn't carry anything, so my parents were carrying my luggage in and out of the hotel room. I had to be careful not to lift my arms above my shoulders so as to avoid stress to my heart. We stopped for breaks frequently so that I could walk some for leg exercise. I see it now: my father and I walking around a parking lot in Iowa, Kansas, Oklahoma, and Texas as we headed west. My parents tried to distract me, but I would end up staring out the window wondering what on earth had happened. I would sometimes try to distract my parents, but my mother would end up staring out the window, wondering, I think, what on earth had happened.

That last night on the trip home, I came apart. The cumulated stress got to me. I was having dinner, trying for pleasant conversation with my parents, when suddenly the whole thing hit me—hard. The idea of going up over the mountains and back down into my life in Los Angeles—back down into forced march with the seizures and the drugs and the way I felt about it all. Facing the task of explaining this heart attack—which had no explanation—rose up in front of me, and I broke down. I began to cry—to weep uncontrollably. My mother took me to the Ladies Room and held me while I wept and wept. She soothed me—as only she could—with sweet and gentle comfort. She stroked the tears from my cheeks, and took my hand, and led me back to the trail on down to my "normal"—my unavoidable—life.

We drove to my house up over the Santa Monica Mountains, with a little snow and a gorgeous blue sky. Another fabulous day in Los Angeles. We got home in the late afternoon, went to the pharmacy for a large bottle of downers, and went to bed that night, January 16.

Do you remember what happened in Los Angeles very early the next morning—January 17, 1994?

The Loma Prieta (Northridge) earthquake.

4 More Dominos

Dealing with the results of the earthquake

At close to 4:00 am on January 17, 1994—the morning after we had arrived home from Iowa City—I woke up to the rumble and the shaking of the Loma Prieta Earthquake. It was a strong one, and lasted for several minutes. I jumped out of bed to go to the guest room where my parents were. They were on a mattress on the floor, and I saw that the TV had slid off its table and nearly hit my mother in the head. I was living in a well-built one-story house which had survived earthquakes before without serious damage. The house began to sway. We could feel the motion and hear some cracking, but the walls didn't fall down or the windows break.

In my experience, some people are simply terrified by earthquakes. The woman who owned the house was in the always terrified group, and she stood there hugging the wall with one arm and clutching her chest with her other. She looked like she was having a heart attack. Some of us, though, don't feel actually terrified, we just feel alarmed. We can act rationally and try to do the safest things. This was the fourth or fifth earthquake since I had moved to California, although it was stronger than the others I had felt. I stood there in the corridor against the structural wall under the huge beam supporting the roof and actually laughed at how ridiculous it was to arrive in Los Angeles *for* this event. I called to my parents to get up out of bed and come stand where I was, protected by the beams of the house.

The quake lasted only a few minutes, but it was a strong one. The swimming pool in the back yard started the dance: waves began to slide up one side of the pool, and then slide up the other, a kind of rocking motion. It was suddenly quiet, and all we heard were the waves in the swimming pool. We waited in their bedroom, unable to simply fall back to sleep, until dawn. The TV had slid off its shelf and crashed onto the floor, so we got on the radio to hear the news. The power was out in parts of the city of Los Angeles and the San Fernando valley to north. My dad and I had to go out to try to get some batteries for flashlights and radios. It was a bizarre morning. I remember strolling on the main street down to the drugstore on an extremely quiet morning stepping over some parts of various buildings which had tumbled down. I had never really felt panic in all the time I had spent in California, but that morning I was hardly feeling anything, because, clearly, my life was now nothing *but* catastrophe. So I think I was less affected than many other people because, by then, catastrophe seemed close to normal.

I had originally planned to go back to my job for a few hours a day, because the doctors in Iowa had told me to go physically slowly recovering from the infarction. Because I was covered by State Disability, I had to fill out some forms with my employer, dealing with my recovery to full-time. That morning of the earthquake, though, I got a call from one of the supervisors at my institute. We of course talked about the effects of the earthquake—he and his family were fine, thank goodness. He asked how I was doing from that medical crisis, so I gave a little brief account, and told him I had planned to come back part-time per week, starting that day. "Well, let me assure you," he said, "that there is no reason for you to come to work today. In fact, we are asking all but the emergency response personnel to stay home."

He told me the story: they'd had some unexpected damage from the earthquake, including damage to particular offices and, perhaps more of a problem, books and journals had flown off the shelves and crashed in awful piles all over several floors of the main library. Some of the big shelves had also fallen over. Nobody, though, had been hurt. They would have to spend several days assessing the damage, and restoring the library. Not only would it be difficult to have the normal staff try to do their jobs in the present circumstances, but the security of access to the library needed to be protected.

So, I stayed home. We walked around a little, but I knew that in such an emergency you shouldn't get in your car and drive around. There might be serious damage to roads and highways and buildings, so the important thing is to stay off the streets to make sure that city and state emergency teams get all the leeway they can to respond to damage or danger. So we sat out there by the pool, in the back yard, assuring my folks that we would find out about the damage as the day went along. Even though our house came through in good shape, parts of the city and the valley had had serious damage. Another crazy idea occurred to me: Los Angeles had just had an infarction.

Then another surprise, a rather serious one, under the circumstances. The homeowner took my father aside a few days after the earthquake, and told him something that she wanted him to tell *me*. Her son had been living in an apartment in the valley, but it was one of the buildings which had been severely damaged. He needed to come home for a while. In fact, because the building was the way it now was, he would have to stay several months, at the least. She needed the bedroom, his former bedroom, that I was renting. She needed me to find another place to live.

So. She needed me, standing there recovering from a heart attack, to look around a city damaged by the recent earthquake, find another place to live, and do the move! Imagine this, if you can: I had a car, but I couldn't drive. I had a certain amount of stuff to move, but I was medically instructed to not carry any of it. I needed to look for an apartment immediately, in between my follow-up medical appointments, to move to. It had to be close to my place of employment because I had to take buses to get there. It needed to be somewhat close to UCLA because I needed to be sure I could get to the UCLA pharmacy, on a bus, to get my not-available-everywhere medications (not to mention the constant blood tests and medical appointments I had there). I needed to do a medical follow-up for the heart attack. And, to top this off, my one-year contract at work was about to expire.

Furthermore, a new director had just been hired—the earthquake happened days after he took over the institute. And, since I had been hired by the former director, I had no idea whether my contract would be renewed by the new director.

Can you picture this? Can you picture me standing there, two weeks after a cardiac infarction, three days after an earthquake, knowing that I had to move right away, unable to drive—in fact, unable to actually carry my own stuff—knowing that my current job contract would end in two months, waiting for the next set of seizures?

I look back now and I think, *Jesus Christ*. But, then, I was going down, down down into numb self-protection. It was unbelievably good fortune that my parents had driven me back home, so that they could drive me around to look for apartments. If I had had to do that myself, taking multiple buses to anywhere I had to go to look for apartments, I would simply have had to take the first one I found, no matter the cost. As it was, my parents could drive me around to apartments listed in that week's Sunday paper as available, checking, of course, whether the apartment building was still standing (!) and not seriously structurally damaged. And whether the apartments available were even do-able for me, much less worry about getting one that I liked.

This is another case of the effects of this diagnosis. Because I had been diagnosed, I could not drive. Because I had to get some medications—on the bus—not available everywhere, I had to be close enough to get to the pharmacy after my work day but before the pharmacy closes. Because I had lots of medical appointments, I had to be able to get to those on the bus as well. Because I had to take a bus to my job, I had to stay close both to that building itself but also somehow close to public transport there. Because I needed to stay employed in the job which (thank god) insured this incredible medical stuff, I had to choose where to live for *those* reasons.

So my personal desires about where to live and how long to search for a good apartment had moved way down the list of factors. With this diagnosis, personal factors can easily become largely irrelevant. They don't control decisions, and in many cases, you have to make choices in direct conflict with what you would otherwise choose to do. And in this particular case, I had to do all of that ASAP.

(And I'm not even talking about the breakthrough seizures. They also moved down the list of important Things to Worry About.)

I found an apartment within a week. I found one close to where I was then living. The tenant there was looking for a professional roommate, and, furthermore, she had lots of her own furniture in the apartment already. I owned very little furniture, in part because I had traveled so much doing research for my doctorate. Finding an apartment which already had furniture was the best possible situation for me. And, also crucial for me, this apartment had a locked garage. This is always a plus for people who need a garage, but it was a serious concern for me. I couldn't drive, and so couldn't legally be moving my car around various blocks to avoid citations. And, also, my job required a lot of travel, and so I would be gone a lot. Furthermore, I happen to own one of the most stolen cars in Los Angeles—so my mechanic told me that—and the very idea of it just sitting somewhere for long periods of time would be an invitation for disaster.

I had found an acceptable apartment. Further good luck: the primary tenant of the apartment was a young woman who was entirely congenial at first meeting. Though we were strangers, I had the feeling that shared living arrangements could be worked out with her. It was a nice apartment, with a good garage for my always at home car.

Next there was the problem of moving. My colleagues at work were dealing with their own problems. And, of course, they had to be at work all day. And there was another factor for me. I had withdrawn a great deal from almost everyone I knew because of all of the medical stuff of the past thirteen months. I didn't want to try to explain, for example, why on earth I would have a heart attack. I had no good answer to that. But I also didn't want to explain why I could not drive and had to choose an apartment where I didn't have to drive and yet had a good garage. I would certainly be asked why. This was another case of knowing that, in order to answer that question, I would either have to tell the truth, which I didn't want to do, or lie.

I don't want to be understood as saying that nobody would have been sympathetic or would have helped me. Looking back, I'm fairly certain that some of those colleagues would have offered to help. But I was still afraid of letting people know, and I was always afraid to lie. As I said before, it isn't that I was so ethically superior that I would never in my life lie. It's just that I would find it difficult to do, and I wouldn't do it well, and it would be clear that I was lying, and I didn't want to do that. That all by itself would cause some suspicion that there were some mysterious problems.

Once again, that was part of my personal response to the situation I was now in. Other people might have felt much better about telling their friends and co-workers that they needed some help, but I sat there and worried about letting anybody know what was happening to me. I didn't want to feel fear about yet another thing in my life. My very best friends, friends who knew about the diagnosis, lived far away. I didn't want to ask them to fly down and help me move.

However, my parents were there. They took the situation in hand and said, don't worry, we will solve the problem. They understood the problem, and they understood how I felt about it. I think they also understood that I was so close to the edge of a breakdown, that they didn't want to give me the additional stress of worrying about asking people to help me. Since they were retired, they didn't have to hurry back immediately. My father, though, still had some obligations, and so they would have to return home soon.

I packed up. We found ourselves in a difficult situation because I couldn't carry any of my own boxes! I had to stand there and watch my parents, my retired parents, carry boxes of stuff out to the car. And boxes of my stuff included tons of books, some bookcases, and assorted clothes. Fortunately I didn't have a normal bed, but what I did have was two large, heavy futons. I remember my father, with one at a time on his back, trudging down the stairs, looking like a slave. And, fortunately, since my parents had driven me back from the midwest, we had both my car and their car to put stuff in.

So, in January of 1994 I stood there looking at another surreal situation. Imagine this: your parents, in their sixties, have to take boxes of stuff out of the car, put it in a grocery cart (which happened, luckily, to be there), take it up in an elevator, walk it down a long hall to the apartment, and carry it in to pile it up in my new room. It took us a while to get all those boxes out of there, because nobody wanted to carry a heavy box full of books. We split them up and my parents went back and forth a lot. My new roommate could help us some, when she wasn't at work. But I couldn't just choose a weekend, I had to move as soon as I could. So by the first day of February, I could sit on my futons in the middle of a pile of boxes full of books and come to grips with the fact that I no longer lived in a house. I was paying more rent, now, for less space, having moved from a lovely house into a second-story bedroom. I sat there feeling the wave of fatigue and loss.

I remember this one moment very well. Because I hadn't been able to drive my car, my dad wanted to use it some to drive it to try to keep the battery charged. So, when I had moved, we went down to the garage to get into my car. But it wouldn't start. My dad sat there, trying to start it up, but no luck. I remember just staring at him. I remember feeling no surprise. I felt no anger. I felt no annoyance. I felt nothing. Of course, I thought, it doesn't start. Nothing, now, in my life, absolutely nothing, is anywhere near normal or pleasant, so of course it won't start.

My parents, of course, knew that they would need to jump-start it in order to take it in to check whether it would need a new battery, or simply need to be recharged. My father wanted to be sure to do that right away, knowing that they had to leave soon. But we couldn't jump start it parked the way it was in the garage, because we couldn't get their car close enough to attach the cords. I had never been inclined, all my adult life, to mess with auto service companies. I inherited that kind of stinginess from my mother. So we stood there just trying to figure out how to do it ourselves. We had to get it out of the garage. "No problem," she said. "We'll just push it out of the garage." But I couldn't push. My mother knew the situation, and wouldn't let me push. "You drive," she said. I stood there almost in disbelief. I looked at my parents. My parents looked at me. My father said, "You drive."

I will remember all my life, sitting in the driver's seat of my car, watching my sixty year-old parents push a car out of a garage with their daughter just sitting there, just turning the wheel slightly. If I had seen that in a movie, I would have laughed. Sitting there doing it, I sat there in shock. *What next? What awful thing is next on the list?*

The cardiac follow-up

I went to see Dr. K_1—the cardiologist recommended by my neurologist—at UCLA. I was pleased to stay within the network at UCLA, in part because of the high quality of care, but also because it would be easy for them to exchange information about the complicated nature of my medical circumstances. I signed some forms so that he could read my *entire* file. Of course, he wanted to repeat some tests, and to do some new ones. So one afternoon I showed up, I got gooped up, I got electroded-up, I got all strapped up, and I took another stroll on a treadmill. Once again, I started walking on the level and I ended up running up a steep hill. I went directly from running uphill to lying on a table, and they did the sonogram goop-up one more time. The technician, once again, was very nice. She knew I was interested in what was happening, and so she let me see what was showing up and gave me a little crash course on how a sonogram does what it does. She was happy that I seemed to be having no problems with the test at all, but the sonogram itself revealed something. My cardiologist came in to see the results, and he was interested in those images that the sonogram produces. Just there, just on the upper right, was a small slightly visible dark spot. Very small, but there. Yup. Mild infarction.

So his examination agreed with the Iowa team. I had had a mild but actual heart attack. But why? I had done "greater than the 85% maximum predicted heart rate for age." My cholesterol levels "have been very low." He couldn't immediately give an explanation, either. He prescribed some additional tests, ones I had not done before, to see if we could find out anything else. One of those was an "angiogram"—I had to return a few days later for that.

In the meantime, back at the ranch . . .

I have to say that my job had also become a little bit surreal. The fact of my heart attack was widely known at work. I wasn't really offended by that, even if it was perhaps an example of the same problem of medical privacy. But since I had to ask for leave after-the-fact, and since I had to file for disability, there was a lot of paperwork. There was also a fortuitous joke about my attack: one of my colleagues, older, with some known medical difficulties and with a family history of cardiac problems, had also had a mild heart attack shortly after mine. He recovered well, and humorously said later: "I had a *sympathetic* attack"—in sympathetic response to my attack. So there we all were, looking at a brief two weeks in one small institution: a new director, two heart attacks and an earthquake.

But there is another reason why I didn't feel so offended by that. Most people view a heart attack as some dangerous, painful thing which sneaks up on you. Most people don't feel at all negative about that—most have nothing but sympathy. So hearing that I had had some weird medical emergency provoked nothing but sympathy in most of those people (at least, in those that I know about). So I knew that I would be asked about that, but I could honestly say that none of the doctors knew why that had happened. So this medical difficulty—the heart attack—didn't present me with the dilemma of how to respond: I wouldn't have to lie.

Although I had returned to full time, I took a day off to go do this next medical test, the angiogram. This one has to do with the structure and performance of your heart, which requires that they actually put some radioactive liquid into your heart and look at the images that the "x-ray films" then reveal. In order to do that, though, they need to put a very thin plastic tube through a major vein *all the way to your heart.* The highly visible radioactive stuff will then shoot directly to your heart, and they can then take images of the blood flow in the heart ventricles which might indicate more than the sonogram can test for cardiac problems. They use the big vein in your groin in order to do it.

The good thing about using that vein is that it is large enough and strong enough to easily get the small tube up into your heart, and so that there would be no damage to the vein itself. The bad thing is that that vein is large enough and strong enough that it will pump a lot of blood out of any hole it might find. It won't actually hurt, they told me. The main thing is that after the test is done you have to go back to your hospital room and lie very still, on your back, with a substantial weight right on your groin in order to help your vein to "clot"—to fix that little hole in the wall of the vein so that your blood won't seep out.

I went into the UCLA hospital to have that done. It is an outpatient procedure. You need to show up early so that they can get the test done early. Then you will have several hours to lie still and recover to the point where you can go home that evening. You don't eat any breakfast and check in very early. They don't want you to eat until after the test is over. A nurse will shave one side of your groin, where your leg joins your pelvis, exactly where it is easy to get to that major vein. A resident specialist comes by to tell you a little about the procedure. It doesn't hurt. You feel a little discomfort in your groin when they insert the tube, but it isn't pain. You won't feel the motion of the tube. When the tube is placed exactly right in your heart, and when they inject the radioactive stuff, you may feel it a little bit. Lots of people don't, though.

My parents were still in Los Angeles, and so drove me there and would drive me home that evening. I checked in early and got "prepped" with the shave. I lay there, in bed, waiting to be taken down to radiology. I waited a while. I waited more. I rolled over to the left side. I got nice and hungry. I got nice and bored. I rolled over to the right side. I talked to my mother. I talked to my roommate. I sent my parents down to get some lunch, of which I could have none. I stared at the ceiling. I looked out the window, remembering looking out the window in the hospital back in Iowa, but it wasn't snowing outside. It was another beautiful California day. I thought to myself: this is just *another* department in medical hell.

Finally, I got told why. The radiologist who was to do my procedure had gotten involved with victims of an emergency situation, and so ended up even later than how late they had earlier thought he would be. He still couldn't do it, but now they had scheduled me with somebody else. So, they could now do the test on me. Down we went to the basement of the hospital, into a huge, very dark room with some more machinery to do this test. My parents, of course, had to sit up in a lobby and wait . . . .

They set a bunch of machinery nearby, and then get the needle. I remember looking at the ceiling, not the same ceiling as before, but it looked an awful lot like the ceiling in Iowa. I could feel the rubber-gloved hands on my groin, and then I felt the prick of the needle. I felt a little poke—not bad—but then the most extraordinary thing happened. I could see a little plume of blood shoot up towards the ceiling.

There seemed to be some quick reactions to that. I could hear some talk that I didn't really understand, and I could feel a stiff shove down onto my groin. It didn't really hurt, it just felt really odd. I had yet another flash memory of that stiff shove on my spine (the bone marrow biopsy), and that stiff grip on my heart (the infarction). I wasn't really in pain, though. I'm not one of those people who have such a strong horrific reaction to blood, either. I knew it was mine. There was very little question about that. But I lay there taking a deep breath and saying to myself, *okay, what next?*

The journey of the tube up the pike to my heart was what was next. Do you remember that they had told me that once that tube was in there, I wouldn't feel it any more? Wrong. I felt it. It was yet another case, in my life, of an extremely odd physical sensation. It wasn't pain. In fact, one of the strange effects of *not* feeling pain is that my attention wasn't distracted by simply fighting the pain. My attention was 100% there. I could feel this strange little series of what I could only call "nudges." I guess they were nudges of the tube on the interior surface of my vein. Maybe it wasn't actually the tube bumping the vein, maybe it was like the little whoosh of wind you feel when the subway train zooms past you. It wasn't bad, it was just weird. And then there was the cold shower. When the tube is in place they inject the tube with a small dose of the radio-opaque stuff, and it has to be colder than your body temperature to do its job. So I lay there, knowing that cold water was coming down the pipe.

Is it possible for you to imagine what it would feel like to have cold liquid shoot into your heart? It's not painful. But it is weird. I guess some people, though, don't feel it at all.

I don't really remember how long that took, but I don't think it took any longer than normal for me. They packed a heavy weight immediately onto my groin, though, and rolled my gurney back up to the room. I wasn't in pain. My groin felt a little tender, and that huge weight was a little annoying. What I was was royally irritated that this had taken so long. And, even worse, what I was was tired, grouchy and *hungry*!!!!

The first thing I needed to do was to drink some more water to stay hydrated. The second think I needed to do, shortly after the first thing, was go to the bathroom. But, you can't just get up and go to the bathroom right after the puncture of your groin vein now under a big heavy pad. You can't do much of anything. So, ... well, maybe you can guess the rest of that story. And then there was the blood flow problem. The normal procedure is to do the test early in the morning so that you have plenty of time to use the weight to help the artery clot back to normal. But they hadn't done me early in the morning—they had done me in the afternoon.

This was directly related to another little problem. After the infarction back on New Year's Eve, I had been on one aspirin a day. One of the effects of aspirin—one of the reasons some patients take it—is that it keeps your blood thin and, therefore, less likely to clot up. One of the effects of your blood being more fluid and less thick is that if, by any chance, it hits a hole in your vein, it will shoot out faster and up higher! Another is that it will bleed longer and require more local pressure to actually clot the vein in your groin. And so it became clear very soon after my catheter test that I should stay the night, lying there with a pile of bricks on my groin, so that I would certainly heal sufficiently from the test.

Having to lie on my back all night would by itself cause me back pain and keep me awake. Doing that with a pile of bricks on my groin multiplied that by a factor of three. But, I agree that it was the wiser thing to do to stay there rather than to have gone home and bled all night. "Sleeping" on my back all night was painful. The test itself had been a piece of cake. When the nurse removed the heavy weight the next morning, the vein had recovered just fine, so they checked me out. I had to call work to let them know I would be "a little late." The only remaining problem was cleaning up a large portion of my lower body which was covered with sticky dried blood.

My mom volunteered to help me clean up, but I had to

make it to work by a certain time that day to attend both an important meeting and an afternoon all-staff speech by the "CEO" of the larger, parent enterprise. My parents drove me madly over to the building, and I walked in—that is, I limped in—to make it to the meeting. Lying still with a weight on your groin for a few hours can make you a little stiff. Doing it all evening and overnight can make you stiff as a board. Walking while stiff as a board can cause pain. I made it up the elevator to my office, and from my office to the meeting room. A very few had known about the test, but everybody noticed that I walked funny. Because the meeting began, and because the person in charge of it didn't want to ask me to give information that I might not want to give, I didn't talk to anybody about it. I think some might have had a clue, though: halfway through the meeting I looked down to see that I was still wearing that little plastic hospital admission bracelet.

At the end of the day the entire staff went to hear the CEO. Because the entire staff was too large a group to congregate in our building, the presentation was to take place in a big hotel convention room just a few blocks down the street. It took *me* a while to walk there.

That angiogram test was memorable, but came back negative. The cardiologist who gave me the second opinion—Dr. K_1— arrived at the same as the first cardiologist had: my infarction was "idiopathic"—it had no known cause. So, based on medical knowledge about disorders, and treatment, and patient response, I was clearly on the outside edge of the bell-shaped curve.

Dr. K_1's advice: keep exercising, report any heart pain, take an aspirin—prescribed drug #6—every day. From now on.

So, breakfast: Mysoline© *and* aspirin *and* vitamins *and* antacid. And *coffee*.

I started to get a side effect of the aspirin: occasional slight ringing in my ears.

In a month or so, my parents returned to their home after they had done what they could to help me adjust to the new, complicated, frustrating, demanding way of life. I remember standing there, watching the car drive away, feeling—irrationally—abandoned. Not feeling that my parents should have stayed with me—for they had given their all to help me—but only that when they left, I was all alone—again—in another medical morass. I wondered whether I could survive it. But, of course, I did. I had to. I had no other choice.

On April 15, 1994 I went to see Dr. D-E again. He had reviewed all the material now in my medical files: the drug reactions, the low white blood cell count, the biopsy, and the multiple medications. He knew about the cardiac infarction, and the cardiologists' consensus—both in Iowa and in Los Angeles—that there was no known cause for that. He expressed some sympathy for how I must be feeling about all of it.

He reviewed for me the complicated possible side effects of the meds I had been on up to that point in time. He was explaining them very carefully, with technical detail. I was sitting there, dead tired, "processing" that information this way:

#4 Mysoline©: depression, fatigue, sleep, depression, fatigue, sleep sleep sleep, depression . . .
#3 Ativan©: downer, sleep, sleep sleep . . .
#2 Dilantin©: low white count, fatigue, constipation, nausea, clumsy, body hair, vitamin deficiency, aplastic anemia . . .
#1 Tegretol©: gait problems, depression, aplastic anemia, and, very rarely, cardiac arrythmia*!!!!*

He said he considered that it *might* have been the Tegretol© that caused my infarction.

I thought: *Jesus Christ.*

He put me on yet another medication, # 5, Neurontin©, and recommended that I go see the team psychiatrist, to see if there was anything to be done about the depression. I agreed to—once again. (I read his notes on that appointment long afterwards, describing me that day as "markedly tearful"—and God, I was. Then he wrote: "Problem #1: seizure disorder at this time appears to be continuing to demonstrate intractability with recurrent episodes of monthly seizures . . . Problem #2 is that of depression.")

On April 18, 1994 I went to see the psychiatrist. My records tell me that I did it, but I have a very vague and confused sense about what that appointment was like. What I recall is that the psychiatrist made the diagnosis of clinical depression. What I remember feeling, again, was: *No shit!* He had no specific recommendations, other than to come back for psychotherapy. I didn't want more medical stuff, or insurance forms to fill out, or checks to write.

I had been working for the interim director of the institute since 1992. When the new director took office, in January, 1994, I hoped to God I could get a job—with insurance—with him. My background—and my Italian language—was directly related to the kinds of projects we knew he would pursue, and so he interviewed me. I waited to hear whether I got the job. In the meantime, my contract expired. I sweated about that. Because the new director was considering me, I got a conditional brief extension of my old contract.

On that same day, April 18, 1994, when I got back from my psychiatrist's appointment, I found out that my new boss had hired me, and I signed a new contract This contract was still for a limited-term—not a permanent job—but this contract was for three years, and was "potentially renewable."

I look back and regret that life was such, at that point in time, that I felt more relief about getting that job at all than I did about the fact—and it was a fact—that I was actually interested in the kind of work I would do for him. But I was glad that the new job also brought me a raise—that my abilities were good enough to be worth that. I was impressed and grateful that the new director would hire me knowing about the medical problems—that is, the heart attack—that I had just had. So, I continued work I had started before on a project for a conference in Germany that fall, and I began to produce some local smaller events in Santa Monica.

But the most recent crazy catastrophe hadn't changed the underlying one. I was still pumped full of the downers. I was officially "clinically depressed." In the middle of February I went to New York City for a conference of interest to the institute for my job. On the evening various of my colleagues and I arrived, we took a lovely stroll around New York and had an early dinner, which was actually a late lunch for people from the west coast. A friend had terrific plans for a fabulous evening there—to go to a Broadway production, to go to a nightclub, to listen to some good music. It would be easy for us to stay up late because we were biologically three hours earlier than New York. But I had taken my downers at dinner, and I was already sleepy and already tired. I couldn't even achieve "wanting" to do it.

I felt regret, not that I couldn't do those things, but because I couldn't manage to feel excited enough to try. I had to apologize my way out of the offer. He headed off for an exciting night, and I went back to the hotel. Unlike many of my colleagues from the west coast, I had no trouble going to bed early. That conference was good, and I spent a lot of time taking notes on scholars that we might be interested in, but I excused myself from a few other evening plans. I didn't want to try to stay up, and I didn't want to explain why I was so tired if I did go out with friends. So I spent a lot of time either at work in the hotel or alone. And, in addition to the way I simply felt, I worried about my low white count. I worried about catching other people's colds. I was afraid to catch anybody else's flu. I tried hard to be careful about touching anybody else, and I washed my hands a lot. I remembered having seen a movie with a character who was so obsessive that he washed his hands all day long. I wondered whether I looked that way. It didn't matter, though. I did it anyway.

So, in April of 1994, I took the *fifth* medication—Neurontin©—along with Mysoline©. I started to have stomach aches with that one. I started to feel even more dizzy than my now-normal constant borderline dizziness. A month after starting Neurontin©, I had seizures. When I would go to the pharmacy to get two "sizes" of Neurontin© to take the actual prescribed amount, with two sizes of Mysoline©, the bill was about $400 a month (I would end up paying $79.11). (It seems to be very often the case that the smaller the actual amount of medication in the pill, the higher the cost per pill. So starting up on medication, or taking a dosage which requires two sizes, will cost more. And, the newer the medication, the more you will pay.) In the month of June I also went to buy some more Ativan© to have some more downers for a trip to Italy. I bought another 8 of them—they don't want you to ever have a full handful of downers like these—for $17.20. And I went to the local drug store to by antacids and buffered aspirin: about $15 per month— not covered by my insurance.

And I would get up early and get on a bus to go do another blood test.

A Return to my beloved Italy

I needed to go to Italy to meet with an official about a prospective project in Venice, and then go back to Germany to do some more preparation for the conference we had been working on for a number of years now. And since I would go to Italy for my job, I took some vacation for myself. I knew what I wanted to do. I had wanted to do this for quite a long time: go hiking in some gorgeous mountains in Italy. So I took my backpack full of hiking stuff, and a suitcase full of appropriate clothes and articles for my job activities. That stuff I could check into the train station in Venice and pick up after my hike in the mountains before I went on to Germany.

My carry-on purse contained: passport, money, one prescription bottle of small sedatives for travel, two prescription bottles of different sizes of the big sedatives, two bottles of big and small pills of the new medication, and three packets of antacids. My checked baggage contained the travel-sized containers of required but over-the-counter multi-vitamins, and extra folic acid, and vitamin E, and aspirin, and antacids, plus my invaluable ibuprofen. Do I *look* hypochondriac to you? I have always traveled with medications in all the annoyingly-sized actual prescription bottles, so that, if there were ever any question—say, in an overseas luggage search—whether those weird drugs were illegal, I would have a fighting chance to prove they were not. Trust me, it's worth the trouble.

So off I went, to the Dolomite Mountains in northern Italy. I stood at the foot of a mountain on day one, looking up the peak I was about to climb, appreciating the paradox of it all. Does anybody else volunteer to climb mountains and take sedatives at the same time? Does anybody else feel the desire to climb mountains with a dangerously low white blood cell count and constant biological fatigue? Does anybody else feel the desire to climb mountains on drugs that constantly make you unsteady and dizzy? My doctor had warned me, one more time, that flying overseas might very well produce "breakthrough" seizures. That I had to be careful with the stress of physical exercise, and I had to make sure I always took my medications with food. And he said, knowing what I was about to do, that I shouldn't ever hike alone. "What if you have seizures alone, up on top of a mountain?" he asked. My answer: "I don't care. I'm doing it anyway."

Here again is one of the effects of the diagnosis and the drugs. You should be more careful about your physical condition and activity, and you should be more careful about being alone, and you should be very careful about not doing things which are known to produce "breakthrough" seizures. In short, you should re-organize your life and stop doing stuff like that. But I didn't care. I didn't mind the danger. I couldn't stand the idea that I should never again do the stuff I had always loved to do: hike in magnificent mountains. So in my pack I put, on the top, two big bottles of water, five nutrition bars, a huge tube of sunscreen, and a pile of bottles of pills and vitamins.

If you saw in a movie a hiker who was taking downers three times a day and staying at 9000 feet or higher, hiking alone, you would think that was crazy. It was crazy, but I did it anyway. I didn't hike as fast as I had in the past, because I got tired very quickly after taking the meds, but after I hiked a few hours, burning the drug, I would feel better and better—until the next meal. I knew that my doctor thought this was a dangerous thing to do, but I felt like it gave me moments of liberation from the salt mines of staying on constant depressants. It was physically like going to the gym (even a little more strenuous), but it was emotionally like a sense of control again, and the ability to imagine my life without feeling doped out all the time. And it was the experience of trying to "enjoy" some aspect of life—the awesome beauty of nature unaffected by human catastrophe.

I decided to do anything I wanted. I climbed up some very steep slopes, without the appropriate rock-climbing equipment. I scaled my way on a goat path, six inches wide, along a steep slope, unable to see around the rocky face of the peak I was on. I hiked on ledges, a little bit clutzy and a little bit dizzy, not knowing what would happen next. I got a recommendation from one of the young men at one of the refuge cabins to go across a certain ledge—wide enough, but there might be some snow still—and to head down a less-used path. I would hike to another refuge cabin at the foot of one of these peaks you cannot climb unless you are a technical rock-climber. I wanted to go see that place. I headed out keeping an eye on the less-used trail, but hit some snow early on. It was deep, but it was melting, so you can see portions of the path every now and then to know where it's going. But I stood there, considering. I've done this kind of thing before. What you can't really see under the snow is the angle of the actual slope or any big rocks which might be there, or any actual damage to the trail. The intelligent thing to do, if you are hiking alone, is to decline to walk that way.

But, like many people who hike alone, you have to decide

whether you want to try it anyway, knowing that, the way life is, you might never have another chance. I headed into the snow bank. The snow had some very deep patches, up above my knees, in part because I would walk into a sudden dip in the ground hidden by the pile of snow. I slipped some, but falling into snow is often like falling on pillows—it hurts less to fall on snow than on clearly visible rock. I went around the bend of the slope onto a steeper rock face, and stood there, frowning, knowing that this was getting dumber every step of the way. But I stood there looking at the past year and a half, and looking at the future on those drugs being more of the past. I said to myself, *What the hell.* I stood there for a few minutes thinking about pitching down off a steep mountain and dying in some snowbank in the wilderness, versus having to stay on level sidewalks and take depressants for the rest of my life. *What the hell.* I headed out along what looked like it might have been a trail.

I didn't feel fear of dying. I hadn't decided to leap off a cliff, but I was in a zen mode of having no fear. I said to myself: of all the ways to go, Amy, this is one of the best. Do what you want to do, no matter the risk. So, I popped some pills, and off into the slope of snow I went.

Depression can be a very complicated thing. I don't want to be understood as telling other people what their depression is or is not. Talking about depression is one of the most difficult parts of my life now. You already know, I imagine, all the general statements we make about it: it affects different people differently, it affects some people more than others, it usually happens in certain human situations, it sometimes happens even when the cause of it is not known. Some people seem to be more sensitive to it—or prone to it—than others. Some people seem to feel that depression is just a case of being grumpy; indeed, some seem to think it is a decision to be grumpy—the word for somebody like that is "curmudgeon." Most of the people who think that way don't suffer depression very often. Most people have had some moments of depression in their lives, but you know, it's kind of hard to tell whether your "depression" is actually similar to somebody else's "depression." It can be hard to judge the caliber and depth of what other people feel. Have you felt depressed about certain things that happened in your life? Have you felt depressed for long periods of time, even after the effects of the event which triggered it are long gone?

Are you one of the many people who seem to be always sensitive to the dark side of things? The eternal optimists often seem to see that as just being pessimistic. Of course, those of us who are sensitive to the dark side—and I am one of them—sometimes see the optimists as shallow, and unwilling or unable to face the undeniable dark side of human life. And when you are coping with a major medical diagnosis and its effects, you wonder whether the optimists have the vaguest idea what your life is now like.

The diagnosis of epilepsy is commonly associated with depression. Dr. D-E had, you may recall, told me that from the beginning. The depression can be directly related to hearing that word used to describe you. It can be directly related to the reactions that other people have when they hear that about you. It can be directly related to the effects that the diagnosis itself has on economic, social and legal issues in your life. It seems, in fact, to be very rare that anybody gets the diagnosis and is not depressed about it (unless they are one of the few people actually wanting to get that diagnosis, and that—from my perspective—seems awfully weird).

Dr. D-E had told me, and I have also read a little about this, that there are some cases—not many—in which the actual location of the seizures in the brain might produce a sense of "euphoria," of pleasure. In those cases the actual seizure itself doesn't produce depression, but the diagnosis and the effects of the diagnosis can cause it nonetheless.

And then there are the medications. I don't want to seem to be saying here that I professionally know all about them—I don't. I know some stuff about them, though. I have had the personal experiences, and I have read some of the studies on the drugs I have taken. Between December 1992 and June 1994, I had taken: Tegretol©, Dilantin©, Ativan©, Mysoline©, and Neurontin©. Many of those are known to chemically produce depression itself. Some are known to produce physical side effects which themselves can cause depression. Dilantin©, for instance, is known to increase your body hair and coarsen your features—that is likely to be a cause of depression for many people, especially women. All of these medications are known to produce fatigue. When you've got both the sense of fatigue and low white and red blood cell count and take downers, let me tell you, you are tired *all the time*. And trying to live while being dead tired all the time is depressing. Knowing that this condition will last 24 hours a day every remaining day of your life can also transform your depression into despair.

Dr. D-E has told me that sometimes patients suffer so much from depression, even to the point of becoming suicidal. For these patients, the physician will alter the medications and try to get the patient in psychological therapy in direct response to that problem. The side effect of depression, in that case, is actually worse than the effects of the seizures themselves. I have had moments of depression during which I would certainly agree.

On that trail in the Dolomite Mountains that day, I slipped on an icy patch, rolling over and over down 500 some feet of steep, slippery slope. It was not a catastrophe. It was a silly fall on a dangerous trail. I had to slog my way back up, taking three steps up and sliding two steps down. Two hours later I was back up to the trail, exhausted. I convinced myself to turn around and go back.

On the next day I ended up on the top of a ridge looking down into a steep, gravelly crevasse. The next refuge cabin, though, on the edge of the less-rocky slope, was 3/4 of the way down that thing. I had no fear. (I am not boasting about this—it is dumb to hike like that with no sense of—at least—caution.) I headed down that slope, skidded, slid and even rolled a little bit. Late that afternoon, I strolled up onto the narrow ridge on the other side of the refuge, and sat there watching the oncoming afternoon storm. I should have gone back down to the refuge, away for the ominous thunder clouds and the likelihood of lightning. You never want to be above tree line in a mountain thunderstorm. I knew better, so I strolled back to the cabin. I popped my pills and stayed that stormy night at the refuge, then headed on. Two days later I hiked up to the razor-sharp peak of another ridge, and stood there, looking down the sheer face of that cliff at the little village 1,500 feet below. Standing there, breathing hard, having burned up a lot of calories and a lot of downer, I looked out that cliff and felt good. That was the first time in a very long time I had actually felt *good*.

Two days after that, I went back through Venice. I know Venice very well. I lived there for a while back when I was doing research in one of the best libraries in Italy for my dissertation. While I had lived there, I had the project of walking on every single street in the entire city—and I think I did it. I spent the last two days of that vacation there, feeling the beauty of the city and memories of the past. There is an amazing Byzantine basilica church in the main plaza in Venice. It has close to unique architecture—very detailed. The interior ceilings of the basilica are paved in mosaics of gold leaf and deep, dark reds and blues and greens, with the names of the saints and of others from the past in black letters and in old, Latin abbreviations and in Greek characters next to the figures. In the basilica of San Marco in Venice, you can sit and see the stories of the Bible in brilliant figures all around you. The muted lighting inside makes the gorgeous gold ceilings not just sparkle, but glow. The floors and walls are done in porphyry or in mosaics of marble. The tile pieces are sets of rectangles, circles and triangles, all set in complicated geometric patterns. The mosaic marble floors are not all smooth and level. They look like frozen gentle waves— the basilica has survived the undulations of that man-made island for going on a thousand years. Nothing in America looks anything like that place.

I sat there and remembered how I had felt in Venice, four years before, when the future looked so good, back when I thought I would write about this place. I remembered some lines from a deeply moving poem I had studied long ago: *Sailing to Byzantium* by W.B. Yeats. I remembered some pages in my diary about how moved I was then, and felt the sadness washing in— for I no longer felt that way. I could appreciate the beauty of the place, and I could contemplate the history of that city, I could think about the meaning of the poetry, but what I felt was fatigue, and sadness. The way that I had felt then seemed to be in the distant past.

I caught my flight north to go do some more work on the upcoming conference on German philosophy and architecture. Then I caught my flight home, took a handful of meds and Ativan©, conked out on the plane, and woke up—from all the downers—an hour later with seizures. Nobody on the plane, of course, noticed them. I didn't sleep, I got the usual headache, and I looked out the window into the pitch black and thought about the fact that I could see the future happening, again and again and again, right now.

And I would get up very early—before I took my meds— get on a bus, and go get a needle stuck into my arm for a blood test. I had started to alternate which elbow they took the blood from.

In August—with a little gauze taped on to one elbow—I took a short vacation to go to Colorado with my parents. They were looking at houses there, having decided to leave Iowa City. I had increased my Neurontin©, and I had begun to have regular bouts of major-league indigestion. I remember lying on the couch at our motel cabin, holding my stomach, in pain. I didn't want to eat, and I didn't digest normally at all. But my seizures remained exactly what they had been before, so Neurontin© did not seem to affect them at all. In October I went back to Germany to produce the conference I had been planning for the preceding years. I flew into Dresden on my way to Weimar, and walked around contemplating the fact that that city had been nearly destroyed by the bombing in WWII. I walked around a little bit there, thinking, again, about the suffering of that generation of people.

A conference like that one is an extremely exhausting non-stop event while it's happening. I couldn't possibly make sure to get enough sleep at the right time. I couldn't just stay in my room feeling bad. I had to stay very sharply awake to run around, do a ton of stuff, solve problems, and stay in control.

I had two seizures there, one having almost sprinted into the ladies' room at a restaurant, and another just sitting there, listening to a presentation on Nietzsche and a famous French architect. When I could go to bed, I would take my handful of meds, pop some more Ativan©, leave a wake-up call and steel myself for the next week or so. I was very lucky that you can get good coffee in Germany. In my condition, whether the coffee was good or not had nothing to do with my drinking it—I required the caffeine hit in order to stay on my feet. Everything else went well. I couldn't help but feel that my job required me to put that kind of performance above my own health concerns. I personally wanted to do that job well, and I wanted to be sure to keep doing my job well in order to keep that job and so stay insured.

Just after Thanksgiving, I woke up with seizures. On December 9, 1994 I went back to Dr. D-E. He listened to my account of the last few months. I told him about the work I had done in Europe, and what we—my institute—had accomplished. We talked about the difficulty of my job and the necessity of travel. I provided testimony that the Neurontin© medication had changed nothing. He asked for my careful account of the seizures themselves. He took some notes. He stared for a while at my blood test reports. He stared for a little while at me. He decided to taper me off of Neurontin©, but keep me on Mysoline©. He started me up on medication #6: Mesantoin© (adding $46.14 to the monthly cost of my medications.) (His notes in my file for that appointment: "drug difficult epilepsy.")

My parents bought a house in Colorado, and I spent Christmas at with them there. I was extremely fatigued. I mean, I was *beyond* fatigue. I was bordering on total inertia. I slept a lot. I "napped" a lot. I stood on the back deck looking at the gorgeous mountains close-by and tried to consider that I was happy to have made it through another year. And yet, Decembers had been scary for me. I was nervous. What's going to happen this December? But I was too tired to be actually panicked.

That was a Christmas without catastrophe.

1995

In January, 1995 and February I did four blood tests—averaging $120 a piece—to monitor the medications and the low white count, but I was *seizure free*.

I was on the full dose of Mysoline© and the full dose of Mesantoin©. There is no point in my saying the word "tired" anymore, because these drugs produce new and awesome dimensions of "tired." I was still alive—sort of. I still had the constant low white count. But I started to let myself think that maybe, maybe the addition of this new drug could solve the problem. I knew better than to think that I would stop taking the sedatives, but maybe I could stop worrying that I would have seizures on the job. Maybe the future would start to look a little bit better.

One night in March, I woke up with the old familiar feelings. "Seizure free" had lasted 4 months, and then I broke through. I saw Dr. D-E soon after and told him, again, about the seizures. I don't think he was surprised, because I had the well-established track record of breaking through everything. He listened to my account, looked at my blood test, and adjusted my dose. In my journal that day I wrote: *I know what this means*. Surgery was the only thing left with a chance of actually stopping my breakthrough seizures.

I got more depressed—if that's possible. I wrote, to myself, in my notebook:

> *I'd like to die in some bizarre accident, so that it would all be over, but nobody would feel guilty. I'm not going to get that though. I'm going to have to do the deed myself, and my parents would never cease to think that there was something they could have done and didn't, when, in fact, there's nothing anybody can do.*
> A few days later I wrote something else I know is true: *I think I am systematically not letting myself hope for anything good, so as not to suffer the letdown when it's taken away.*

In April I went back to the pharmacy and got two sizes of Mesantoin©, two sizes of Mysoline©, and a new drug, #7, diazepam. One of the brand names of diazapam is much better known: Valium©. So, picture this: I was on two major-league downers plus another one known to risk aplastic anemia. My bill: $222.55. Five days later I had to go to the lab before breakfast and have yet another fasting blood test done: low white blood cell count. There was a new technician there, so I started to get to know blood-lab technician #3. And I saw Dr. D-E again. I decided to try to consider surgery—that is, provide Dr. D-E with the kind of information he would require to consider it—and got put on the list for another in-patient EEG.

In April my job review was due on the 17th. I had to see that before I decided what to say to my boss about the upcoming medical procedures. But I didn't get the review. My boss was out of town, so it would have to wait. So *I* would have to wait. From my diary: *I'm slipping away. Even I can see it. I haven't cared about anything for so long. I'm totally faking it at work, just trying to do so unpretentiously so as not to look like I'm claiming to know stuff I don't know about. That's one tiny little piece of relative honesty I can maintain: silence.*

Towards the end of April, I went to Bologna, Italy. I was part of a team of people from my institution discussing a joint-project proposal with a number of Italian agencies and institutions. On my way back, I had a long layover in De Gaulle airport, so I planned to take the subway into the city and go to the Louvre to see a few paintings. Then I would walk over to the Sorbonne to revisit a part of Paris I had enjoyed during a trip there long ago, back in the first years of graduate school. But I got to De Gaulle and sat there—in the airport—for a while, so tired. So drugged and so tired. I walked down to the entrance for the subway, but I found myself just standing there, feeling mostly fatigue. I sat there wishing that I wasn't so tired, and wishing that I could work myself up to go into the beautiful city of Paris, and to visit the *arrondissement*—the neighborhood—I remembered well. The fact that I didn't feel like I had the strength to do it made me cry, right there in De Gaulle airport. I couldn't make myself do it. I went to find an airport bar, not to get a stiff drink, but to get some strong French coffee and then pop some more downers. I sat there and remembered Paris, and my pre-drug life.

In May of 1995 I took my long-planned vacation to Sicily with the same friend I had traveled with that on that fabulous trip in 1988. That first trip was the one which gave me the bug bites which sent me to Student Health which gave me a bunch of conflicting diagnoses which led to the one that started all of this. I was deeply depressed, once again, by the breakthrough seizures. I was deeply affected by the Mysoline© version of phenobarbital and so tired and so scared what the future would bring. We did what the two of us had always loved to do—hiking. My hiking speed had gone way down, and she was very sensitive to how I felt about that. We made it up a cliff over the ocean and stood there, looking out to sea.

I remember thinking, again, that I would rather die hiking than stop hiking. We drove most of the way up the south side of Mt. Etna and took a hike further up, into the volcanic fields of the peak, enjoying the strangeness of it all. That night, we sat out on a porch in a small restaurant, and I swallowed another handful—the third that day—of drugs. I was enjoying that vacation, but I was also doing what was now actually normal for me: thrashing back and forth between enjoyment and depression. I was mercurial—I was sometimes just silent and depleted, and other times irritated and short-fused, about the stupidest little things. I had been doing that for a long time. My friend has known me well enough, and known everything that was happening to me, that she was holding on for me, trying to cheer me up but knowing that the depression was always there, wide and deep.

That night she woke up in the middle of the night, sick as a dog, and spent the next two days in our hotel room. I did everything I could do for her, but time was the only cure. I was the only one who could speak Italian, so I went to get some stuff from various stores for her. What she wanted to do most, of course, was lie in bed and try to pass out. I thought about the irony of it all—I had bunches of drugs to pass out with, but I wouldn't wish them on any other human being. What I wanted to do, knowing that there was nothing further to do for her but wait it out, was to drive up to another trailhead on the north face of Etna.

But. You may recall that I had surrendered my driver's license in December, 1992. I had gone two and a half years without my license, but I stood there, knowing that I wouldn't be able to do much of anything while my friend—the driver—was so sick. I would have to stand there, in Sicily, looking up at the place we both wanted to go to, but just walk around the small town regretting that I could not go there. And I stood there saying to myself: maybe you should get in the car and go up to the trail . . . . I contemplated that it wasn't the case that I would drive in the city streets, or on the highway. It wasn't the case that I would have a *gran mal* while driving and slam into somebody. I would know, in advance, as I always had, that I was going to have a seizure. And I would stay off the busy roads. I stood there for a while, going back and forth, knowing that if I didn't do it then, I would probably never do it. I got in the driver's seat, turned the key, and sailed away.

The feeling was strong, not because I hadn't been in cars all that time, but because it gave me what the experience of driving almost always gives some of us—a sense of *control*. I could go anywhere. I could stop anywhere. I could go faster. I could drive as long or as far as I wanted to. I could change my mind and turn right instead of left. I could go case a particular trailhead, decide maybe that I didn't like the looks of it, and just turn around and head out. I found an enticing little path, and took it, but not all the way to the top. But that didn't matter to me, because I just hiked up to where there was an impressive view and then sat for a while, just enjoying the fact that I could get anywhere near there at all. And then I cruised, literally, along the back roads up the gentle slope of Etna, and looked back at the past two and a half years: my sense of control had been close to forcibly removed.

It isn't the case that people who can't drive can't do anything they want to do. That of course depends on the circumstances of your life. And it depends radically on whether you never got used to driving. For those of us who got used to the freedom to go wherever and whenever we want to, the *sense* of that loss is one of the worst. So, on the one hand, I absolutely loved that cruise on the north slopes of Etna. On the other hand, when I came back down, and gave the keys back to my friend, and knew that I was back among the deprived, I slid down to despair.

When I came back home, my review had still not been done. From my diary then:

> *Twice a week now, sometimes more, I'm having trouble making myself go to the gym. All I want to do is sleep. I don't think I can stand it. I'm actually dreaming about driving—I haven't felt that free for years. It's gone now, though. I have to talk to [my boss] soon. It's all going to crash and burn . . . I know I'm going to cry. He'll be flustered by that . . . . I don't get to choose my leave-takings now. Not even that. It would be one thing to feel boxed in by the needs of a husband and children; to feel boxed in and alone is another . . .*

> *Maybe I'll get all the time off anybody could need. I have a feeling I'm in for some more instruction in how little I'm worth to anybody.*

In June I started to fill out the paperwork for the in-patient EEG at the Santa Monica Hospital.

Another blood test on June 13: low white cell count. $223.36: (I paid $44.67).

Almost at the bottom

At the very end of June I went to Colorado for a few days. We would put some picnic stuff in the truck and just wander around a little, in the mountains, enjoying the beauty of it all. My parents weren't hikers, but they did love the scenery. My father would walk some, but my mother couldn't manage that. She just enjoyed the drive, and felt, constantly, a deep sympathy for the fact that I could not have done that for myself. We drove up a gorgeous but not a heavily-touristed pass—Waunita pass—one day and got out to walk around a little in the aspen groves. That day was beautiful, as most are in Colorado. I sat and tried to enjoy the beauty, trying to fight the despair. My mother could not hike, and I could not drive, and we communed with each other's sense of loss.

Driving back towards home, we passed through a big slope full of lupine—beautiful lavender-flowered plants, and stopped again to enjoy the beauty of the landscape—wild and empty. She and I had always enjoyed wild beauty more than many people; it was one of the experiences in life for which we were very close to each other. I sat there, feeling deep sympathy for her, for she and my father, long ago, used to hike in the mountains she loved in the summer. So she looked over that valley and felt, I think, that that was a part of her life now clearly over.

We drove back. I was trying to keep the door closed on my sense of despair. At the fork in the road, we decided to try to head home over the old version of the mountain pass we had to take. It was a gravel road, not full of tourists, with a magnificent view. So up we went. In July that year there was still snow on some of the peaks, and, as we discovered, on some of the ridges. We made it up to the pass from the west, and I hiked the 150 feet up from the road to the peak itself to see the view—for myself and for my mother. And then, as the afternoon was waning, we decided to head down the east slope towards home. So we got back in the truck, took the curvy gravel road around one edge of the peak, and came around a corner face to face with a huge snow drift over the road.

It sloped from the west side of the road, four feet deep, across to the east side. On the east edge, it was only about a foot deep—that is, it looked to be only about a foot deep. When you can't see the trail—or the "road"—underneath, you can't know whether the trail itself slopes, or is washed out. We could see the road again about 25 feet away, naked and looking just fine. My dad and I stood there, looking at the snowbank, and then looking at each other, and then looking at the snow bank, and then looking at the truck. It was a big, wide truck. Four-wheel drive, but wide. My mother was all gung-ho—let's give it a try! We got into the truck, drove carefully into the drift, and got stuck, starting to spin the wheels in a slick patch of snow we had just crushed into near ice. We had two choices: get stuck or slide sideways. My dad and I began to discuss the possibilities, knowing that we were tired, and that it was getting dark. If we had serious problems, and got seriously stuck, we might have to spend the night there before I could take the hike down to get some help. I thought about my trip in the Dolomites, and I knew that I would have tried it anyway. But then again, I might have gone rolling down the slope just like before, only this time in a huge, heavy, rolling truck. And, more importantly, I would risk having my parents roll with me.

We knew better. We shoved the truck back to where we could turn around and headed back down the west side of the slope, knowing that the drive home would take much longer now. It was a smart decision—like ones that have to be made every day in the mountains, and maybe even twice a week in normal life. But for me, it was a decision which symbolized loss—another thing I could not do.

I sank down in despair after that. By the time we pulled into the garage, I was losing control and weeping. I couldn't even move to get out of the back seat of the truck. I could hardly even talk. My parents sat there, confused by why I was so upset at that moment, but of course knowing, as they had known for a long time, why I was so depressed and had been for so long.

I finally spoke about the horrible sense of loss—loss of control, loss of freedom, loss of hope for anything to get any better, loss of the strength to carry on. I said, for the first time to my parents, that I knew I was suicidal, and that I couldn't find a reason anymore to take another handful of drugs and live another day knowing that I wouldn't ever feel any better than I did at that moment. And that there wasn't anything that anybody could do for me to change that. And that I felt very alone. And that I couldn't find any pleasure in life anymore.

My mother knew exactly how I felt. She had had the sense of deep depression in her life as well—we knew that, too. She had had the sense of loss, and the sense that there isn't anything another human being can do to fix loss itself. Other people can be as kind as they know how, and they can be emotionally supportive, but she is one of the few people I have ever know who could nakedly face the brutal reality of loss. Most people try to persuade you to see the world differently, to "look at the bright side." They think that the best way to deal with life is to turn away from the sadness, to "recognize" that everything which seems to be "loss" has the flip-side of good fortune—it is actually all for the best. Maybe life is that way for them. It's not that way for me. What in the hell could possibly be the good side of those last two and half years?

But my mother is also a constant reminder of the fact that one person should never assume that she can judge the level of despair of another. She is an example of someone who has suffered loss, but very seldom talked about it. People who don't talk about it seem to give the impression that they haven't suffered loss, even though they have deeply suffered. But, paradoxically, people who seem to be able to look at the good side can give the impression that they haven't suffered anything very serious—and that is sometimes also wrong. She is the most emotionally sensitive and supportive person I have ever known because she doesn't ever correct how you feel or how you "should" feel.

After all the efforts to comfort me had been given, she said to me: "Amy, think about the beauty of nature, and remember the lupines on Waunita pass"—the beauty of the wilderness. I know that part of why she loved the mountains so deeply is that they have nothing to do with the difficult details of human life. They are unaffected by whether you look back and think that you should have done this or that, or that things would change if only you change. Mountains, for her, refute that the only significance in human life is interaction with other people or achievements or success, or even the understanding of others. Try to feel the beauty of the world. Love the few people who love you. And remember that.

After my July 4th vacation, I came back home. I was imploding—it is hard even to describe how I felt then. I walked around with permanently gritted teeth, and I tried to do as much of my job as possible alone in the backwaters of the library or in my locked office. I was extremely nervous because my employer, the director, had not yet actually done my one-year job review—"due" on April 14. I wondered if that implied that there would be some negative responses. And I felt that I'd better tell him the truth about needing the time off for what was about to happen—the in-patient EEG—and about why it was about to happen.

I knew that I would have to make multiple appointments for the various exams, and that I couldn't really control when those would be. I knew that I would have to check in to the hospital when *they* were ready, and stay there as long as necessary. I was still worried about whether my medical problems—and the insurance—and the time off—had influenced or would influence a decision about my job. I was worried that my absence from my job might be misinterpreted. I knew that my boss would be gone for some weeks several times that summer, and I didn't want to give anybody the impression that I was just not showing up. That feeling I had had the previous year, having just had the heart attack and having to wait two excruciating months to find out whether my contract would be renewed, had hit me again in full force. If he knew what I was about to do—and why—would that affect the review? Would it affect that possible, future "renewal"?

I talked a lot to my parents about this problem. My dad certainly encouraged me, as he always had, to tell people about the problem. He was confident that my boss would support me. I had no reason to think that he would not, but, on the other hand . . . . And I had not yet seen my review! If the review was not a good one, even if it was a lukewarm one, that might very well affect any decisions about salary, or contract renewal, or support of my medical issues. And, even worse, I worried that if my boss had not *yet* written that review, telling him about my medical condition—and its upcoming effects—might actually affect what that review would say. And it was another round of the game of chicken: do you want to make sure that people think highly of you, and review your performance before they know the personal stuff?

And here's another factor—a big one. This institution is one of the few which "indemnify" their own health insurance. That is, the company pays its own health insurance benefits. Some part of the staff of the institution itself processes all the forms, reviews the medical information, stipulates "approvals," writes checks for service providers—doctors and hospitals and pharmacies—and, in essence, knows just exactly how expensive you are—and why—and may well continue to be.

Now consider this problem: I had nothing but respect for my boss. I had a certain amount of confidence that he would be a) honest in my review and b) personally supportive of my difficulties. But, I didn't actually know that. I didn't know whether being personally supportive would actually include being professionally supportive. And I lacked confidence that the other staff members who would be involved in decisions about my job would be personally helpful. I didn't feel that they would be vindictive, but I worried that they wouldn't be supportive. I had heard rumors about other experiences that seemed comparable.

I didn't want to let my boss—or the staff—know that I was asking for strong, committed support until he had actually given me the review and the raise for my performance. It was a high-stakes waiting game for me. I had to be reviewed and then have my contract renewed—and signed—before I asked for the time off to do what I was about to do. And I knew that I had already been an "expensive" employee—the multiple appointments, the constant blood tests, all the medications and the cardiac infarction. I also knew that it was entirely possible that some people might already know all of this. It was possible that decisions would be made based on that knowledge.

Now I know what you might say—other people have said it: I was being paranoid. There were legal restrictions on circulation of that kind of information. There were legal restrictions on use of that information with respect to employment decisions. But, keep in mind, I was a contract employee. If this institution didn't want me, they wouldn't have to fire me. All they would have to do is let my contract expire. Indeed, since my contract didn't actually, legally guarantee my job, they could very likely be able to "let me go" before then. And, keep in mind, losing that job would be awful, but losing that insurance—and suddenly becoming a case of "pre-existing condition"—was even worse.

And, keep in mind how I felt about it. Dr. D-E had told me that many people were prejudiced against people with epilepsy. Some of his patients had lost jobs. Some had literally never gotten jobs again. Some patients lose friends. Some—just like me—lose lovers. So, I was afraid of the consequences.

But I was about to leave for London for a conference. And my boss was about to leave for Europe for a month. I needed signatures. I needed support. I faced the job/insurance/public knowledge mess again: should I tell the truth? Will I *have* to tell the truth?

And how long can I hold out?

5 Catch-22

One of my best colleagues at work—L—was the office administrator for my boss. I had learned to like him and to trust him, but I still hadn't told him anything about this medical stuff. But he could see that I was nervous about the issue of the job performance review, and so he gave me something very valuable: confirmation that the review had been done, but had simply not yet been "processed." He was careful about what he said, but helpful: "it's not negative."

I stood there, at the edge of that cliff, and decided to trust my boss. And I decided to trust L. So I told them both the story. I'll remember all my life how that moment felt—I got instant kindness, instant sympathy and instant support. I felt enormous relief, and yet some nervousness remained. I felt trust for those two people, but I didn't know whether I should trust them. And I still didn't actually have my review. Of course, that is ultimately what trust is about. My boss said: "let L know what's happening, and do what you need to do." And then he got on a plane and went to Italy. I got on a plane and went to London.

On the 26th of *July* I got my April 14th job review. I want to actually quote some of this review because I think it's important that you see the actual content, not just my representation of it. My purpose, here, is not self-aggrandizement, but rather to document the evaluations made by my boss. This review listed the multiple projects I had been involved in—some of which involved a number of outside and foreign guests who had "remarked on the efficiency of her arrangements and the grace and warmth with which she served as host." I had "helped to bring the complicated international ... conference to a successful close."

I was now the "main coordinator for [another] complex ... project," coordinating with a number of international agencies and consultants. My "ability to work under [the director's] direction and yet independently has been crucial to the success of the project (and, indeed, to all of the projects for which she is responsible)."

I was so glad that, in the opinion of my new boss, my performance in and production of those complicated events was very positive. And there was more:

> "While working for me and for X, in his capacity as Acting Director, she was responsible for primary research on and for evaluation of (in collaboration with others, including me) the work of 30 or more candidates per scholar year (reviewing original research in four languages). This component of her job demands high-level research skills, organizational ability, and the capability to critically review material outside her own field of expertise . . . ."

I had always loved that aspect of my job, but I was very glad to have confirmation that I had not lost my abilities in scholarly research. Under "Plans for improvement":

> "occasional problems in working with other units of the Center . . . sometimes expresses her points of view in a way that might be perceived as categorical. This could easily be overcome through a more flexible attitude."

"Overall Performance Rating: Excellent."

With that review, I was promoted to a new position, and given a raise (and salary for that raise backdated). But: my promotion was to a new contract job, for the remaining two years of the previous contract, and then "potentially renewable for one additional two-year term." Again, I was relieved that I could stay insured. I thought to myself: *maybe being promoted means you are closer to being made permanent.*

One of the reasons why I had always found this medical stuff difficult to talk about was that it brought me close to an uncontrolled emotional response. That is one thing with close friends and family, but another with colleagues at work. I came very close that day, giving some information about the medical difficulties of the last year and a half, reviewing it myself, rather than suppressing the mess and moving on. But I also felt moved by the sympathy of the two colleagues I had told. You cross some of your own emotional boundaries when you reveal something like this about yourself. I began to cry a little out of relief. I had felt that exhibiting loyalty to him was part of performing my job. And now I felt personal respect for him as well.

My Ph.D. degree had been in the Humanities, and part of why I had pursued those studies and that degree was that many of the disciplines in the Humanities involved the high-ground of ethics in human civilization. It involved moments in which people had to make choices about what was ethically and morally right, even if it wasn't what seemed the most expedient. I had just seen one of those acts, and was impressed.

The next day I got on the plane to London, took my handful of pills and passed out. From my journal: *This doing the Grand Tour on sedatives with aplastic anemia is something else.* At the National Gallery, I sat on a bench looking at the Arnolfini Marriage painting by Van Eyck. I wrote:

> *At least, I tell myself, I'm not faking love where I don't feel it. That's one tiny 5 centimeters of relative honesty, maybe. I don't know that I'm proud of it. I*

> *just feel like a cornered animal, unwilling to perform. No, that's not right. I don't know what I feel. I don't feel much except anxiety and pain, flinching from the past, looking away from the future.*

I went up to Oxford, and sat there on the steps of the Bodlian library. From my journal: It might be nice to come up here and disappear into the Bodlian, but then again, what for? I've been trying to find the part of me that was a scholar once, but I can't. She's gone. I did my job—attended a conference and took extensive notes on scholars we might be interested in. I'm good at that in part because I can handle being alone. I could actually want to be alone, or at least be afraid of being very social. I got on the plane, popped some sedatives, and flew back home. From my journal: *Jet lag w/ aplastic anemia is really something else.*

I began to prepare for the inpatient EEG testing for my seizures. The plans were that I would check-in, get wired up with electrodes on my scalp and get put on closed-circuit TV monitors 24 hours a day. I would then go cold turkey on my medications, and "hope" for seizures. I had spent most of my time, of course, trying to avoid seizures, but now I was on the flip-side. But in order to make this worthwhile, you want to have them while you are plugged in and on-line so that your doctors can both see and measure what exactly happens in your brain.

First I did a PET scan—a Photon Emission Tomography scan—to provide my doctors with some "pictures" of my brain activity. This one involves an injection of some radioactive liquid, but it isn't painful. (The insurance bill for that one was $936.) I also did a "WADA" test, where they measure the locations of certain brain functions with a fairly simple set of injections. That summer I also went to see a psychologist (not a psychiatrist), whom I had not seen before, for some performance "behavior" tests—reading and puzzle-solving and picture recognition—in order to get some ideas about the way my brain currently functioned. I did those tests as a medical procedure, not as psychological therapy. (But let me tell you now that I began a long, complicated series of inquiries about the insurance coverage of that.)

At the end of July my parents came again to help me deal with doing this stuff. Dr. D-E had told me to begin to taper down on my medication before I went in to the hospital in order to raise the chances that I would have seizures while all wired up. I had my concerns, though, because I had the feeling that the seizures would "normally" occur very soon anyway. I was afraid that reduction of the medication might bring them on too fast. But he advised me to do it anyway because it would increase my chances of having seizures while I was wired up in the hospital. That issue remains a constant difficulty in this procedure. For many people, you can't predict exactly when their seizures will happen. The doctors want to try to ensure that they will happen while you are being monitored—that's the entire point of this complicated and expensive project. I was to check in to the ward the very last day of July.

I think I was suppressing the fear that I was about to lose more control over my life—to get strapped into a bed and just sit there, contemplating a) my life in general now and b) the stupid futility of doing this now. I remember standing there in the hospital room, actually gritting my teeth to do this. I was in a kind of manic mode at that time, only I wasn't going back and forth between elation and depression. I was going back and forth between anger and despair. I think I wondered to myself, even then, whether anger was my emotional defense against despair. But there is at least one other major factor: the side effects of Mysoline©—a kind of phenobarbital.

The battles with anger and despair had been going on long before I stood there in the hospital room. I remember some moments of naked fury, something I had felt very seldom in my pre-drug life. One day, at Dr. D-E's office, I sat there in the waiting room. My appointment time came and left. I sat there. Waiting. I paced a little bit. I sat there waiting. All the other patients in that room were called in to see their doctors, and yet I just paced around. Hours went by. And I'm not exaggerating this time:

literally hours. I got furious. I remember going up to the check-in desk to start to actually argue with the staff there: I have a job for Christ's sake!! I can't just sit here for a week!! If he has too many patients today, tell me now!!! I am not going to sit here anymore Make me another appointment—on a day when he doesn't have 43 people in one afternoon!!! I was yelling at the staff. One of the assistants took me back into the hallway nearer the offices and tried to calm me down. "You are next. You will be seen today." She had me sit there in the hallway, closer to my neurologist's office, and told me, for the umpteenth time that it wouldn't be long now. I remember sitting there with my teeth clenched, gripped onto the arms of that chair, feeling that kind of naked fury—above and beyond what was actually happening to me.

It took a while, but I did see him. And he didn't criticize me. He didn't tell me to calm down. He asked me the usual questions about how things were going, and whether I had had any seizures, and were there any other problems. I think I calmed down a little. I think maybe I had just burned some of my jet fuel. I think I sat there and told him, again, that I had had seizures, and that I hated my meds, and all I could do was my job, and **dammit**, I couldn't even do that if I had to sit out there in the waiting room all day, and wasn't there any other treatment, and would this **ever** end??? He sat and listened to me. He sat and watched me break into tears and cry. He kept me there a while. By the time I left that appointment, I think I had swung back to despair. (From his notes on that appointment: "Needs telemetry/report MRI/PET/Psychiatry!")

By the time I got home on the bus I felt literally awful. Two or three days later I went back to that office to apologize to the staff for how angry I had been. I nearly cried trying to say that. One of the women at that office reached over and stroked my arm, and said, "It's alright. We understand." Her kindness made me cry. What I found out later was that the appointment before mine was with a patient who was falling apart—emotionally. And what Dr. D-E had done with that patient was the same thing he had done with me—and more than once: stay with him (or her) and try to help the patient cope with that. I left, embarrassed by the way I had treated this department full of people who were, in fact, trying to help people like me.

There had been a series of tests to be done before I checked into the hospital for the in-patient EEG. My parents took me to the smaller medical offices to do one. We sat there sat there sat there. Again. This test had been scheduled close to dinner time, and yet dinner time came and went. And, of course, missing dinner time might make almost anybody grumpy, but I had to take my dinnertime meds with food, or I'd get close to sick. I went up to the staff to ask why on earth this was taking so long—the scan is known to take x amount of time—what's the problem? The answer was that they were late in their schedule, and had to still do another PET scan before mine. I got pissed off about that. *Why didn't you just **tell** me that?* The answer: we called your home number, but nobody answered. Me: *I gave you my work number!* Them: we didn't have it. Me: *why didn't you just **tell** me that when I checked in?* Them: no answer.

It was another case of difficult experiences. Anybody might have been angry about that, but I had a very, very short fuse. My parents took me on a walk: several loops of a few blocks, to try to get me to calm down. I did. A little bit. But I stayed angry. I had another appointment with the psychologist for tests. I thought this one was silly, but it had been scheduled, so I went to the office to do it. And waited. This one I don't even remember, because, for some reason, things screwed up. I think the appointment had been made in error, but I don't remember whose error. I got angry about that one, too. My mom took me out in the hallway and we walked up and down. She wasn't trying to tell me that I was overreacting, because she knew exactly why things like this made patients angry. But she told me later that she could see that I was right on the edge. I think I spent a lot of my waking hours—when I could get some—on the edge.

And I still had seizures.

I went to work with my teeth gritted, knowing that I had to do that well, and that I had to control myself to the absolute maximum. Fortunately, then, a lot of my job was research, so I could sit in the library or at my computer work alone. But when I had to interface with others, I had to stifle that short fuse—and that of course meant that I would get pissed off even at the slightest difficulty with the rest of my life and with my friends. It was another kind of paradox: if I stayed sleepy, I was less irritated. If I jacked myself up, I could do my job better, but I had to work harder to stay calm. I was angry at myself for wanting to give up and sleep.

That part of my life is an example of one of the more complicated aspects of treatment. I was on a drug—Mysoline©—known for these kinds of effects. I was at a point in my treatment where it was clear that my drugs weren't stopping the seizures. Dr. D-E, though, wouldn't take me off those drugs—so my sense that things would get any better had left town, never to return.

1995 was already a very tough year. It was a very emotional year. I have been—let me correct that: I *had* been—in much better control of my emotions than I had become. I had some of the very best reasons why that was happening, but that doesn't change the effects of that condition, on yourself and on the people who deal with you. It pulled me ever deeper into despair. No, let me put that differently: it *strapped me down* into despair, because I knew that I had to work harder than ever for control, and yet achieving that control wouldn't actually change anything for the better. All it could possibly ever do would be keep things from getting worse. So: anger and despair fought for the upper hand. And, once again, that control in my job was what I had to do, even if everything else had to pay the price. And it did.

A few days before I went to the hospital for the EEG, I went to another big seminar produced by a colleague, on a topic I was very interested in. I remember being so tired, and so afraid that I would have seizures there, that my attention was wandering. I was just about to strap myself into a hospital bed. One of my colleagues noticed that I was tired and in a bad mood, and asked, but I didn't want to tell her why. All I did was apologize for the fact. Since I was only a spectator, not the producer, I knew I could leave if necessary. Fortunately, I didn't need to do that.

The in-patient EEG

The night before I checked into the hospital, I took my reduced amount of meds, said goodnight to my parents, and went to bed, very tired. I woke up with a start early in the morning of the last day of July with that tidal wave of fear. I got the icy chills, with a burning metallic taste, and I knew . . . . The world telescoped away from me, and the wave washed up my stomach. I had seizure after seizure, stronger than they had been for a long, long time, freed by the reduction of my medication. I was nearly sick to my stomach with the visceral feelings of the seizures themselves and the horrible sense that my warning to Dr. D-E about the seizures all happening *before* I would check in had come true. I took some diazepam, which acts more quickly that the other meds, but to no avail. I lay there, awake, seizing and feeling tidal waves of despair. I got the usual brutal headache and lay there, furious at the futility of it all, once again.

My parents took me to the EEG ward, and I checked in anyway. I had told the medical nursing staff to get hold of Dr. D-E and tell him the news. My past experience was that the seizures would cluster together in one night, and then I would occasionally, but not always, have one or two much weaker ones the following day. However, since my medicine level was very low, I felt like I might very well have had them all. The decision was made, though, to check me in anyway, since the set-up had been scheduled and since they were somewhat hopeful that I would have some more seizures soon. I told them that my guess was that I would not have more for quite a while now. But, because the arrangements had all been made, and because the reduction of the drugs might actually make me have more than I would normally have, they checked me in.

I was royally *pissed off*. I had *told* Dr. D-E that this would happen if he reduced the meds, but he did it anyway. *God damn it!* This, for me, would be yet another exercise in futility—*in stupid futility!!!*—but this one would be an *expensive* one.

Now, I can look back. Now the person no longer on Mysoline© can tell you the story about these events with a little detachment.

It takes a little time to get you set up for this procedure. They have to do some paperwork, check you into the appropriate suite of rooms, and get you wired up. They also need to collect the medications you've brought with you so that they can follow the doctor's instructions as to what to give you and when. I found out later that the nurses there in the ward actually locked up that stuff because patients had been known to try to sneak some during their stay. Me, I wanted the medical results, so I wouldn't have tried to sneak anything.

And in any case, I felt almost sure that my seizures had come and gone. So, feeling resigned, I handed over bottles of pills and got wired up. And for your own protection, they also have to insert the needle gage into your vein and then just tape the small plugged tube onto your arm. If you had seizures that were dangerous, they could give you the right medication intravenously and immediately. Most of the electrodes are simply glued onto your scalp, but there are two that they need to more or less inject you with—into your jaw joint. Those two hurt. I sat there thinking that it was just pain which would serve no purpose because they wouldn't get the seizures I was there for. I tried to grit my teeth—again—but that time I couldn't even do that because it made an ache a sharp pain. So, I got stuck with electrodes, strapped to the wall, trying to keep my jaw still, and sat there, sat there, sat there . . . .

If you've never done anything like this, it's hard to imagine the experience. Since you are wired up to some machines in the room, and since the cords are only so long, you can go only so far away from the edge of your bed. And you have to stay on camera, too, so that the nurses will be able to record what your body is doing during the expected seizures. They certainly want to follow all the possibilities, but most especially know when you are having a *gran mal* because you might very well hurt yourself. You get to have company every time you go to the bathroom, and that alone can be very hard for some people. It didn't bother me much. Be comforted that your nurses can't possibly be bothered by those kinds of things because they are there in order to help your body do whatever it needs to do. But the bottom line is that you need to get approval to go to the bathroom, and, furthermore, if, for some reason, the nurses are too busy to come right away to help you, you need to make an appointment!

You don't have to stay in bed all the time. You can get up and sit in a chair right next to your bed—not just any chair—and watch TV, or read, or talk or knit. And sometimes they need to adjust the cameras when you get out of bed to sit in that chair, so sometimes you have to get an appointment for getting out of bed, too. And then there is the awesome problem of taking a walk. It might be allowed at some carefully scheduled moments, but they have to unplug you from the headboard (or the box right next to your bed), plug you back into a little box strapped on you, and take you for a little stroll down the hallway and back. Whether this bothers you will have a lot to do with how physically active you are. For me—used to going to the gym everyday—that was just one notch above being tied down to the radiator.

But I understood why. There's no reason to be there unless you are being visually monitored 24 hours a day. For those of us who are used to exercise, though, sitting sitting sitting and then, once a day, maybe twice, walking slowly down 35 feet of corridor and then back, the more we sit there the grumpier we get. The nurses are prepared for that. They probably don't like it, but they're not surprised. Some of them, in my experience, have a degree in grumpy. They don't let it bother them, and they are nice to you no matter how you act towards them. (My life has given me enormous admiration for nurses: they are people who can do whatever is needed to take care of others and in a kindly manner.)

And then there's the sleep deprivation drill. For people with a history of seizures, lack of sleep is one of the most effective seizure-inducing activities. They start out giving you far fewer hours of sleep than you want, and in some cases they proceed to give you less and less, with the hope that it will ensure that you have seizures. In order to stay awake long after you become sleepy, you have to watch TV, or keep on reading, or do some kind of game, or talk to other people. And if you start to fall asleep, the nurse will use the microphone speaker plugged into your bed to wake you up. That might make you a little grumpy, too.

For most EEG patients—and certainly for me—you could eat whatever was available from the hospital kitchen. One of the "side effects" of being stuck on a leash and constantly kept awake is that food becomes one of the few sources of outside stimulation you can get. And even if your friends and relatives do their best to bring you stuff from the outside, it's not likely that they will be able to produce every meal for you on time. And even if you don't especially like the kind of food you can get, at least you can get some stimulation from putting things in your mouth while you are strapped to the radiator. Here's my advice: be warned.

So I got less and less sleep. But they had tapered me down off my medications—those downer drugs—entirely. So I sat there feeling somehow like I was floating back up to the surface of a murky lake. I started to feel less angry, more calm, and even, for God's sake, more *pleased*. My parents told me that I started to make more jokes, and to talk more about the larger world, and to laugh at life more easily. My mother and I played an uncounted number of complicated card games which we have always enjoyed. My parents did their best to help me stay awake, and I remember one night my mother, who could always stay up late, and I were playing cards, while my dad would sit and watch CNN and talk to us. Before long, though, he would drop his newspaper and slide slowly down on his chair and begin to snore. I wanted to send them home—I didn't want them to start to feel deprived just because I was. Finally they agreed to go sleep some, even though my mother wanted—as always—to stay with me.

I read somewhere that deprivation of sleep is one of the simplest and most effective forms of torture. I believe it. But even with no sedatives, and with no sleep, I felt ten times better than I had for years. So there I sat, strapped onto a machine, on camera 24 hours a day, having no sleep and no seizures and getting happier with every waking hour. Why? *I was off the downers.*

I liked my hospital roommate. Unlike me, she suffered from *gran mal*. She had gone down on her medications as well. She also was supposed to have given the nurses all of her medications when she checked in. But she had a long history of severe seizures, and told me stories about having them and then what would happen afterwards. Her mother was constantly there entertaining and taking care of her, knowing, she told us, that the seizures which would come would be brutal and very painful for her daughter.

She told me that she knew that her daughter would have *gran mals* at any moment now, and that she didn't want to take her entirely off the medications because she was afraid her daughter would have even worse seizures. She had seen the horrible ones her daughter had had prior to getting the medication Tegretol©. For that reason, she had kept some meds in her purse, and was sneaking some to her daughter when the nurses weren't looking. And she would stay there late at night, talking and comforting her daughter. She also got to know me a little bit. She was a very kind person. It was clear that she had struggled for many years helping her daughter deal with the seizures. And I could tell that she had been very supportive all along.

As she expected, it happened one night. (I think it was a night, but it might have been a day, because when you are deprived of sleep and plugged into a machine two feet away, you lose any sense of what time of day it actually is.) My roommate and her mother were chatting about something, telling stories about the past and laughing. My roommate suddenly, in the middle of a sentence, went stiff, and her head snapped to the left. Her mother knew exactly what was about to happen. She buzzed immediately for the nurses, then got up to try to hold on to her daughter when she began to bash into the side rails of the bed. I have seen some representations of *gran mal* seizures in a movie or two, but I had never seen a real one right in front of me. She went totally stiff, curved up from head to feet, and then started to jerk.

The nurses rushed in to help hold her down. It took three of them, and even three of them couldn't keep her from the tonic-clonic full-body powerful jerks so classic with *gran mal*. It's hard to understand the force of that kind of bodily motion if you have never been close to it. One of the nurses, however, had the presence of mind to pull the curtains between my roommate's bed and mine, to protect the privacy of the one having seizures. I understand that problem. I don't think that the patient would have worried about that—she had had hundreds of *gran mals* in her life in every possible kind of activity human beings do. But the nurses were doing what was both professional and kind. I'm sure that they would have done it for me.

But, for me, they never had to do it. I just sat there, noticing that I felt better and better now with absolutely no sleep and being wired up in a bed and being watched and filmed 24 hours a day and eating cold hamburgers for some meal and not being able to go to the gym and not being able even to get out of bed without permission, even to go to the bathroom. My roommate had done the deed, and so she checked out early, and left me alone in the "compound." So, even then, even with all that, I felt more alive (if not exactly more awake) without the phenobarbitol drugs—the downers. I remember asking myself if I truly remembered what life before diagnosis had felt like . . . . Sitting there chained I paradoxically felt finally free.

But I was also "seizure free." I had some slight weird feelings. I felt some compulsive swallowing, not knowing why I was doing it but not able to stop doing it. I had the lightest possible sense that I could just barely smell or taste something slightly suggestive of some metallic aroma. So, I sat there sat there sat there.

Seven days later, when my insurance company would no longer pay for me to stay there, I checked out. Because I had gone through the necessary withdrawal—as it were—with that horrible downer Mysoline©, Dr. D-E put me on another med—drug #6—Mesantoin©. They pulled all those electrodes off and tanked me up again with a huge load of those new downers. It's probably on my record that I "fell asleep" soon afterwards, but what I did was pass out. My father tells me that my boss came by to see me that day, but I was totally unconscious by then. So: six nights, no sleep, high on the absence of drugs, highly complicated and technical but decidedly insufficient tests, and then over the cliff—back to the awful, depressed, spaced-out bummer reality. There are lots of factors in making decisions about a surgery like this, but one of them was certainly that I had had a brief look at how I biologically *felt* before these drugs, and it made me ask myself whether I could ever get back there again.

But they did not have enough information from this episode.

Initial bill for that in-patient EEG: $21,443.60. Second, adjusted bill: $15,634.03 . . . . (This particular bill would take the next six months to sort itself out.)

August 22, 1995, I did another blood test: $199.20.

On September 1, I went to get some more Mesantoin© (100mg/100ct @ $49.05) and some more antacid.

On September 27, I came back for another test: the WADA. This test allows the doctors to "numb" one side of your brain—independently of the other—in order to see if the other side can perform the same kinds of processes which would be affected by a proposed neurosurgery. Just as in the cardiac angiogram back in 1993, they stuck me with a needle—not into a vein, but into a big carotid artery. They injected me with a short-acting barbiturate, which more or less numbed the left side of my brain, and then showed me some flash-cards of objects and asked me to name them. It was weird! One moment you feel normal, and the next moment you get a rushing sense of cold up your arm, and then you can't *name* anything. I recognized the thing, but I couldn't think of the name. That only lasted a few minutes. Then the drug wore off, and they showed me the cards again, to ask if I *remembered* having seen them—and I had. When the drug wore off, I could name them. The WADA test was measuring whether the right side of my brain—the part called the hippocampus—could process language and memory if the left side were impaired. Surgery, after all, might do just that: affect the functioning of the left side of my brain.

My God, neurosurgery?

In mid-September, my parents came with me to talk to Dr. D-E about the results of the EEG and about the possibility of *brain surgery*. We had a long talk—he gave us a lot of his professional time, and made some careful points about the complicated history of my case. I was unable to process what brain surgery would actually be like. But we discussed the issue as to whether the fine-tuning of drugs or new drugs would ever solve the problem for me—that is, suppress the seizures. He had been prescribing various medications for me since the fall of 1992—close to three years. I had confidence in his judgement because of his position—a professor of Neurology at a major University hospital in the United States, involved in research about epilepsy and on medications. He certainly knew all the drugs which might be effective for me (because, as I have learned, different kinds or locations of seizures respond to different medications).

So his considered opinion was that if I didn't do the surgery, I was certainly guaranteed to stay on the medications the rest of my life and, as was clearly the case, likely to break through medications the rest of my life. He would be able to put me on whatever new medications might be promising, but I had clearly established my tendency to break through. There is, he said, a certain percentage of people with my kind of seizures who always break through.

But it wasn't guaranteed that surgery would entirely solve the problem, either. My case was clearly difficult.

He told me that if we decided to do surgery, he would recommend surgeons whose work he knew well. And, based on what he knew about my case and about me, he would recommend those known for the complicated kind of surgery that he was confidant I would need. None of them, though, were at that time in Los Angeles. I would like to say that we "discussed" these possibilities, but in reality I just listened.

He would recommend a surgeon either in Montreal (Canada) or in Paris (France). I remember sitting there, listening to him, with a complex mess of thoughts in my mind: travel abroad? Is it possible that my insurance would cover that? Would I want to do it anyway, at my expense, because of his recommendation? Does that mean that he wouldn't recommend any surgeons at UCLA or anywhere else in the US? Does that mean that the required surgery for my case is *that* complicated, *that* different, *that* difficult? Does that mean that my family would have to travel with me, and pay for hotels and cars? Would he also be there? How long would this take? Could I fly back home right after the surgery? Does everybody in my family have a passport? Who will help my family talk to the doctors during that period in which the only member of my family who speaks French— me—is unconscious? How long will this take? Just how crazy would this be?

I don't think I even said very much. My parents didn't push me to talk.

I went home and spent some time thinking about that possibility. At work, I was doing some library research for my boss for some material on topics he was interested in. But I was also in the middle of a huge, complicated, multi-year project, producing a number of conference events in Europe. That kind of work requires the ability to travel, to deal in foreign languages, to do as many hours in a day as are necessary to produce such a complex event, and to stay right on top of everything that is happening or might happen. It is intricate and highly demanding. I could not possibly defend doing some kind of challenging medical procedure like brain surgery in the middle of this extremely complicated project. I had to go to Italy for more planning meetings in the fall, and produce the first big public event the following spring. Maybe, I said to myself, *maybe* after that . . . But, that first big scholarly event was part of a series, and I was already working on the second for the year after. I couldn't imagine being able to do the surgery in the middle of that project.

On August 16, 1995, I got my new contract—for two years—and a promotion. This new contract stated that the position is potentially renewable for one additional two-year term. I took that as a good sign of the value of my job performance. I went out to the beach after work, with an upset stomach, slightly dizzy, and relieved that I could do my job well anyway. I considered whether it would be much smarter to produce that next major event to prove my performance, and then make the case that I should be made permanent. I'm not sure I could actually imagine doing brain surgery at all. I was focusing on the issues having to do with work because, for someone in my position, those issues are neck and neck with personal considerations. I wanted to make sure that I could do my job well for an interlocking set of reasons. I wanted to satisfy myself for my own efforts, and to do well at this particular complicated project. I wanted to do well at all the things involved in my job. I wanted to give my boss, and that organization, every reason to make me permanent. I wanted to stay employed and insured, so that I would not hit the "pre-existing condition" barrier with another employer's insurance company.

I wasn't confident, either, that the EEG had told the physicians what they needed to know—after all, they hadn't actually seen a single seizure. Dr. D-E seemed also to be less than totally confident. He had discussed the case with the other specialists who were part of the group reviewing my case. But he was presenting to me the various factors of making the decision.

I know now, indeed, I knew then, that I was suppressing my own personal fear. I remember wondering, at some point, how I would emotionally feel about all of this if I didn't have to immediately worry about several crucial things: if I do this, will the aspects of arranging for and having such a medical procedure affect my performance enough to reduce my chances of being made permanent? If I do it (or even ask to do it), will the cost and the effects of that affect my employer's decision about whether to make me permanent? And then I would consider another, equally crucial question: would the effects of the surgery actually alter my intellectual ability to do this job, or to do one like it? For it was my brain which got me that job in the first place.

If I don't do it now, while I am insured, and if, for some reason I am not made permanent, does that mean I might *never* have another chance? (You can perhaps guess how much this kind of surgery would cost—it's not like I could just put change in a piggy bank to save up for it.) If I don't do it, does that mean I'll be on this set of downers all the rest of my life? If I don't do it, does that mean I will *never* feel any better? And I will always regret that I did not do it?

The Future on Drugs would be more of the Past. Dizziness, indigestion, clumsiness, constant debilitating fatigue, constant risky low white count, and depression, depression, depression.

But then there was the trackless wilderness—the unknown country of the consequences of the surgery. That kind of surgery alters your brain function. It can induce new and different kinds of neurological and psychological problems. So, ultimately the question is: take the side effects you now have and will always have, or gamble for something new. In my careful considerations of the consequences of this, I would have some flashes of naked fear: My *brain?* My god, how could I possibly volunteer to have my head sliced open? How can anybody volunteer for this? I got paralyzed by that huge, interlocking web of factors for that decision.

Catch-22.

I needed to do my job well at that point in time to stand the best chance of getting hired permanently. That would keep the larger number of options for whatever the future might offer.

I wouldn't have to deal with the fear. I wanted to be able to do my job well to get at least some pleasure out of my sleep-drugged life.

I gritted my teeth. I said no.

Down the Appian Way

In October of 1995 I got some more meds (Mesantoin© 100mg/120ct @ $53.77; diazepam 5mg/20ct $8.41), popped a bunch, passed out on another plane, and went to Rome to take care of some major factors of the upcoming conference in the big, multi-year project I was producing. I spent some time with our Roman collaborators, scouted out some locations, organized some material, and faxed some crucial information on that project home. On my last day there, before taking that pile of pills and passing out in an airplane to come home, I took a long walk down an ancient road out of the city walls of Rome. I thought about several Roman emperors and politicians, from long ago in the past, who were thought to have had epilepsy. I thought about how much I loved my job because I was producing a big project in the humanities, and because that job had put me in Rome that awesomely beautiful autumn day. I walked alone, thinking about the future.

I thought about the fact that one reason I was so good at that job was because I could easily do the required travel. I can entertain myself, especially in a beautiful city like that one, or in a city which has an interesting art museum or an archeological museum—indeed, Rome is just one huge museum of civilization itself. And I could stay involved with a number of scholarly institutes and with scholars themselves, even though I hadn't gone down that path exactly.

I spent some time trying to consider whether I would ever know why I hadn't gone down the normal scholarly path, or what would have happened if I had. Looking back at the past five years, I knew that if I had been on all of those medications while I was in graduate school, I would very likely never have gotten my Ph.D. I wouldn't have had the energy to do the work that that requires. Looking back at the previous three years, I knew that even if I had finished my degree, and then gotten the diagnosis and the medications, and then gotten an assistant professorship in a university—which was what my academic training was for and what I had wanted all along—I would have had all the same medical problems, all the same personal difficulties and all the same drugs and, therefore, all the same side effect problems. I would be in exactly the same position with respect to the insurance issues—for unless you get tenure in an academic position, you are on contract, and if anything goes wrong in the current job, you need to look for another job. You will face, again, that ominous "pre-existing condition" issue.

I would have had to cope with my own depression and despair while trying desperately to be positive and supportive of my students. And that, for me, would have involved some flat-out lying about how I felt about those endeavors. It would have been painful for me to try to keep from speaking "the truth" as I saw it. It would very likely have involved flat-out lying about what I *did* care about. I would have felt absolutely compelled to do a lot of my own scholarship, to read hundreds of books in five languages and think deeply about complicated, intellectual, historical problems while taking big handfuls of downers and sleeping nine hours a night. I would have had to write and publish as much of my work as possible in order to keep a job like that: "publish or perish."

I would certainly have had seizures every now and then while lecturing to 200 students. I would have had the same constant low blood cell count, making me very susceptible to infectious and contagious diseases, while working everyday in a university full of thousands of people. College students are well known to have lots of contagious diseases (like mono!). They, of course, almost always recover easily. I wouldn't have recovered easily at all.

I knew I wouldn't have made it. I don't want to be understood as saying that I would have been successful and had a fabulous academic career but for this medical catastrophe. I might not have been good enough at that anyway, independent of all the rest of these factors. I'll never know. But at least I was good at what I had to do for the job I had gotten, and that job was intellectual enough that I could stay interested in the content as well. And I could also give all the time I needed to give to be good at it. I was in there almost every weekend to make sure that I accomplished what I needed to do, and do well. Since part of my job was to read scholarly publications on a lot of different topics in the humanities, my job let me enjoy what I had always loved about graduate school: reading scholarly work. Learning, for its own sake.

And there was another factor: I wasn't involved in the complex issues of anybody else's life. I had no spouse or children to take care of, my parents didn't need my constant presence or direct support, and I didn't have to schedule my travel or my 18-hour-a-day production of conferences around anybody else at all. I was also one of those people who can cope with being alone a lot. And for me, that long cascade of disaster—the diagnosis, the abandonment by my lover, the drugs, the severe side effects, the simple fear of physical susceptibility to contagious disease, the necessary medical tests, the heart attack, the constant anemia and the constant despair made me more and more withdrawn from other people. I couldn't possibly have developed another close personal relationship, and I couldn't possibly have given much to anyone else because I had nothing to give *other* than disaster and withdrawal. Disaster and withdrawal were, for me, side effects of the diagnosis.

And, while I'm at it, let me just go ahead and tell you another private, and embarrassing truth. One of the potent side effects of many of the meds I had been on was to literally kill any sexuality I had ever felt. And once again, I was in the maze, with the trail of biochemical and emotional depression interwoven.

And here's another problem. Many of the medications for

epilepsy are "teratogenic"—they can be damaging to fetuses. So even if I had been in a position to want children, I and my partner would have been forced to face the chances of birth defects and the consequences of my withdrawal from the medication—more and stronger seizures—to try to prevent those defects. I didn't face that, but many other patients do. Even though I wasn't directly in that position, I found an enormous sadness in the fact. I would have faced that even if everything else—including how I felt about life—had gone well.

I thought about what Dr. D-E had said: a lot of the cases of epilepsy resulted in damage to or destruction of personal relationships. I think I know why. I don't want to speak for anybody else, but I personally have nothing but sympathy for this problem. And I want to say that I feel sympathy not only for people with this diagnosis, but also for friends and family and partners who end up having to cope with all of this. They have to cope both with the medical problems and with the depression and the emotional withdrawal of the patient. I suspect that my emotional withdrawal from the medical diagnosis and from the immediate abandonment by my lover was close to autism itself because suppression of emotion was a kind of survival mechanism for me.

So I felt very alone, but I saw very clearly that I was also choosing to be alone.

Catch-22: the fact that you don't want to feel that way, but you do feel that way, makes you feel that way even more.

So on I walked, down the famous "Appian Way," reflecting on how sad it was to be alone, and how much worse it was to choose to be alone.

And let me tell you about some friends of mine. My closest friends, the ones that I had known since junior high school, all saw me have that big *gran mal* on that Thanksgiving Day in 1992. So they knew. It wasn't that I had to decide whether to tell them—they knew—they saw the thing happening. But I think that I would have told them anyway, because I was close to them and because I trusted them. And I knew that their relationship with me had nothing to do with what I was doing on that Thanksgiving Day—it was about a lifetime of friendship. But I withdrew anyway, even from them, not because I was afraid of anything they might do to me, but because I didn't want to talk about all of this. I didn't want to have to account for it. I didn't want to have to say what I would do. I didn't want to talk about how I *felt*. They would certainly ask me that, out of deep personal concern, out of kindness, every time I saw them. But I had to suppress. I didn't want to talk about all of this, I was just remembering that day with my mother—those lupines on Waunita pass—and trying to survive the blast.

Once again, some people respond very differently. They need support, they want support, they want to be able to talk about all of this—about the seizures, about the consequences, about how they feel. They need to get immediate support. If I had gotten immediate support from my lover, I think I might have, if not gone the other way, at least stayed a little closer to everybody. (Of course, I'll never know that.) But the compounded emotional effects of that diagnosis and his desertion caused me to freeze, and to try to stay frozen, which can easily be seen as pushing friends away. Those of us who do that are often interpreted as not feeling much at all, but for lots of us, the opposite is true. We feel too much. Some people feel better if they can express their emotions. Some of us feel fear of emotional nakedness. I had gotten a lesson in what my doctor had said about the possible negative effects of the diagnosis itself—loss of friends and lovers. I sat there, rigid, asking myself: *who's next?*

I have no defense for that. It's hard to deal with. Those closest friends, I think, tried to decide whether to probe any deeper for more of my emotional responses or to make sure that I wouldn't feel pushed or interrogated. At that point in our lives we all lived in different cities, so we couldn't just see each other on some random, painful, Tuesday night. For me to go see any of them would have involved effort, and I had very little strength for anything. I'm sure that any one of them would have gotten on a plane for me, but I didn't ask for that, and I didn't want that—I didn't want to want anything. I wanted to feel as little as possible. It was never that I didn't trust their reactions. It was my own that I didn't trust.

One of my closest friends told me how difficult it was for her to deal with the effects this had on me. She knew that I wasn't talking to my acquaintances down in Los Angeles, but she felt the need to talk to some of her friends about the disaster. I understand the needs of friends, too. They have to cope with having to cope. She had some good friends there—they were not only supportive of her, they were supportive from afar of me. I would go visit my friend often, and sit with her friends and talk some. They were also kind because they didn't interrogate me, but they did give me some chances to talk. I'm grateful for that, but I'm even more grateful that they could provide support to my beloved friend.

And I lost those of my friends who were actually my lover's friends. And, even more painfully, I lost his family as well. I have no criticism for that—none at all. That was a classic case of a no-win situation, and of course they felt the need to support their son, whatever he felt he needed to do. I have nothing but sympathy for that problem, and I have nothing but respect for them. There was no argument or blame. I just had to say goodbye.

So here's the bottom line for me: I had lost a lover and some of my dear friends, and I didn't want to lose any more by letting them know. I didn't want to make any new friends, to increase the number who might walk away. I didn't want to let myself care any more than I already did. So I emotionally withdrew from damn near everybody.

I stayed as close as I could manage to my best friend, who never wavered. I stayed as close as I could manage to my family, who never wavered. But I had put up The Wall.

November 13, 1995: I woke up early and lay there while a long series of waves of cold biochemical fear washed over me. I couldn't sleep. I got up, took the bus to the lab and did my routine blood test. Then I got onto the bus to go to work, and had a series of quasi-seizures all that day. I noted them all in my journal. Results of that blood test: low white count, low neutrophil.

November 16, 1995: Mesantoin© 100mg/400ct @$159.45. I took *four* of them a day.

December 18, 1995: blood test: low white and red blood cell count . . . . Mesantoin© is known to cause depression and aplastic anemia . . . .

At Christmas, 1995, in Colorado I had a sudden and fierce fight with my older brother, about something which had nothing to do with my epilepsy or my treatment. In a sense, it was nothing actually new, for he and I had had fights in the past. But this one slammed me in the face. I got up and walked out of the house—into the snow in Colorado at 8000 ft. in the dark in the middle of winter—and stood there, holding myself, crying with *rage*. I don't think I had ever felt that way about arguing with him in the past. I'm not sure I had ever felt that way about anything in the past. I stood out there for a long time. My mother came to find me, and to hold me. My brother left for his home the very next day.

It was a gruesome celebration, I think, of my sense of helplessness and the effects of my drugs. But I can't blame that fight on my epilepsy. And I can't blame it—entirely—on my drugs. But my drugs were co-conspirators. They were there. They had been on the premises for the preceding three years of my life.

1996

That previous fall—1995—I had started dealing with my insurance company regarding bills from that EEG stay in the hospital in the previous August. There is always some delay between the procedure itself and the issues having to do with insurance and patient payments, but by October my insurance company had not paid Santa Monica hospital, or maybe Santa Monica hospital accounting hadn't processed a payment yet—I'll never know that either. So I started to get serious (leaning towards threatening) bills from the hospital for a week-long stay in the EEG ward and all the medical services associated with that. In addition, my insurance covered only a certain portion of a restricted number of the "Neuropsychological Assessment Battery" and the "WADA" tests I had taken as part of the medical considerations concerning the possible surgery. The insurance company insisted that it wasn't a medical necessity, and therefore it wasn't completely—even at the percentage of an "outside provider" service—covered. I had to start a complicated series of inquiries about that decision. I got the support of one of the technicians involved in those procedures, insisting that it was indeed a medical procedure, not a "psychological" one. I began the process of inquiry with my insurance company concerning its payment of one—only one so far—of the two sets of tests.

I was of course waiting for several official statements from my insurance company so that I would know how much of the payment I was responsible for before I wrote the check. In the months between September 1995 and February 1996, I got to the point where I was faxing my insurance company, telling them that I was getting billed even more for past due charges. I also finally got a response from the state telling me that they were not the ones who could solve the problem. They "forwarded" me to another agency. I forwarded the inquiry, and waited.

January 16, 1996: blood test: low white count and low neutrophil. The bill: $199.20. My payment—including my deductible: $114.93.

Finally, in February, I got the insurance company's statement on their entire coverage for the year 1995: $22,989.90. Given the exemptions, the rules, the nature of the service providers, the never-ending blood tests, etc. I paid close to $3,000 myself. The issue of the psychological tests, though, remained unresolved. Even the psychologist who performed them had encouraged me to push that inquiry.

But there was one good thing as well. Finally, finally, finally Dr. D-E decided that he would recommend that the State of California reinstate my driver's license. Even though I was breaking through my medications, it was only at night, when I was asleep in bed. He had known some of the details of my life without being able to drive, and he knew that this would be an achievement for me. But he warned me again: be as careful as a human being can be because it is still the case that you might be sued for any accident that might happen. Months after he filed the request, the DMV made an appointment for me to come in in January 1996 and take the exams again (I passed them). For the first time in over three years, I could go home, get in my car and drive down to the lab for my blood tests.

And I could drive up the Pacific coast.

But my getting in that car is another example of how deep the personal effects of the previous three years had been. I felt myself *trying* to keep from feeling like this was a victory because I didn't want to set myself up for more pain. I was guarded about the realization that maybe this wouldn't be permanent—if I began to have seizures during the day, I might lose the license again. And, all the same legal issues remained. Driving did not feel the same as it had before all of this mess. It was now a valuable freedom, but it was also a risk. The effects of the previous three years were not just that I had lost my driving privileges, but that I had lost my ability to let myself just feel. I always had my emotional teeth clenched. I got in my car and drove up the coast, looking out to sea, feeling as close to free as I could, remembering that day in 1992, when I had sat on the beach and faced the loss.

On February 7, 1996, then, I wrote another check for my portion of medical expenses so far, and on the 8th I went back one more time to my family doctor, with another bout of vaginal infection. She was worried that I might have ovarian cysts related to my constantly suppressed immune system. But she prescribed some more treatment ointment, and told me we'd keep a close eye on that. At the end of February, 1996, I was finally notified by the State that my inquiry about why my insurance company had refused to pay for the psychological studies done for me the preceding year (for the EEG) had no merit. Even though I did those tests, not because I wanted psychological treatment, but because that was a prescribed element of the neurological analysis for possible surgery, my insurance company did not cover them. As you might imagine, I guessed that they would certainly not cover anything "psychological" at all. I wrote that check for a bill for $660.00, knowing it would be in addition to my official "out-of-pocket" costs. However, as I soon discovered, that first check covered a certain set of charges and a certain set of paperwork, but it did not cover *all* the expenses of that battery of exams. I soon received the invoice from the psychologist who had done those exams covering the outstanding charges: $640.

On March 25, 1996, I took another blood test: $190.70 (I paid $57.21). A few days later I went to my appointment with Dr. D-E. He took one look at that most recent blood test: in January, my white count was a low 3.4—you may recall that the "normal" range is considered to be 4.5-10. This time, two months later, my white cell count was *2.7*. Severe aplastic anemia can, literally, kill. My red cell count and my neutrophil count and my sodium were all low. He was nervous, too, about the fact that I had constant vaginal infections. And my cholesterol, which had always been low, was now incredibly high at 255! I had never had cholesterol problems before, but the level had risen steadily since December. Dr. D-E immediately started me down on medication #6—the one which had actually been the most effective in suppressing my seizures—Mesantoin©.

We had yet another conversation we had had a number of times before, about the problems with these drugs. He asked again, for that reason, if I was having sex, and if I was on birth control pills. My answer to both questions was no. We discussed some possible side effect problems of getting pregnant on these kinds of medications (because they are associated with birth defects). There is some evidence that some epilepsy medications reduce the efficacy of birth control pills as well, so that you might very well get pregnant even though you are trying to avoid that. That would of course put you in a horrible dilemma.

He started me down on #7, and up on #8—a relatively new supplemental med—Lamictal©. He warned me that I might be allergic to Lamictal©, so if there was *any* sign of that, I needed to go immediately the Emergency Room. And then we discussed the side effects: this drug binds to melatonin in your skin, so you need to be careful to stay out of the sun. It is associated with a tendency to gain weight, so be careful about that. It is associated with headache and dizziness. And, unlike the drugs I was on, this one was related to insomnia—difficulty sleeping. I went to the pharmacy, getting ready for more headache, dizziness and weight gain, and wondering if I even remembered my normal sleep patterns. I bought 100 25mg pills for $251.10. I started slowly up on Lamictal© and went in the following week for another required follow-up blood test.

Because I had gotten my driver's license back, I could now make a quick trip to Colorado and help my parents with their own serious family emergency. My grandmother had had continuous medical problems, and my parents' decided to move her across the state to their house. My mother had had her own medical problems; indeed, she had gone downhill some since having moved to Colorado. And now she took on the responsibility for her mother's care as well. I'm sure my father was contemplating the fact that now all the women in his family had serious medical problems.

April 10, 1996: blood test.

In mid-April, I had a series of auras—the prelude to a seizure—all day one day, and then a series of seizures that night. A week later I had some more, and some periods of mild but persistent compulsive swallowing, and, just for something new and different, some pain in my pelvic region. So: back to my family doctor, who decided, given my low blood cell count, to test me for chlamydia. A week later I went back for another blood test. My white cell count: down to 2.6.

I started to actually *lose* sleep on this drug. My seizures had almost always happened very early in the morning—they would wake me up. And I know that some disturbance in a person's sleep patterns can be a brain-function problem all by itself. On this drug, I would go to bed with a headache, fall asleep and then wake up again 45 minutes later. I would be awake a while, and then fall back asleep for an hour. Then I would wake up, and not be able to sleep for an hour and a half. Then I would fall asleep again, but wake up very early in the morning and know that I wouldn't be able to sleep any more. So, I'd get out of bed and consider that no matter whether I slept far too much on one drug, or not enough on the other, I still felt exhausted. But I didn't want any coffee. I really didn't want any coffee at all. If I had my "usual" daily fix of phenobarb-fighting caffeine, I would start to fidget. I felt a little dizzy on that stuff anyway, but the caffeine would make me start to feel manic. To feel like I wanted to run up and down stairs. I close to cold-turkeyed myself off of coffee. I had had low-grade headaches from the start of that drug, but mid-mornings were major league. I "de-caffed" myself anyway. I did the third blood test for the month of April, 1996. All total for the month of April: $463.90 (I paid $30.15).

It began to be normal for me to get up several times a night, take some ibuprofen for a slight headache, and pace a little bit—something I had very seldom done in my pre-drug days. This was a new kind of exhaustion: *tired and wired*. My portion of the cost of this drug was about $50 a month.

Tired and wired, though, was better than lying in the mud of constant downers. And here's another major side effect—for me—of the Lamictal©. As I went down on the Mesantoin©, and up on the Lamictal©, my missing and presumed dead sense of sexual desire came welling up, like a diver from the bottom of the sea. It was an astonishing surprise. It isn't that it just crept back, it's that it leapt up like a dolphin. I would pace around at night, staring at my empty bed, with the despairing feeling that I'd be cruising those seas alone.

But I used that time—waking up in the middle of the night—to gear up for another major event on my job, a conference I was producing at our own institute at the beginning of May. I was actually glad that I started to sleep less, even though I was tired as always. But I could stay awake for the unavoidable crises which always happen in events like this. And, for the first time in a long time I could drive around myself to do anything I needed to do for this project. I drove carefully. I had always been a careful driver, but now I was nervously careful. But, of course, exhausting yourself and not getting enough sleep can cause seizures, and so I had some more. I spent one of the days working like a dog at that event with a truly brutal post-seizure headache, but I couldn't possibly not do the difficult and exhausting tasks for this project because I was in charge of them. Fortunately I didn't actually have seizures in front of a room full of our guests.

That seminar went extremely well, and I was grateful that our efforts had paid off. It was on the work of two painters less-known that the more famous ones, but who had produced strange and interesting paintings involving both Christian religious and classical mythological figures. Then I started immediately on the next seminar, number two in that multi-year, complicated, international project, to take place in 1997.

I got home and opened my mail: the bill for my Neuropsychology Tests in August 1995 remained at $660. My inquiries to my insurance company were going nowhere. I faxed my insurance company *that* the inquiry was going nowhere, and I wrote the psychologist who had done the tests that I was still trying to solve the problem. He wrote me back, thanking me for that endeavor.

Right after that, I went back to my family doctor for the normal yearly exam. The good news was that the test for chlamydia had came back negative, and my PAP smear looked normal. The bad news was that what she did find was a small lump in my breast. She looked at my records, and then looked at me: "We need to do a mammogram for this." I just sat there, looking at her. From the page in my journal that night: *I just can't process this stuff anymore . . . .*

Have any of you had a mammogram? I've been told that for lots of women it might be just a little uncomfortable, but for some it seems to be painful. Guess which group I'm in.

Some women seem to be frightened by the examination, but I wasn't frightened. I was emotionally numb. I just stood there, cringing a little because of the pain, thinking about the fact that my grandmother had had a breast removed, and remembering having read somewhere that breast cancer often skips generations. I had a crazy thought: let's see, the bone marrow biopsy had me lying face down; the infarction had me lying face up; the angiogram had me lie under a pile of bricks. Now I have to stand up straight with one arm above my head to get this painful squeeze. So, next will be to do some test while hanging upside down. I did the mammogram, and on my way back to the car I went by the pharmacy and got another $251.10 of medications.

Two weeks later she told me the good news: the mammogram had shown some slight irregularities, but they were "benign." Let's keep a close eye on this, she said.

In the middle of June I did another blood test: low white and red count and high cholesterol. Then I had another full set of night-time seizures. I got up early, having slept very little, took two ibuprofen with the meds, the aspirin, and the vitamins. I started in on the coffee, not so that I would wake up—on that new medication, I was on overload awake—but because it seemed to dull the headache pain a little. My neurologist increased the medication a little, so I went back to the pharmacy to get some more pink and yellow ones, plus some more diazepam.

My medical bills for the month of June, including blood tests and the mammogram: $844.70. This set of bills was complicated, and involved some charges discounted or eliminated by my health insurance. I paid $49.71.

For the Fourth of July I went back to Colorado to see my folks. I decided they didn't need to know about the mammogram.

And one of the weirdest things began to happen. I started to lose my hair. Not in big patches, just in small handfuls, almost one by one. (By one by one by one . . . .) It was a side effect of the Lamictal©. I would wonder sometimes if this was the beginning of baldness.

On July 12, I sent a three-page letter with two pages of attachments to the Benefit Specialist at my insurance company, inquiring why his or her response to my earlier inquiry referred to only one of the multiple charges on only one of the Explanation of Benefit forms referring to the complicated set of charges for the multiple battery of exams on the two dates in question, therefore leaving a substantial amount of charges both unpaid and unaddressed. Then I sent a two-page letter with twelve pages of attachments to the Department of Corporations, as advised by the Psychologist who had performed the battery of tests, informing them that these exams had been "approved" in advance through my insurance company and performed by a "preferred provider" and that I was now being billed directly for over half the charges incurred. That even though I had contacted my insurance company repeatedly, I had been given no response as to why certain charges are not covered. That even though I had made sure to receive prior approval, I could get no specifics on what, exactly, was actually approved. To its credit, the Department of Corporations responded within five days, informing me that my Request for Assistance (RFA) had been forwarded to my insurance company along with the department's request for investigation.

On July 15 I did a blood test: even *lower* white count, high cholesterol. ($190.70—I paid $12.40.)

On August 3 I woke up with seizures.

On August 12, I did some more blood tests: low white count and low red count and low neutrophil and low platelet volume and high cholesterol. ($235.10—I paid $15.28.)

On August 14, 1996 I got my yearly review:

> "Amy has been instrumental in developing the program and arranging the logistic for the first seminar and in starting the organization for the second seminar, which she suggested be held in Italy in order to maximize the [institute's] international audience . . . has also been very active in helping me organize and facilitate the Scholars Program, including reviewing scholarly material, making recommendations, discussing the

program . . . joined the project team of one of the opening events for the new [institute], the "State of Art History" conference . . . she also contributed to the conceptual organization of a seminar on "Memory," originally proposed by some of our scholars . . . Amy, with the help of a Research Assistant she supervises, is constantly showing high-level research skills, organizational ability, and the ability to review scholarly material outside her own field of expertise . . . Her interdisciplinary academic background as well as her considerable discretion and her ability to understand our institutional needs and my own directions are important to me and to the [institute] . . . Her interaction with other members of the staff, as well as with representatives from other institutions, especially the Museum, is good and efficient. I value her work highly."

Plans for Improvement: "Due to the excellence of Amy's performance, I am not proposing any specific plans for improvement."
Overall Performance Rating: "Excellent."

I got the raise.

On August 16, I woke up with seizures. Later that very same day, I saw Dr. D-E. From his records: "*Total neutrophil count is dangerously low.*" He started me down further on Mesantoin©. Less than a week later (August 22), I did another blood test: white count *lower* than August 12, low red count, low neutrophil . . . .

On August 26, I wrote in my notebook: *400mg Lam + 200mg Mes: seizures anyway*.

In August, I started to get some odd little bumps on my fingers—they would swell up and hurt, for no reason. They would last a while—a few weeks—and then go away, mysteriously. I didn't know what they were. (I still don't know what they were.) I wondered if it was a side effect. I wondered if it was something which had nothing to do with the drugs. I wondered if I would ever know that.

On my birthday in 1996 I popped a handful of drugs and got on a plane to Hamburg, Germany to help plan for another upcoming scholarly event. I sat there in the plane thinking about the futility of it all, taking uppers and downers and aspirin and vitamins and sleeping pills. I worried about getting the flu. I washed my hands a lot. I would stand there, in the bathroom, just washing my hands, and thinking about how psycho that looked. I went back to my seat and contemplated the fact that I was careful about touching any thing, much less any body. If anybody noticed that—and I don't know that anybody did—it would probably be looking like obsessive compulsion, or frigid paranoia. And an explanation—if I could give one—would look like hypochondria. If I gave the Big Explanation—well, I wouldn't do that.

In Hamburg I spent time at a major institute in Art History, talking with some perspective institutional partners and scouting out information for another upcoming seminar—feeling, once again, both tired and wired at the same time. I flew from Hamburg to Amsterdam for a conference, and ended up on a boat on a rainy day, kind of wandering around the old city, wishing I could have a nap and then actually feel as though I had. I spent a week there with interesting presentations and visits to the museums, taking notes for future projects, and then going back to the hotel to "sleep" at night. (I have a lot of notes I wrote to myself in the middle of the night.) Then I popped some more drugs to pass out on the plane coming back.

On the way home I flew through London to meet with another prospective project partner for a future event—a seminar on visual perception. He is a research neurologist who focuses on the biophysical processes of vision itself. We discussed some possible future events, and he gave me a kind of crash course on some of the aspects of brain function. I sat there feeling the irony of that—talking to yet another neurologist about what happens in the brain. He was good at making sure to define some terms for me, not knowing—of course—that I already knew more than most people about the anatomy and function of the brain. But I didn't talk to him personally about my brain.

September 16—three weeks after my last blood test—I did another: low white, red and platelet. I was averaging two a month—sometimes more. Dr. D-E was keeping very close track of the level of medication. Even more importantly, he was keeping track of one of the most serious side-effects of my medications on my white and red blood cell count. As fortune would have it, I had never been afraid of a needle. I didn't enjoy the prick of the needle, or watching the blood seep out, but I wasn't terrified of it. I wasn't grossed out by it. As time went on, it had become so normal that I didn't react at all. I started to get a kind of education in how to do it, and what it measures. I went to the UCLA labs to have it done, and so the people who did it were career blood test takers—most of them were very good at doing it as painlessly as possible. Most of those blood tests were just tracking my medications. Every now and then I'd do a big one—tracking many more factors. For those, they would pull more blood, and I would go back out feeling a little more dizzy. Sometimes I would sit in the lobby and wait to see if I could feel better before I went to work. And I had gotten used to the sting of pulling the cotton wads back off.

I got a phone call that afternoon from an agent in the Department of Corporations—the agency I had written back in July about the issue of my insurance company's refusal to pay for tests done over a year previously. He had contacted my insurance company within a few days, but my company had informed him in August that they were a PPO which did not "recognize the jurisdiction" of the Dept. of Corporations. My insurance company had not informed me of that. I would never have known that if the agent from the department had not called me to tell me. He referred me to the Department of Insurance. I wrote another letter. (Copy to the psychologist.)

At the end of September, I got a letter from the Claims Services Bureau of the Department of Insurance telling me that they had been "recently" advised that my health plan was a "self-funded" one, and so the Department of Insurance had no jurisdiction. They would therefore send my inquiry to the U.S. Dept. of Labor.

At the end of September I popped another big handful of meds and got on a plane for Italy to do some more work on the big conference I was producing. I took the train from Bologna to Venice, and woke up early that next morning with the sense that a seizure was on its way. I lay there and wavered on the edge—just felt cold and odd. I didn't get the full event, but I did get the anxiety that it would happen. I did get the headache.

I had some work to do in Venice. I know that city very well—I had lived there for a while in my graduate student days doing a lot of my dissertation research in the big library there. So I took a long, aimless walk, thinking about the past. This corner or that *campo*—a little town square—would provoke the strongest of memories—not only for my everyday life in that city, but also for what I then thought would be the future. I went to sit in the Basilica of San Marco again, to think about life. I met with another possible future project partner in the city, taking notes for my boss, and thinking about what we might do there in the near future. I ate dinner alone that night, and took a long walk, trying to remember how I had felt in Venice six years before. I went back to the hotel and faked some more sleep.

The next day I got on the train to go up north to where we would actually produce the upcoming seminar. I did my job, took my notes, and met with our colleagues. We talked again about the particular history of that place in Italy—the city of Trento—at the time of the painters we were working on. And we talked about some of the details of its history in WWII. The politics of that section of Italy are complicated—the politics of every section of Italy are complicated—and so I could spend some time thinking about long historical series' of other people's problems. And I could sit in the castle there and contemplate what we know about the lives of the painters we are doing this series of seminars on. I would take some more walks, and go back to my hotel to at least lie down, if not actually fall asleep. I was at least happy that plans were going well, and I was confident that the event—to take place the following spring—would go well. I was proud of the work I had done. I took the train back to Venice, took another long walk there, and then popped my pills and got on the plane home.

More blood tests. September 16: low white and red count. October 7—three weeks later: low white and red count. I saw Dr. D-E, and told him how things were going. He considered—again—the possible connections between my seizures and my menstrual period, and so recommended I take diazepam at the start of my period. Every month. He decided that I should start to taper off the Mesantoin© *altogether*. Even though it was a strong suppressant of my seizures, its side effects were too threatening. I went to pharmacy for some more generic Valium©.

I stayed up one night that October—nearly the entire night—thinking about the past. I did something I think I had done only two times before in my life—write a letter to my older brother, the one I had blown up at the preceding Christmas. It is one of the best things I have *ever* done in my life because it was a deeply felt apology for that argument, and for my part in all the arguments we had had in the past. I think it was one of my most lucid and reflective moments in all my life. I tried to achieve some kind of honest admission about how I was then—how I felt then. And looking back at that letter, I feel a little bit of pride. Nowhere in that letter did I cast blame for that fight on my epilepsy or on my drugs. Nowhere did I even mention them. Looking back, much later, when I was off those kinds of drugs, I wonder whether they—their side effects—were involved. I wonder whether my sense of despair at the previous three years of my life was involved. But I think I knew, even then, that the disorder and the drugs couldn't be blamed for everything. I think I was trying for both self-control and for some understanding of the bigger picture of my life. I was *trying*.

October 17, 1996: more seizures. October 23: more blood tests. November 1: more diazepam. November 7: more seizures. November 8: more Lamictal©. November 15: more seizures. December 3: more blood tests *and* more seizures. December 10: 240 ct of Lamictal© and 8 ct diazepam—$300.32.

Merry Christmas.

1997

I did my yearly follow-up (since 1994) with the cardiologist: no problems. I had increased my Lamictal© dosage over January. In February I woke up with an odd rash all over my body. *Jesus Christ.* I grabbed the pile of medication bottles, lobbed them into my purse, and got in the car for the Urgent Care clinic at Family Health. I was responding to Dr. D-E's warning that Lamictal© had been known to produce dangerous rashes, but I was also remembering just how long it can take to get some medical attention in the emergency room in a hospital like UCLA, constantly full of horrible crash victims and deathly-ill people. I'm not criticizing that hospital; I'm just speaking the truth. That Urgent Care clinic happened to be right across the street from UCLA hospital in the office complex where my family doctor worked, so I decided that was the way to go.

I wasn't looking forward to this at all. I don't know anybody who looks forward to something like this, but I was facing another difficult aspect of anything medical in my life: trying to give a doctor who doesn't know me an account of what kinds of medical problems I have had and of what kinds of medications I'm on. Indeed, can you imagine me sitting there with one of those one-page forms which asks you to state your past medical problems and then gives you 3.6 inches of blank line? All I could really do was write down a list of medical terms and wait for the questions.

I hit Urgent Care, though, on a good day. It wasn't that busy, and the doctor who saw me first seemed willing to listen to my information about why I might be there and what they should look for. He was looking at the rash to see whether he recognized it immediately, but he did not. He looked up the name of my medications in the big drug book—the one that gives information about known side effects—but mine wasn't in there. He asked another doctor who was there if he recognized it, and that one did not. Doctor #1 went to his computer and got on the system to see whether he could find updated information on my medications. Doctor #2, who had not heard my summary account, started to ask normal questions: "Do you have any current medical conditions?" I sighed. *My god, here we go again . . . .*

But they got interested almost right away. They understood the problem, and sent me to an affiliated dermatologist to make sure I wasn't having some kind of allergic skin response. Off I went across the street. The dermatologist indeed had 15 free minutes, and was kind enough to see me as a walk-in. He looked at the "rash," told me it wasn't a "rash" at all but seemed to be seepage from tiny blood vessels. I had a flash to the past: sitting there at Student Health with some funny bumps and getting one after another diagnosis of stuff which had absolutely nothing to do with bumps on my arm. "Why is that happening?" I asked. "Not my specialty," he answered. "But, you do have, in addition to this, a minor skin disease in a few places. It's not at all threatening, but you need to treat it." He made the diagnosis, and wrote me the prescription. "Go back to Urgent Care and tell them your 'rash' has nothing to do with dermatology problems." So I stood there in the hallway looking at another prescription (#12 on the big all-purpose list). *I don't care about this just at the moment.*

I trotted back to Urgent Care, and those doctors had gotten up to speed on my medications. The doctor I had first seen told me that he concurred with the dermatologist that it wasn't a rash, so I shouldn't worry about that. What it looked like was burst capillaries, which might be related to one of the side effects of my drugs, low platelet count. If so, that might require a *transfusion*. (*Jesus Christ.*) It might be a related tendency to bruise easily. It might be an effect of a strenuous physical exercise and the increased amount of the prescription drugs. It might also be related to the aspirin I took. "Go take a blood test. Take it easy for a few days and see if it will just go away." I was thinking: *those bumps in 1988 had just gone away . . . .* These red spots went away, too.

February 18, 1997: Lamictal© and diazepam: $300.32 (I paid $60.06).

February 27: blood test: low white and red count. $233.60 (I paid $12.58).

March 17: another blood test. I saw Dr. D-E a few days later, and he told me something unusual! My white count had gone up in the previous December, nearly—but not quite—to the lowest in the normal range. But now, three months later, my white cell count had plummeted to 2.9. And the small burst capillaries might be a side effect of the connection between the aspirin I was taking—since January 1993—and the meds. He recommended reducing my aspirin slightly to see if that would solve the problem. He knew I was about to leave for Europe for a major event I produced for my job. I had been his patient for going on five years, and over those years he had gotten a fairly good sense of what I did in my job. He had also been to meetings there, so we talked a little about the culture. And he asked me to talk about what I was about to do in Italy. He told me to get lots of sleep, even though I had told him that I would not be able to do that, and do another blood test when I got back.

At the end of March I piled up a purse full of bottles of meds and got back on a plane to Italy. I flew to Rome to talk to some prospective conference partners about a project we were thinking of doing—the same project I had talked about with the research neurologist in London the preceding fall—on issues of visual perception. I had been doing research on that—that is, reading the work of scholars important to the field—and, because of my background in various aspects of cognitive science, I was personally involved in developing some proposals for a seminar. I sat with those scholars in a piazza in Rome, discussing the network of complicated issues about how we understand our visual processes and how we interpret what we see. I sat there and thought about trying to write a paper on what I knew about the brain.

Then I got on a train east, to go visit the family of a colleague. They had invited me to stay a while and enjoy the small town and its ancient ruins. I staid there a few nights, enjoying not only the city, but the kindness of my hosts. My colleague and I planned to go on to the major event together. But it didn't work out that way—she caught a bad cold and ended up staying at home. I caught a deep sense of fear that I would get the cold—as susceptible as I am—right before this crucial event. But it didn't happen. I left her at home, and got on a train north. I stayed overnight in Florence, and took a long, meandering walk remembering that year I had spent as a student in the University there long, long ago. I stood there looking over the Arno river, trying to physically remember how I was then. *Who* I was then.

The next morning I got on a train to the city of Trento in northern Italy, to go produce that second of a multi-year series of events on a Renaissance Italian painter. To produce that event had involved hard work for two years before, but it was hard and grueling work for the week it took to actually do the thing. But things went extremely well—I'm very proud of that. I will always be proud of that, especially because I could accomplish it even while on drugs and with a 2.9 white blood cell count.

And my boss was very pleased with what I had done. As a reward for that, I caught the flu—and I caught it full-force—towards the end of that conference. But I couldn't just rest because it was my responsibility to do the project no matter what, and I personally wanted to do it well. After getting everyone else on the way to the train station or the airport, I went back to my room and essentially passed out. I "slept" a long time. I woke up the next day having missed my flight. So I had to get up, check out, stagger to the train station, take a train south to a different city and a different airport and talk my sick way onto whatever was the next flight home. Got the seat, took the meds, passed out. I had the flu for three weeks. I had some minor seizure "auras" right after I got home.

April 11: blood test: white count down even more. Three weeks later: blood test: low white count ($221.72—I paid $14.41). In April, when I had gone to get a month's supply of Lamictal©, the bill was $251.60. In May, when I went to get a month's supply, the bill was $411.67! $2.06 *per pill.* "The previous price had been an error," they told me. So now I was paying about $80 a month for this stuff.

And I wrote another check. I got some end-of-the-line responses to my inquiries on the insurance coverage issues for the Neuropsychology testing I had done almost *two* years before. In response to my inquiry to the U.S. Department of Labor: "The Department of Labor does not interpret plan documents or determine whether individuals are entitled to benefits." Bottom line: consult a lawyer. From the Department of Insurance Claims Services Bureau: "the insurance company's position is tenable." Bottom line: pay up. I wrote the check: $640. Total, when all was said and done (and written and faxed) since the tests themselves: $1300.

My next trip would be back to Germany at the beginning of July (1997), to another conference I had helped produce. I knew I would be doing that, so I had spent some time trying to plan to take some vacation time right before then and travel some more in Europe (Italy was my beloved place). But somehow, I couldn't achieve excitement about what I might do, and I felt the irony of an American with foreign language abilities being unable to be excited about going to Europe for vacation. I think my friends had trouble understanding that as well. What I wanted to do was get in my car and drive. I would have to do it solo, because nobody else had the same time off. I packed my hiking stuff and drove up into the Sierras, enjoying the simple drive itself.

I ended up in Sequoia National Park, standing there in awe of those trees, thinking about being with my mother, about the fact that the world contains many things which have virtually nothing to do with the human life span. I hiked the dizzying Watchtower trail right on the edge of the plummeting canyon of the Kaweah River, and enjoyed the thrill of how dangerous it could be. I did three hikes up to the peaks in the Sierras and sat there, thinking about my own sensitivity, now, to those aspects of life which are natural or biological, and which have nothing to do with what you do or say or think. I sat there thinking about depression. Any crisis like the one which changed my life—and there are many different kinds—can produce an immediate depression in almost anybody. But I sat and thought about another aspect of this kind of medical experience: you can get a sense of life as fragile. You get a sense even of personality as fragile.

I was not the same person I was before that diagnosis, and I never would be again. Not only had my exterior life changed, but so had my interior life. I know, both intellectually and personally, that the medications can directly affect your sense of yourself, and they can cause changes in your behavior. I had lost an ordinary sense of pursuing a "career"—I had been spending years now just trying to stay awake long enough to do my job, to stay above water. I had lost the sense that I had the physical energy to pursue a career. But I had also lost the sense that I could do anything to change the way my life was. People would certainly argue with me about that, and tell me that I could change things if I just changed my opinion. And I would say that I could not just decide to change my opinion—my opinion involved what my life had actually been. And, in my experience, it is often the case that the people who tell you to simply change your opinion have never been through anything like this, and have no sense of that sense of fragility.

I'm not saying what other people should or could do. But I often have the desire—which I immediately suppress—to say: "Alright. You do this. You have the seizures and the diagnosis and the medications and the medical catastrophes and the pain and the abandonment and the unending, unbelievable, incurable fatigue, and then you show me how happy you can decide to be!" But I know that that's the wrong response, because, in most cases, your friends are trying, not to criticize you, but to encourage you. So how do you deal with that? They are doing the best they know how, but you feel like you are a million miles away.

At the beginning of July I went to Hamburg, Germany again to help produce the conference I'd been working on as part of a team. Ironically, it was about memory of horrible events in the past. But it dealt with larger issues than just personal difficulties—some of the presentations involved events in Germany and in Japan in World War II. They reminded me, not only of what I intellectually know about those events, but also about how I had felt about them standing in the remains of a concentration camp in Weimar, Germany at a conference I had produced back in 1994. I felt some empathy with the complexity of dealing with catastrophe, but once again I put mine in perspective with the events discussed in that conference. I hadn't been in Germany in the war, or in Nagasaki when the atom bomb hit, or in South Africa under military control. But my life had been radically altered. There was a "before and after" a single event: the diagnosis.

Fortunately I was only part of the background, so I didn't have the kind of responsibility I had for my big conference in Italy. A colleague of mine, though, was having enormous and constant problems sleeping—because of the jet lag and because of the stress of his more public job duties. (Maybe he also had other problems—I don't know, and it was none of my business to know.) I was about to say to you that I had nothing but sympathy for him, but that's an overstatement. I had a lot of sympathy, but I also had that suppressed response: "Imagine what your life would be if you always felt, every hour of every day, the way you feel right now." But I didn't say that to him, or to anybody. He didn't deserve my saying that to him. And I didn't feel the need to say that to my colleagues in part because of my boss's constant encouragement, and his review of my performance as excellent. I didn't need to express an excuse because I was performing my job very well anyway. That conference was an interesting one, and I'm glad I was involved in that project.

In a hotel in Hamburg I woke up very early one morning. *Here come the freezing cold waves . . . .*

In late July I did another blood test, and went to see Dr. D-E, again. He asked about the event I had produced in Trent, and how things had gone. He reviewed my blood tests, heard about the flu from Italy, heard my description of the seizures I had had, and decided to put me on yet another supplemental medication, Klonopin©—medication #9. He decreased my Lamictal©, to see if that would reduce the side effects, including suppression of my white blood cell count. I went across the plaza to the pharmacy and got the smaller dosage Klonopin© pills to taper up in the next month: $32.49, the month's worth of Lamictal© $413.49, and a month's worth of Diazepam, $8.28. The cost of my medications for the month of August: $454.26. I paid $90.85.

My contract renewal would come up in August, and I had made the request that, given my performance—especially my production of that major series of events—and my boss's reviews of my performance, he make me permanent. I knew that some major administrative policies were being revamped, but his appreciation for my work gave me confidence in him. It was a complicated month because of his required travel, and because of administrative issues in the larger picture of that institution. So things dragged on a little.

I got my job performance review—four pages long—in early September. As I said before, the major reason I'm quoting that review is to provide official information on my performance of my job. But, I can't deny that I'm personally proud of it. My review acknowledged that my job demanded "scholarly ability as well as administrative skills." It noted that the projects I had been working on for several years now "required efficient planning and operation as well as diplomatic and communicative skills." The second seminar of my multi-year project "was a complete success." It involved "intense effort to meet necessary deadlines." I had "significantly contributed to the conceptual organization of [another] recent seminar . . . in Hamburg, Germany." I had "helped with reviewing proposed papers" and prepared "material to be an alternate moderator" for that seminar if necessary. I had taken "detailed notes" which were "crucial in helping to reconstruct a record of the seminar itself" and "producing written summaries." I "contributed substantially to the group effort to evaluate applications for the Fellows for the upcoming scholar year" bringing in my experience with "searches for previous scholar years," "reading and providing summary information and discussing various constellations of scholars." I was continuing to "play a distinct role in the ongoing discussions with me [my boss, the director] and the Scholars department concerning the transition from this theme to themes of future scholar years."

I continued on a project I had been working on for quite a while, "to investigate independently current developments on research on Visual Perception, producing a large annotated bibliography." And "the production of a written proposal will be a substantial part of her work in the upcoming months, and will include a list of possible collaborators on such a project in local, national and foreign institutions. . . . To summarize, Amy's activities at [the institution] in the past year have been intense and successful. She performed the duties of a project manager with distinction." "Her work was essential in many respects, especially in the (x) project, where she showed a good ability to interact at the international level." This review also notes that I didn't publish anything that year, but did note that I could "contribute conceptually in projects" where my "training might be useful." My boss ended this review with "I appreciate Amy's considerable discretion and ability to understand the institutional needs of the [institution] and my own directions."

In the review's "Plans for Improvement" section: "Due to the excellence of Amy's performance, I am not proposing any specific plans for improvement."

In the "Overall Performance Rating": "Excellent."

I felt enormous pride that I could do that job that well notwithstanding the life-altering medical condition I was in. But when I spoke to my boss again about the excellence of the review, and the issue of making me permanent, he told me that he could not make me permanent at that point in time. The issue involved administrative planning of the institution as a whole. He didn't give a reason specific to me, but repeated that my performance was excellent and that he would certainly continue to try to achieve that. And, furthermore, instead of simply renewing my three-year contract, he said that what he would do at this point in time was to extend it another 18 months, ending December 31, 1998. So he assured me that my performance wasn't a problem, and that I should just continue to do the work I had been doing. He would have to delay, though, permanent decisions. This kind of thing—administrative reorganization—was nothing new in that institution.

He mentioned that it might be a good idea to check out the market for another job possibility in case something "better" was available. So I went home *uneasy* with that situation. But all of the same issues applied. I was constantly given excellent reviews, on my production of events and also on several ongoing projects, and I had confidence that my boss was telling me the truth. After all, he knew all of the aspects of my performance and my medical situation, and had given me nothing but positive response. And I wanted to continue to work with him, given both the kinds of projects he was interested in—and how well I could produce them—and the fact that he was an excellent boss. He trusted me to work the way I thought was best so long as I did the job he asked me to do. Furthermore, I would certainly prefer to stay with that job (and that insurance policy!) rather than have to deal with the scary issues of whether—or how—another insurance company would cover my costs.

A few days later I went back to my cardiologist—Dr. K_1—for the yearly follow-up. Arrythmia (irregular heart beat)—yes. Danger signs—no. (Insurance paperwork and payment—you bet.)

In August I went for vacation to see my parents and my grandmother in Colorado. But while the family was there, my grandmother, not well, at the age of 93, went into a coma. My mom would stay up, stay with her, knowing that these might be her last days. I stayed awake as well, not only to be with my grandmother, but to be with my mother. My grandmother never woke up again.

My mother was right there, telling her mother she was right there. Her mother died peacefully that night. The family held each other and wept. When the mortician came to take my grandmother's body to the morgue, one of the nurses who had known her came with him. All of us held each other and wept together, and said goodbye. I wept also for my mother's sense of loss. Her own health had suffered the previous year or two, but she had done the best for her mother that anyone can do. I was glad—her family was glad—that she was now released from that burden, and might be able to take more care of herself. I hoped that she might come to terms with her grief and be able to feel released. To be able to feel better herself.

I sat there trying to remember *feeling better*. Then I would pop some beige downers and try to stay awake, until I needed to pop some little white downers—in addition—and try to sleep.

I went home to say a kind of goodbye to part of my life. My institution had been located in the lovely city of Santa Monica ever since I had worked there, but it was now to move to a complex of buildings at a new site. I stood and looked out the windows of my soon-to-be-former office to the mountains and the ocean, feeling like that part of my life was ending. I certainly wasn't alone in that respect—many of my colleagues there felt exactly the same way! I felt a little silly that I was feeling that strongly about "losing" a place, in comparison to my mother who had only just lost her mother, but I felt it anyway. It wasn't just the place, or the view. And it wasn't the sense that the previous five years had been magnificent, for they certainly had not been—not for me personally. But I stood there, looking out to see, contemplating the fact that I seemed to have lost the ability to look forward to the future. What I mostly felt was the sense of loss itself. And the sense of uneasy, nervous angst for what the future would bring. The last day there, having put all my files and four bookcases of books in moving boxes, I said goodbye to the horizon and walked away.

August 25, 1997: Klonopin© 5mg/30ct @ $32.49. Major side effect: somnolence, i.e. made me feel sleepy.

September 11, 1997: blood test: $149.21 (I paid $9.70). At the end of September I went to Harvard University for a conference on "Internet II"—developing a network designed for academic and high-level research institutes. I had done some research on that already. On the last day I got a phone call from my father. My mother had just had a scary experience which made him take her down to the local hospital immediately: she had suffered an apparent heart attack! We were both silent on the phone for a little while. I was stunned, and he was stunned—again—having seen that awful thing happen to me before and having to say it out loud again. On top of this, they had some guests arriving from Australia the next day. Those guests were already on the plane. Dad wondered if I could come to help out.

I called my boss's office with confidence in his sympathy and, true to form, got immediate permission to go to Colorado the next day. It was—again—the reward for the fact that I made sure to do my job well, and the proof that he was in full support of his employees in these kinds of situations. I got on the plane for the five and a half hour flight to Los Angeles, then trotted down the terminal hallway to get on the three-hour flight to Colorado Springs. My father had taken my mother down to the local hospital, and their diagnosis was that, since it had been a kind of heart attack, she should be moved down to Colorado Springs to see a specialist.

My mother felt very weak, but seemed to be okay. She had had a kind of chest pain. The doctors wanted her to stay lying down on the gurney in the back of the ambulance, not because they felt that she was in immediate danger, but because they wanted her blood flow to be as little affected as possible. If you know the area west of Colorado Springs, you can immediately see what's coming up: she got strapped down on the gurney, put into the back of the ambulance head-first, and driven down the narrow, curvy canyon of the Arkansas River. She told me later that that would be a good way to make people throw up.

The specialist in Colorado Springs gave his opinion: it hadn't actually been a heart attack. It was a response to the stress of her lung system—already damaged—affected by the effects of living at the altitude of their house (about 8000 feet). "What you need to do," he said seriously, "is move to a lower altitude." My mother had, of course, already known that. But she loved the mountains, and so they had decided to move there after my father retired. But now her chest pain—a new experience—had reinforced the advice to go down to a lower altitude. As a solution to that complicated week, we decided that my dad would go pick up their friends arriving at the airport, and drive them back home the scenic route.

I drove my mother home—not up that canyon again, but over the other, longer but less curvy route. She loved that route, too, though, because she simply loved to see the mountains. On the way down into the valley from the east we passed the very place where she and my father had stood long ago looking at the peaks which were now in their backyard. She loved Colorado. She felt better back at home, even though it was 2,000 feet higher up than the hospital in the Springs.

I had to go back to work. On October 7, 1997, I went to the pharmacy: Klonopin© 5mg/30ct @ $32.49. Lamictal© 100mg/200ct @ $413.49. I was in the tug of war between the two drugs.

My parents began to plan to go down to Arizona to find a house. The plan was to spend the larger portion of the year down at a much lower level, and then come back up to Colorado for vacation in the summertime. They began to pack some stuff to take with them to look for a house. The weather in Colorado turned nasty, and they knew they were about to be hit by a major snowstorm, so at the end of October they threw some stuff in the back of their car and drove south, trying to beat the storm. My dad tells me that my mother just sat in the front seat, looking backwards, watching her house and her backyard mountains out the back window of the car until they disappeared from sight.

She had been on oxygen for part of the day for a long time, and so she kept the bottle with her always, to use whenever necessary. She started to feel better, though, for every 500 feet down in altitude they went. By the time they got to Tucson, 5,000 feet lower than her house, she could function all by herself without the oxygen. So they both knew that she would feel much better there. They found a nice apartment to stay in for a month or two while they looked for houses. I heard the stories over the phone: this house was too old, and that one had no garage, and this one was in a bad rundown part of the city. The one they found, though, thank God, was a house half a mile from the Tucson Medical Center with a backyard view of the Santa Catalina mountains to the north. The mountains weren't the same caliber as the 14,000 ft. peaks in the backyard in Colorado, but they were mountains.

I did another blood test the end of October: $176.75 (I paid $11.49). Low white count, lower than it had been in September. I hated the new stuff I was on, Klonopin©. I took it at night. It made me slur my speech, and I felt truly crummy the next morning—like some kind of hangover. I hadn't had a hangover for a long time. I had stopped drinking alcohol five years before—the day of my diagnosis—and I had never drunk much anyway. But this hangover was a direct result of a medication taken the night before. Dr. D-E began to reduce it. From his notes in my file: *Problem #1 Epilepsy, TL . . . Problem #2—mild anemia and depressed white blood cell count and depressed platelets.* In layman's terms: problem #1 is the disorder, and problem #2 is the treatment.

November 5, 1997: blood test: $88.80 (I paid $5.77). More meds: $243.23 (I paid $48.69).

But even though my mother was feeling better down in Tucson, she still wasn't feeling well. Just after Thanksgiving, she felt so bad that my father took her into the hospital. She had pneumococal pneumonia, and so needed to be in the hospital for a few days. At Christmas time I went back to Tucson and she and I would sit out in the yard of their apartment, looking at the very tops of the mountains, talking about the fact that she could look at the whole range when they actually took possession of the new house. We would tell each other some stories about Colorado, and I knew that she deeply missed it. While I was there, she had developed a bad cold again, and slept a lot. She had been feeling poorly since Thanksgiving. But she just took things easy.

She started to feel worse, though, and she started to feel back and abdominal pain. She took it very easy, didn't walk around much, hoping that it would get better. It didn't. On New Year's Eve she knew she had to get medical help. She called her family doctor in Tucson, who told her to take some Tylenol, and if she didn't feel better, come into emergency the next day. My mother had been taking pain killers, and had been in pain for a while, and had never called any doctor until she was actually very sick, and so she was angry about the insensitivity of the doctor. But she went to bed.

Early the next morning she was in agony and she knew she had to go in. We checked her in, and they went to work to make her feel more comfortable. My dad and I stared at each other in the hallway, remembering the New Year's Eve exactly four years before, when he and my mother had stood in a hallway looking at *me* in the hospital bed.

Happy New Year, 1998.

6 Hitting the Wall

1998: The Year from Hell

On New Year's Day they made the diagnosis for my mother: herpes zoster—a virus in your nervous system which is often incredibly painful, but never dangerous or life-threatening. It was a severe case of the shingles. Her response to any disease, though, was stronger than that of other people because her immune system wasn't strong. I stood there feeling that I might know how she was feeling. I had the same immune-suppressant problem, though for different reasons, and had now for five years. Aspects of disease can put people like us in a much worse situation than people with a normal immune system. And her lungs were already damaged as well, so she had more trouble with a problem like this than other people would have. They didn't think it was a "heart-attack" either. Thank God.

The day after I left to go back to work, the doctors had decided to do another test for her, a liver scan to see whether there was anything else going on. In order to do that, of course, you have to clean out the patient's gastric system—that means that she had to eat nothing and take some kinds of medicine that clear out her stomach and all her intestines. That kind of thing is misery. But she did it, still in horrible pain from the shingles, suffering even more than you would think anyone could bear. When they took her down to do that scan, they discovered that their machinery didn't work, and so they couldn't do the test that day. They sent my mother back up, telling her that they would have to try again the following day. She looked at my father, and said, "No. I won't do it again." Her life seemed to have nothing *but* pain. So they prescribed some medications for the shingles and sent her home.

My parents had bought the house with the view of the mountains, and they needed to move into it right away because they couldn't stay another month in the apartment they had rented. But my mother certainly couldn't deal with the move at all, and my father couldn't leave her in Tucson and do that himself. My brothers (and their families) and I decided on a plan. I would go back to Colorado to handle the move. My dad and I made the plans about the Colorado house—what to move and what to leave there—and I headed home to make sure I got my own project work done so that I could take a week off and go to Colorado to pack for my parents. My boss was so sorry to hear about my family troubles, and signed my vacation request immediately.

I packed, and popped some meds, and got on a plane, and rented an SUV and drove through the snow up to that gorgeous house at the foot of the mountains. It seemed like all a dream: the sky was deep blue and the mountain peaks had snowpack and the temperature, standing on the back deck in the sun, would be up in the 60s. I stood there on the back deck looking at the view my mother loved. Even though the diagnosis was herpes zoster—the "shingles"—we knew that she still had the lung problems which had put her down in Tucson in the first place. Because her health wasn't strong to begin with, her response to any other illnesses would be weak. I knew it might very well be the case that she wouldn't be able to come back up here for any length of time. I looked out at our favorite back yard peak and let myself wonder if it might even be the case that she wouldn't be able to drive up this high *ever again*.

I have a deep and abiding sympathy for the personal loss that that would be, and, indeed, she had taught me just how to feel sympathy for other human beings. She had always had a deep and abiding sympathy for me—for all of her children, for all of her loved-ones. So I stood there on the deck wondering if I could somehow see that beautiful place for her. I started to take all kinds of pictures, of the house, of her kitchen, of the yard, of the views down to the valley, of the fireplace, of the etchings on the walls and the pottery on the bookcases, of the big pines in the back yard, of the peaks. I wanted a record—images—of how that house was when she had left it, knowing that it wouldn't ever look that way again. And then I started to pack the house up.

I had made the arrangements to have the movers come and pack most of the furniture and garage stuff themselves, but because of the scheduling of my job, I couldn't stay long enough to be there for that. We had some very kind neighbors who would take charge of that for us. They would let the movers in and try to supervise that process a little. What I had to do was to determine which stuff—furniture and clothes and dishes and whatall—to leave at the house as a kind of stripped-down summer cottage package. And I had to organize that stuff and actually mark it in way that would be clear to the movers: pack anything and everything that is not clearly marked.

It would be hard to have someone else to look through your house full of the last 40 years of your life and decide which things to pack and which to leave. I could make some of the logical decisions—make sure we leave this number of pots and pans, that number of towels, that one chair, the floor lamp with the old shade—myself, knowing that my parents wouldn't be upset about any of that. My dad and I made the rest, based on what he knew he and my mom would want down in Tucson. And we decided to leave a lot of kitchen dry-goods, so that there would be some food there next summer. I had to clean out the perishables, of course, and also pack the valuables myself: some pottery and some glass. But we had some painful moments, too, for we had to decide about those little personal items that we all have—which to move, and which to leave. My dad and I spent hours on the phone as I walked around the house, deciding on things like that.

We both got so tired that we couldn't think any more. I would just stay up late and plan and mark the things to stay, and eat some canned food, and say goodnight to the peaks and go to bed, exhausted. The task of moving is never easy, but I did it knowing that for my mother, this was marking the end of one of the best times in her life—living here. I basically stripped that house. I packed, I cleaned, I took pictures, and I wept. I would try to talk myself into a better mood, thinking that we could all come up here in the summer, but I had a hard time getting past the sense of loss. On the very last day there I put the small package of invaluable personal treasures in my bag, put my personal stuff back in the rented SUV, said goodbye to the mountains, and drove two hours east back to the airport. I flew down to Tucson.

On the day the movers arrived, I dealt with them moving stuff in through the front door. There were a few things at the back of the house which still had to be done—fix some cupboards and install some replacement carpet—and my brother was dealing with that through the back door. My dad stayed at the apartment, helping my mom, organizing the medications, getting her food, helping her move a little. All together the three of us could do the deed. When we were ready, we put a banner up at the entrance. It was a scarf my mom had bought when they had visited me in Italy, years before. It was her flag, so to speak. It was from the small Italian town of Siena—the flag of St. Catherine. We wanted her to feel that this new house belonged to her.

I flew back home to Los Angeles, exhausted. I made an appointment to see my boss again, needing to know about the position of my job. He couldn't tell me anything new. A new CEO of the parent organization was about to take over, and we all knew there might be some administrative changes. I went on working.

In the middle of February I did another blood test, and then went for a weekend to Tucson. My mother was just as bad—still having horrible pain from the neuralgia following the herpes zoster.

Towards the end of February, I went to the pharmacy: Lamictal©
100mg/100ct @ $210.74. In early March, I made another
appointment with my boss and, for the first time in the history
of that job, I actually pushed him: "I *need* to know." And so he
told me. He was sorry to tell me that my position would not, in
fact, be made permanent. That of course meant that I would not
be made permanent. I had to cope with that sense of
disappointment right away. But at that point in time my mother's
health problems had become as important as the various aspects
of my contract position. But the worst was yet to come.

Neither would my contract—then in its sixth year—be
renewed. I sat there one more time in my life in actual shock. He
kept talking: the problem was not with my performance, but
with the reorganization of the institute itself. He was
sympathetic—I could tell that he had some sense of just how
hard this would be. I sat there trying to freeze up again and not
feel what I was beginning to feel about the professional
consequences of this job ending—and, even more powerful, the
personal consequences of the irrelevance of my "excellent"
performance. I was trying so hard to numb my pain, that I couldn't
arrive at the point of "arguing" at that moment. I stayed mostly
silent, and when he was done I just looked at him. He apologized
again that things were that way. He was affected by my silence. I
didn't want to try to talk about the sense of betrayal I was
desperately trying to suppress. I asked if we were done—and we
were—and I got up and left the room.

An acquaintance had said to me, way back when I was in the
throes of producing the second major conference, that I should
just walk into my boss's office two weeks before the event was to
happen and insist that either he make me permanent or I would
just walk. I wouldn't have done that. To me, the importance was
to demonstrate my abilities to do that job well, and part of doing
it well was to avoid producing some additional difficulties myself.
And I needed, I emotionally and ethically needed, to know that
my performance itself would be valuable enough to be rewarded.
If I had played hardball, and insisted that I get the permanent job

or would abandon the institute's major international project, I would never have had the confidence that being made permanent was recognition of my abilities. I would know that it might have just been a case of tactical blackmail.

The constant renewal of my contracts—and my promotions—with each of the last two directors, and the present director's reviews of my performance had given me every reason to believe that I was proving that I was a valuable—and an ethical—employee. His personal knowledge of, and support for, my medical difficulties gave me every reason to believe that his review of my performance was not affected by the issues of medical care. I didn't want to play hardball—I wanted to be rewarded for performance itself. And, just as importantly to me, I wanted to be respected and rewarded for the fact that I *did not* play hardball.

This was, and still is, a case of ethics for me. I was working for an institution in support and performance of the "Humanities"—not Wall Street. I was working for an institution which ostensibly seeks the highest intellectual endeavors—in support of the "Arts and Humanities"—and I had taken the bait. Six years of performance, production and loyalty—including the ethics of choosing not to play hardball—got me renewed contracts, raises, promotions and excellent reviews. Those six years included my decision, at a certain point, to be honest with my boss about the medical issues because they would influence certain aspects of how I did my job—not, as my reviews show, how well.

And then, that year, the "reorganization" of this institution made four other project managers permanent—only one of which had worked there as long as I had—only one of which had the level of the job that I had—but not me. I wondered why. Do you wonder why?

So let me talk about some of the bigger issues here. If you find yourself in this position, know that you will be in a difficult position. I was a contract employee. I wasn't fired. But at the point in time when positions similar to mine were made permanent, mine—with me in it—was not. And, furthermore, for the first time in six years my contract was not renewed. And, six months after I left, a position very similar to mine, with the same title as I had held six years previously (from which I had been promoted), was made available, advertised, filled and made *permanent*. These employment issues might be different for people in permanent positions to start with, and the insurance issues might consequently be different. But it's hard to know whether the total package—your "position" with a company—will be different.

I understand that the institution was being reorganized, and I believe that there were other factors involved in this situation. One of them might have been the cost of keeping me at my current salary level versus the cost of replacing me with an employee who would be paid less. And then there might be the issue of the cost of keeping me employed—of my medical treatment and my prescribed medications. Of course, there are legal issues involved in what kind of information an insurance company can give employers concerning their employees. But then there are the issues of how many people in a company, involved in administrative issues, can and will tell others about medical circumstances. And remember, this institution indemnifies its own health insurance.

If you are a contract employee, or if you are in a position still subject to approval, my advice is: be very careful who you tell. And, for me, there is another lesson, one which is painful all by itself: be very careful who you *trust*. This issue for me—exactly who found out about my medical situation (and how)—doesn't end here. There's more to come.

That weekend—another gruesome weekend ironically like the one five and half years before, just after I got the diagnosis—I drove up the coast and took a long walk on the beach, contemplating the awesome effects of losing that job. I tried for self-control because I had to think about what exactly to do, and because I wanted to suppress my emotional reaction to what had just happened. But I failed, and I ended up sitting on a small rocky point, just looking out to the horizon and breaking down.

I had hit the wall.

I didn't sleep at all that weekend. I walked along the beach, I lay in bed and cried, I drove up the coast and stared out to sea. I was actually trying to work up to anger, but all I felt was despair. My education, my excellent job performance, my loyalty, my honesty, my belief in the value of ethical behavior, my respect for the intellectual endeavors of the humanities—they were all worth nothing in the end. I sunk even deeper: the medical and professional crisis I was in had nothing to do with my actions or with my performance. I didn't do anything to cause the disorder, and I couldn't do anything to change it. I couldn't be angry at myself for having made mistakes, for having caused that epilepsy, or for having failed, somehow, to do my job. I just held myself, like a child does, and wept for the deep and abiding futility of it all.

But there was one big decision that I still had to make, even feeling the futility of it all. Unlike in 1995, when I had first considered surgery, my back was against the wall now. I was facing the fact that I would be epileptic the rest of my life. I was facing the fact that the next job I went looking for might have everything to do with that. I've already talked about the "pre-existing condition" issue, and I know that some legal changes to that have been recently made, but the fact remains that I wouldn't be able to control exactly how and to what degree a previous condition might be covered. I had already been told that the insurance benefits with this job were some of the best available in the market. I knew that I would very likely have to settle for a plan—assuming I could find a job—which covered less. I would still be looking at the cost of my medications. And all the problems I had thought about in 1995 remained. What I had to face, and face it *now*, was the question of surgery.

If I didn't do it, it wasn't at all clear that I could arrange to do it in a future job. It would certainly require, for example, close to a month of absence, and then part-time recovery, not to mention doctor's appointments and medical tests—virtually none of which could be done except on a normal work day. I would need a lot of leeway—which my boss had always given me—to do any of the medically necessary stuff. I would need vacation time, which I certainly had earned in my present job, but which would take a while to earn in a new job. And of course there was the issue of medical coverage. It was difficult to know whether the coverage in a new job would in fact be the same as that in my present job. I wouldn't take a job which offered only HMO.

And then there remains the issue of whether information on my medical records would affect a decision about my employment. Officially, legally, it is not "allowed" to affect those decisions. But I know, as I discussed before, that it might affect a decision to not pursue me as a candidate. And I knew then, from personal experience, that the environment I was in was a tiny group of institutions, who inevitably knew lots about each other. Knowing the history of my institution, and, indeed, knowing what I "coincidentally" know about others—things I should not know—I had every confidence that the information would indeed be made available off the record.

There was another issue as well. Dr. D-E had told me that it was clearly better to do the surgery at a relatively young age, because the ability to heal from such an experience goes downhill with age. So there I sat, on the beach again, hugging myself, weighing the possibilities. If I didn't do surgery now, I might not be insured to cover it in the future, and I might never again be able to do it. But if I decide to do it, I have to do it *now*.

But *brain* surgery? My god. I had never felt fear of the actual physical reality of that—I don't know why. Many people would certainly be afraid of that. I had felt fear of the effects of that on what was essentially the center of my existence and of my personality. I am an intellectual, not only by choice and by career, but by personal nature. My job depended on my several languages and my ability to deal with intellectual material. And my intelligence and my personality had everything to do with my abilities in language itself. The surgery would have to remove a small section of my left temporal lobe, and language is nearly always located right there. In many cases, the doctors decide that they need to do an "intracranial" EEG before the surgery to map out exactly where the seizure origins are. That kind of EEG involves placing electrodes, not on your skull—which was done to me in 1995—but *inside* your brain tissue, and to leave them in there as long as it takes to actually record your seizures. Then you need to recover from that procedure itself—normally six months or so, before they do the actual surgery to remove those portions of the brain.

I considered again the futility of it all. If this kind of epilepsy originated in my right temporal lobe, or anywhere other than where language is located, I think I would have had much less fear of the results of the procedure. But, my doctor had already talked to me about the fact that because I was so highly verbal, this kind of surgery might affect me more than others. It would affect—it would alter—where my skills themselves live. So my decision would have to do, not only with the effects of serious medical treatment in and of itself, but with the very origins of my intellectual abilities themselves—and with the very origins of my personality.

I stared out to sea and considered the way things were at that moment—the seizures and the side effects of the drugs. The bottom line is that all of the meds I had taken are known to produce variations of sedation, cognitive impairment and some psychiatric disorders. So, in that sense, it was a no win future. It would be, in the best possible circumstances, a damage-control future. The future would just be more of the past. It wouldn't get any better—the one and only question would be how *much* worse.

I can give several explanations for why I made the decision that I made, but even I don't know which of them are actually reasons, as opposed to acknowledgements of the issues I had to think of. I suspect that the actual reason is that I couldn't bear the idea of continuing to feel the way I felt about my life at that moment, and so I had only two options: suicide or brain surgery.

For the very first time in my life I could see that my parents were in one of the toughest times of their lives. My mother had never felt pain like the pain she now felt, and the doctors told her that even though it was severe, it wasn't life-threatening. It would certainly cease, but they couldn't tell her when it would cease because there seems to be a wild variety of recovery periods for the herpes zoster neuralgia. And there is no cure for this—all the doctors can do is to try to treat the pain itself as well as possible. And so my mother was on a set of complicated drugs—my god I understand how that goes!— which had some effect on lessening the pain, but which didn't actually eliminate it. She was physically weak, too, not being able to exercise much at all, and not being very interested in food. And my father was doing the best he could, both to make sure she took the medications as they were prescribed, and to help make meals for her and to just help her emotionally get through a painful day (and a painful night). We all felt that way for her. After all, she had spent her adult life taking the very best care of all of us.

I think that under any other circumstances, I would have needed to have their support and comfort for this decision. After all, they had always been nothing but supportive of me and my problems and my emotional status. But now I had the deepest sympathy for them. I didn't want my mother to feel any more pain—and she would feel my pain as well as her own—and I didn't want my father to feel that he had to cope with my crisis— again—as well as his own. I decided to wait until my mother felt better, or at least could see the light at the end of the tunnel, before they would have to deal with yet another crisis in the never-ending stream of crisis.

I knew I had to tell my dad that I had finally been told that my job was over, but I was trying to suppress my sense of despair. I don't know whether I actually achieved that. He of course would know how I felt about that loss, but I tried, anyway, not to push that situation. The decision I made I chose to keep to myself for a while, waiting for my mother to begin, at least, to feel better.

I stared out to sea and said a kind of goodbye—to that part of my life now over.

The Decision

That night I emailed Dr. D-E: "I have just learned that my job will end soon. Is there anyway we could do the surgery before January 1, 1999?" He emailed me back two days later: "Call and get an appointment with me. I'll start the process now." He told me he would check right away about scheduling the tests needed, and that he would see how soon they could check me in for the intracranial EEG. Then maybe I could heal enough that they could actually do the surgery before the end of the year. I made an appointment to see him.

Once I had made the decision, I had to deal with some other difficult personal situations. Once I made the decision—to do some "horrible" and "frightening" thing—I didn't want to waffle. *If I have to do it, let's go.* I had felt that before when I was discussing and considering surgery in 1995. It was emotionally harder to get into the long process of stuff needed. The very idea of another in-patient EEG with even more complicated inserted electrodes, and then having to recover from that and then waiting six months and then going in again was itself causing me despair. I wanted to keep my nerve, and do the damn thing. But a medical procedure like this can't be done the next day. You have to try for resolve, not just nerve. You have to deal—somehow—with seeing the approaching train on the horizon. You have to resign yourself, in a way. You might want to start to run towards the train, but it's not up to you. You have to grit your teeth and persevere.

At the end of February I had gotten a month's worth of Lamictal© ($210.74), and began the process of scheduling medical appointments. Towards the end of March I got the next two months' of Lamictal© ($545.12!), and went to Tucson for the weekend. My mom was no better. I said nothing about the medical decision. At the beginning of May I had a weekend of mild seizures. I made an appointment with my boss in the middle of May. We spoke for about an hour, but no more, because he had to get to the airport that evening for a trip to Europe. But in the hour that we spoke, I told him the present situation.

He knew, of course, my medical situation, but I repeated some of the serious issues: that medical insurance in America—totally unlike the insurance in his home country—is directly related to the job you hold, and so I would lose this insurance with the job. I might be covered for a short time directly afterwards, but I would have to find a new insurance policy soon. That it was possible that a new job, and therefore insurance company, might regard some aspects of my condition as "pre-existing," or that they might not cover it in the same way as my present insurance. That it was likely that I would continue to break through my medications, and so if I was not completely covered, I would be paying close to $300 a month myself for the drugs. I told him that under these circumstances—that I was losing the job which insured me—I had to make the choice for surgery. I told him that I would need to go to a number of appointments for preparations for the surgery, and that at this point in time I would need to do them whenever they were scheduled to try to get this done in the time I had left. I assured him that I would without fail be in in the evenings or all day on the weekends to get my job done. I looked at him when I said the word "done," wondering if he got the irony of that. He gave me "permission." So I began the trial of doing very little else in life other than show up at the hospital for a stack of tests and spend the rest of my conscious time at my desk.

My boss had some emotional reactions to the idea of my surgery. He told me—what I already knew—that he had gotten to know well one of the scholars who had been visiting the preceding year. That scholar had suddenly been diagnosed with a brain tumor and had it surgically treated while he was in Los Angeles. But, sadly, they couldn't remove all of the tumor, and this scholar had died earlier that month.

I didn't reply to that, for what could I say? He then spoke about his hopes that the ability to treat brain problems might get better and better every day, and that I should consider waiting to have the surgery. I was quiet for a little while, but then I said, *again*, that I wouldn't be able to do it without my insurance—and my employer—supporting it. I think he understood the problem, but had not entirely processed the consequences for me. (After all, he is a native of a country that insures its citizens independently of their employment.) Maybe he didn't want to process the consequences for me. I don't know.

I told him that my neurologist had begun the necessary procedures to schedule the necessary tests and the hospitalizations. I explained that there would be more than one hospitalization, and I explained what my doctor had told me back in 1995. The first stay in the hospital, the intracranial EEG, was actually the most dangerous part of the upcoming procedure. And I couldn't tell how much time it would take. I had lots of vacation hours accrued, though, and I said that I wasn't going to use them as a vacation—they would be available for this event. He was quiet about that.

I told him that I would have to recover from that procedure before they would actually do the surgery itself. I told him that my doctor was working on trying to get this all scheduled within 1998—knowing that my job was ending—but that it couldn't be guaranteed because of the complexity of all the factors involved. I wanted him to realize, though, that my doctor was doing his best to respond to the fact that my employer would not make me permanent or even renew my contract.

I repeated that it wasn't yet clear that they could schedule everything to take place before the end of the year, and I asked him whether this institute would consider extending my contract into the following year in recognition of the fact that I would, at the very least, need time to recover—involving a large number of post-surgery medical tests—before I could go looking for another job. I sat there, hoping that he was considering what it would be like to look for another job a month after having brain surgery. I think he did, but I don't know for sure.

He told me that the current budget for the institution could not handle that. I told him that I had been told by a colleague—a friend of mine—that maybe the parent trust would, under these unusual circumstances, agree to provide some funds for this particular difficulty faced by a long-time trusted employee. He said he would try to find out whether that was possible. He was clearly aware, now, of the consequences of my loss of the job, but that made no difference. He was personally sympathetic, but that made no difference either.

In early May I saw Dr. D-E and got a sketch of the plan and some discussion of the consequences. He was very sympathetic for my present position, but he had made clear to me all along—and I have enormous respect for this—that his decision about whether to recommend the surgery would not actually have anything to do with my job situation. His decision had only to do with the medical facts. But he would do what he could to try to get the procedure on a schedule which might work out while I was still employed. My first in-patient test was the "extra-cranial" EEG—the one I had done in 1995—in which you check in for a week or so and they attach electrodes to the surface of your scalp in order to measure the brainwaves during your seizures. The big question here was whether that kind of EEG—*extra-cranial*—would give them enough information about the seizure locations to make a decision, or whether they would decide that they needed to do the next step, the *intra-cranial* EEG. That would be where they had to insert the electrodes deep into the brain tissue. That would be the painful and dangerous one. For the moment, though, his staff had scheduled that first EEG for me at the UCLA hospital.

The week after that I was headed downstairs into the library to find some of the research stuff I was working on, and I ran into a colleague—K—there in the stairwell. She was one I had liked immediately when she took the job there, and her job had recently become working directly for my boss. I didn't know whether she knew all the details of my medical circumstances. I thought perhaps she knew some, as part of her job. She asked me, in a perfectly pleasant and normal way, "How are things going?" I felt the need to tell somebody the whole story, and even though I didn't know her well, I felt a strong sense of trust for her personally. So there we stood, in the stairwell of the building where we worked, and I told her the awesome story of what I was about to do.

K didn't give me the impression that she knew about it, but she didn't give me the impression that she was shocked, either. She let me tell her the story, and gave me nothing but support for how serious—and how scary—she knew it would be. I will never forget those 10 minutes in that stairwell. She had been a fun colleague with a delightful sense of humor, but in that stairwell she became a precious friend with an abiding sense of support. It's hard to tell in life who your friends really are, but sometimes you will find one in a stairwell when you least expect it.

Later that week I found myself in another difficulty. I was asked to meet with an associate director, not my boss but the director of a department affiliated with some of the work that I had done. I went in to find that he was suggesting to me that I take on another project to produce a conference which was scheduled to happen in early fall. I had to sit there and look at another tough situation, for that summer would be one of the worst possible for me to have to produce a major event—I knew that I would need a whole series of tests and examinations, and I knew that I wouldn't be able to schedule those to my convenience precisely because my job was ending.

And furthermore, for this particular project, I had been part of a small committee of people who had done a lot of research and organization of material for this event. Several years back, though, that committee had been dissolved and then reorganized. A few of those of us who had done that kind of work were omitted from the reorganization of the project committee for a number of complicated personal and professional reasons. The details of that are not relevant here. What is relevant is that, at that point in time, having been told that my job was no longer "needed," I was about to be handed a major conference—one from which I had in the past been formally removed—to produce for the upcoming fall.

So I sat there with two big problems. I was angry that I had

6 HITTING THE WALL | 181

just been told that the institution no longer "needed" my expertise—therefore no longer "needed" to even renew my seven years of contracts. Yet they wanted to hand me a project which I had not planned for or organized—from which, in fact, I had been removed—but which I was now being asked to produce. I would have been professionally irritated with that in any case. But the other problem was worse than that. I needed to try to get all of the details of this complex and major-league surgical procedure organized before my job ended. And, now, I was being asked to take on a major-league project that would require intense commitment and performance before the surgery (in addition, of course, to tying up the loose ends of my seven years of projects for my job). I knew that I certainly could accomplish the project. I knew that they knew that I certainly could do it, no matter how difficult it would be. But I also knew that I couldn't do both the project and the surgery. I knew which one I *had* to do.

He had suggested that producing that event might be a good project with which to end my affiliation with the institute. Under other circumstances I would have addressed that issue all by itself: I wouldn't want an event which I had not organized to be handed to me as my "last" professional performance for that institution.

But there was another factor he was not aware of—as far as I know: my last "performance" would be surviving the brain surgery I had to do because my affiliation was about to end.

I told the associate director that I needed to speak to my boss, the director, about that project. I went in that afternoon to talk to my boss. His reply was careful but somewhat sympathetic—he hadn't himself decided that I should be asked to do that project because he knew what I would actually have to do that summer. So he would support my declining to do it, but, he said, we needed to give some explanation to the associate director as to why. We all briefly met, and my boss told the associate director that I would in fact require some complicated medical procedures which would compromise my ability to produce that upcoming event, and so it was better to make other arrangements. He didn't give any more information on what those procedures were—he had always respected my privacy—and the associate director, to his credit, did not ask for more details. I know you are wondering why I am bothering to talk about these details, but there is a reason. Stay tuned.

The day after that I went in for an MRI—the magnetic resonance imaging test of the brain. It isn't painful at all, but it is expensive. The insurance bill for that was $1200. A week later I went for another test, the PET scan—the photon emission tomography test. This one, just like the test I did in 1995, involves an injection of some radioactive liquid, but it isn't painful. The insurance bill for that one was $950. Three days later, at the very end of May, I got on a plane to Tucson to visit my family. I knew when I was checking into the hospital for the EEG, but I still hadn't told anybody in my family about it.

That weekend I found myself talking to one of my sisters-in-law, whom I have loved for a long, long time. I trusted her absolutely, and so I found myself, in a grocery store check-out line, telling her that the surgery was looking likely, but that I hadn't yet told my parents in consideration of the problems they themselves had. She was the only person in my family who knew at that point in time.

On the 10th of June, I began my "vacation" away from work. I checked in to UCLA for the in-patient EEG. You may recall that I had been so annoyed and angry about all the aspects of doing this the first time—in 1995. This time I had made the decision myself to do things differently: to proceed as cooperatively as possible. I remembered how grumpy and pissed-off I had been the first time, and I made the promise to myself that I wouldn't do that to the staff and to the doctors this time.

I checked in officially—they strap the medical info band on your wrist—so I was officially in the care of the hospital staff who had to take me up to the ward with the beds in the EEG suite. But, for some reason, there had been delays, and the inpatient coordinator had checked me in, but couldn't officially—and so, in a sense, legally—give me over to another member of the staff. She had to walk me around a little, and take me to the cafeteria for lunch, and then take me back to her office. I sat there knowing that I would have been furious with that the first time around, but this time I did the best I could to stay cool. She was very grateful that I managed to stay cool. After the first hour of waiting, she apologized again, and asked if I wanted to sit in one of the doctor's offices and maybe read some stuff on the procedures I was about to do.

So, that afternoon, I got a crash course on the history and development of the EEG test, as well as the aspects of the test for epilepsy. I read about the information that the test process could provide, leading up to some discussions of the treatment options indicated by the results of the test. So, in the couple of hours I had to wait just to be checked in, I got a kind of Bachelor's degree in EEG.

The office coordinator realized that I was interested in studies on this stuff, and so she assured me that I had permission to take some copies of some of those articles if I liked. And I did. So, by the time they actually put me in the suite, I had a stack of research articles on the various tests my doctors were about to do. Three years ago I would have said, "about to do *on* me." This time around, I could say that they were about to do them *for* me. I have to say that I have enormous sympathy for the emotional difficulty that procedures like this can have—I have first-person knowledge of that. I felt differently this time around. I look back and think that part of that was because of the emotional effects of medications I was on in 1995, but part of it was still my defense against the very idea itself. This time I wanted to do the best thing possible to get the best possible information for my doctors' decisions. I had resigned myself, I think, to the fact that all kinds of tests and procedures would be part of the ballgame I had chosen to play.

It was also a sense of Fate. I was entering the rapids now, and I had very little control over anything. This time, I chose to do it alone, without the abiding presence and touch of my sweet mother. But I made that choice.

This time around Dr. D-E had not told me to taper off my

medications before checking in, and this time around I had not had any seizures, not even the mild break-through seizures, before I checked in. We had arranged the schedule as close as possible to when my break-through seizures might occur. That was, to me, a sign of good fortune. And when I checked in, I knew the drill. I had brought my bottle of prescription meds to give to the nurses so that they could lock them up, just as before. On the first day, of course, they spend some time just attaching the electrodes to your scalp in precisely the positions necessary to get the information they need. That takes about a half-hour. So I got wired up and then sat in my bed so that they could adjust the closed-circuit TV camera to be sure to cover me, and settled in to the next week of asking for appointments to go to the bathroom. And I began to read that stack of articles on epilepsy that I had gotten from the office of the head of the Neurology department at UCLA. Because I went cold-turkey off my medication, I started to get some of those odd feelings, but just random odd ones, not actual seizures. And, of course, the whole point of this was to get those actual seizures on tape.

The second day I was there Dr. D-E brought his group in to add two more electrodes to my head. These are the two which need to be placed actually inside your skull, rather than on the surface, and so you need a specialist to do that. I had had those in 1995, too. They are injected into your sphenoidal joint—your jaw joint. My doctor told me what I knew from that previous EEG—the injection hurts because there's no way to anesthetize that area in order to do this procedure. I remembered it had hurt like hell that first time. This time, he did the first one himself and it hurt like hell this time, too. He had one of his associate post-doctoral colleagues do the second one, and that one hurt even more. But you have to believe that it's worth it. It aches, though, for a long time, and it makes using your jaw at all hurt. Before he left to go see his other patients, I volunteered to sleep-deprive myself right from the start if he thought it would increase our chances of getting the seizures we needed. So he gave the instructions, and I got ready for the *Tired But Wired* dance again.

6 HITTING THE WALL

And just like clock-work, twenty minutes later, as the staff was adjusting the cameras and the technical EEG specialist was standing there fooling with the machinery, I got lucky. What I felt was the "aura"—I knew the seizure was about to happen, but I was still functional enough to tell them that it was just about to arrive. So there we were, plugged-in, wired-up, and ready to go and then I sat there and had seizure #1 for my audience. This was just exactly the kind of thing for which you do this procedure, and the staff was pleasantly surprised. This is another paradox of this kind of hospital stay: you have some kind of scary and unpleasant seizure, but you, and the staff, are actually delighted that you are having one. That first seizure, though, was a very, very mild one—not really a full one. But it was a start . . . .

My hospital roommate this time around had also had *gran mals* since she was a teen-ager. She told me about her story. She had been taking "recreational" drugs, including heroin, in addition to her legal meds, for a number of years. She had been trying to come off heroin to methadone for a long time now. But for this EEG study, she had to come down off the methadone, and down off her medications (Tegretol©) and go cold-turkey on 2 packs of cigarettes a day. On top of that, she talked about the fact that she and her husband would have to pay some of the expense of the hospital stay. In withdrawal, and worried about the cost of that, she was feeling BAD! While she was there, she would call her husband on the phone and pray with him for the strength to do this. But, after two days, she couldn't stand it, and she and her husband decided to stop trying and just go home again. My heart cried for her, and for him.

So I sat there. I had brought my laptop computer, so I could read all those articles and take some notes. One of the projects I had been working on for my boss ever since he took over was to do some research on current studies on "visual perception." There are of course some connections between the discipline of Art History and work on visual perception, but the connections between science and the humanities are seldom direct. So he had asked me to do a bibliography of recent work on that topic in both the humanities and the sciences to see whether our institution might be interested in producing a project on precisely those issues. I had on my computer a number of bibliography files and notes on visual perception, which involved, directly, anatomy and function of parts of the brain. Because of that research, I already knew some stuff about the brain. But my personal experience had put me through another course—a crash course—in brain anatomy and function, so I know that visual perception takes place in locations different than those of language.

So there I sat, in the hospital, with a complicated series of electrodes attached to *my* brain so that they could learn what was happening and where it was happening, while I was sitting there reading a stack of research on *other* people's brains—on what was happening and where. That was Plan A. But the longer I stayed awake, the harder it was for me to pay careful attention to the scientific stuff I was reading. I ended up falling back to plan B. I put that stuff away, and started in on a novel: Herman Melville's *Moby Dick*. I had some confidence that the 600-plus pages might last me the week I would be there.

The nurses were excellent. They would literally stop in for a few moments every now and then just to chat—to give me a little outside contact. They offered to take me on walks—down the hallway plugged in to a different, moveable machine—whenever I wanted to do that. One of the nurses was a specialist in epilepsy cases. She would come to talk about some of her cases and I could ask her some questions about the medical articles I was reading.

That second night I used my credit card to call my dad to ask him how things were, how my mother was feeling. Things had not changed. I didn't tell him where I was calling from. K—my new friend from the stairwell—came to see me and to find out how things were going.

I stayed awake—once again with the help of the staff—and read and read and read. Indeed, I was starting to think that I might actually get through *Moby Dick*! That Saturday afternoon I had one of my "normal" seizures—a partial-complex—but stronger than it had been on medication. That was why I was there.

Then on that Saturday evening, I "woke up," sort of, feeling odd, and not knowing where I was. If you can imagine having volunteered to be strapped in and having been awake for days and having talked to almost all of your nurses and having read seven articles on seizures and yet "waking up" very confused—not knowing where you are. But I was in pain, too. All over. I felt like something had slammed into me—my arm and my shoulder were in sharp pain. And my tongue hurt like hell.

I could hear this voice before I knew who was talking to me. "Amy, do you know where you are?" I didn't. "Do you know what city you're in?" I didn't. "What year is it, Amy?" I couldn't even think of what year it might be. "Do you know what happened to you?" I just stared at the nurse talking to me. I couldn't remember much of anything. "You just had a full seizure—a *gran mal*."

My God. They are awful. That was the kind I'd seen but never had happen to me since that Thanksgiving Day in 1992. And this one was worse—I literally felt like I had been beaten. My body had pulled almost all of its own muscles, and locked almost all of its own joints, and slammed itself into the bed railings. It took me a few minutes, maybe, to come back from that sense of confusion, and to know where I was and who I was talking to. And yet, when I came back to "reality," I lay there in pain and I was glad. That was the kind of information that we needed. That was exactly the kind of information that we had never gotten that first time in 1995. I stayed awake. I talked to the nurses who had been there during the seizure and I took a short—and painful—walk. Then I picked up *Moby Dick* and said to myself: let's do it again.

And I did it again. Shortly after that seizure my good friend, K, who knew the entire situation, came to see me, and heard the story. And my boss called me to see how I was. When my apartment roommate called to see how I was doing, I was out cold. I wasn't asleep, I was unconscious. I had two more *gran mals*. A seizure like that just scrambles your brain—when I "woke up," I had literally no idea where I was, or even who I was. That "scramble" is so strong that when I woke up from the second seizure, I didn't know where I was, and I didn't even know what had just happened to me even though it was seizure #2. And, they tell me, I had actually fallen asleep when I had seizure #3, and when I woke up from that one, I still had no idea. Not until I would come back to "normal"—then I knew.

Dr. D-E had came to see me every day that I was there, but one. On day seven, he told me that he had the kind of information that he needed, and that he would check me out and send me home. "Your seizures," he said, "had all begun in the left temporal lobe." Seizures which begin in a specific location can generalize to the rest of your brain. That is what produced—for me—a full *gran mal*. My experience had been an example of the complexity of this disorder, though. He was confident that my *gran mals*, even though they weren't "normal" for me, gave him the kind of information about my normal seizures that he needed. He talked to me a little bit, again, about the fact that it was likely that the withdrawal of the medications caused my seizures to be actually worse than they had been before I had started on the medication.

But none of my seizures had begun in any other part of my brain, so they knew more than they ever had before.

When I checked out, my apartment roommate came to pick me up and take me home. I went home on a Sunday and slept, slept, slept. The initial bill for those seven days in the "laboratory": $15,158.30. My neurologist decided to put me on yet another supplemental drug, Topomax©—Drug *#10*. I went to get a month's worth of those little beige pills: $160.27.

I went to work the next morning, and met with my boss. He asked how things had gone, and I told him that they had learned what they needed to know in order to move ahead with the surgery. So the actual reality of that began to sink in. He told me that maybe I should consider waiting on the surgery. Medicine was moving ahead at an advanced pace: "They discover new things every day." I reminded him again that waiting was a dangerous thing. The fact that my job was ending changed *everything*. He knew that, but he didn't address it. He knew about the entire problem of the insurance and the employment issues—I had previously explained them.

I told him that my neurologist and the group he was part of needed to review the information they had and make decisions about the surgical procedures for me. That review and discussion might take some time, so I didn't know whether they would decide to do the second in-patient EEG session—the more dangerous one in which they insert the electrodes into the brain rather than attach them to the surface of your scalp. If so, I would need to recover from that experience before they would actually do the surgery. That might mean that I couldn't complete all of the necessary medical operations before Christmas—before the end of my contract. Based on that possibility, I asked whether under those extraordinary circumstances he would consider extending my contract a few months into the next year so that I would be able, not only to have the operations, but also to recover back at my job. Then I wouldn't have to go looking for a job with my shaved head still wrapped in bandages. He was moved by that, and said he would see what he could do.

By the beginning of July I started to discover one nasty side effect of drug #10, Topomax©: my speech was slurred. I would stand there—a person with a doctorate in literature in three languages—an extremely verbal person—*slurring* my speech. I was a little dizzy—again some more still. I sounded and looked drunk. I suspect that many people might have thought that was the case.

The situation in Tucson

I flew to Tucson for the 4th of July weekend. My mother was still in pain—we had no clue about how long that would be the case. It was such extreme pain that she was literally bed-ridden, and on a set of complicated sedative drugs to try to manage the pain. She had been to one of the clinics for pain itself—in addition to treatments for the diseases or disorders causing the pain. She had been given another prescription drug: Neurontin©. I asked my dad: "are you sure you got that right?" He was. I stood there surprised that my mother was being treated—for pain!—with the same medication I had been on for seizures! This is an example, though, of the complex nature of the human brain, for the physical events of pain and of seizure seem to be somehow related. That drug, however, did very little for me. And, so far, it had done very little—maybe nothing—for her.

She had a very kind in-home nurse coming once a week to help her, but my father spent all of his time taking care of her, trying at least to make her feel less pain, even though he couldn't do anything to actually cure the pain. I sat next to her bed and tried to tell her some good news—there wasn't much, so I more or less made some up. She and I talked about her pain, and about the fact that nobody seemed to know how long it would last. I just kissed her hand and held it awhile, and tried to do what I could to comfort her. I knew that I didn't want her to have to deal with the issues of my surgery, and because my father was doing all he could do to help her through the pain, I hadn't said anything to him either.

After a while she dozed off, and I sat out on the patio and contemplated my options.

How can we do this? If I needed to do the second in-hospital EEG test, that would be scary, scarier almost than all the rest of the procedures for this process, including the actual surgery itself. For it involves your having, essentially, several constant "open wounds"—and that requires careful attention to prevent infection. And if I needed to do that, I would need to actually recover from that. And to both do it and recover from it, I would need to have some close care and some actual physical help. I would need to do it in Los Angeles, where my doctors were. But I wouldn't be able to get on a plane three days later and fly to Tucson to be taken care of. In fact, I couldn't get on a plane and fly anywhere for quite a while. I would need someone to take care of me there. And who could that be? At that point in time, very few of my friends in Los Angeles knew anything about this. And all of them had jobs and in many cases a family. They couldn't do this kind of thing even if they wanted to. Both of my brothers had similar commitments—they couldn't just leave their homes and kids to come to Los Angeles for a couple weeks, and I couldn't get on a plane to fly to them either. Indeed, I wouldn't be allowed to even get in a car and be driven anywhere because you have to be very careful while your body is healing.

My apartment roommate—P—would certainly be as helpful as she could be, but she also had a full-time job and personal commitments, and had never actually taken care of anybody in circumstances like these. Under some kind of "normal" circumstances, my parents would simply come, as they had in the past, to take care of me for however long it would take. But the way things were at that point, of course, there was no chance that my mother could make the trip at all, and my father would find himself in a position similar to mine: who could take care of her for the weeks he would have to be taking care of me? We were hoping fervently that her neuralgia would simply heal soon, as it might very well do, but none of us could be sure of that.

And that intracranial EEG would be only the first event. The surgery itself, called a "resection," was actually less dangerous. But, nonetheless, it would incapacitate me for a while. I would need to sleep a lot to recover. I would have trouble even talking for a while. I would need to be careful to heal the wound itself, and that would take some time. I would have several follow-up appointments with my doctors so I would certainly need someone to drive me there and back home. I would have to be sure to take the right medications, and careful that I didn't faint or fall down, so I would need to have help always close by. If I started to have seizures right after the surgery, I would need medical attention. I sat there, thinking about all of this as technically as I could manage, to try to keep from feeling the personal fear of being the one to actually do all of it.

So I sat there doing the math: if I did the second EEG, that would take probably a week, and maybe more. Some patients have required several weeks plugged-in like that before they had seizures. And since the procedure of getting you plugged in—the medical procedure of the *intra*-cranial "test" itself—was so serious, they would need to simply keep you there—strapped in—for however long it would take. And then, unlike with the first non-invasive EEG, I would need to recover. The surgeons won't do the resection until they are sure your body has recovered from the invasive EEG. So even if I did that before the end of that month—and that didn't actually seem likely because it can take a while to get all the scheduled procedures organized—I might need two weeks to give the results. And even if that worked, I would need a while just to recover from that test itself. And so I would very likely need at least a month—more likely two or three—to recover. So, the very soonest I would do the surgery itself would be the end of August. I thought: *I can go in for surgery on my birthday.*

But it was more likely that I wouldn't be able to get into the ward to do the first procedure before the end of August—you can't just call the hospital and tell them you will arrive on a certain Tuesday. Then I would likely be in the hospital doing that for two weeks, into September (and my god, maybe more). Then I would probably need six to eight weeks to recover, and then, if all was well, go in for the surgery itself in late November or early December. *Merry Christmas.*

Back when I was finally told that my job would end, I had felt as though I had hit the wall. But now I sat there feeling even worse, up against another wall, saying to myself: *try like hell to stay numb so that you can reason your way through this.* My mother's doctors had told us again and again that she would certainly recover, but nobody could even guess, much less know, how long that would take. I didn't sleep that night, trying to decide whether I should in fact cancel the plans for surgery. Or "delay" them, knowing full well that "delaying" might end up being "canceling." It was another in a long line of sleepless nights.

My dad and I sat the next day on the back patio, and he talked a little bit more about how he was able now to control the pain somewhat, with careful treatment. Maybe, he said, my mother seemed to be feeling a little better, and so he was hopeful that maybe she was close to starting to recover. I sat there also knowing that he would be upset at my not telling him about my situation.

"How are you feeling, dad?"

He looked at me. "As well as I can. I do the best I can."

We were quiet.

I bit the bullet and told him the story: my job was clearly over, and I had decided that I had to do the surgery, and I had begun the preparations. I had already done the week-long inpatient EEG. But I could clearly see that he and mom were having their own long, drawn-out medical crisis, and so I hadn't yet arrived at the conclusion about what, exactly, I should do or not do, right now.

I will remember all my life how that hit him. He sat there, literally, with his mouth open. Not finding any words. I knew his problem of finding no words. I felt for his pain. But I knew that the only choice I had had was to decide when to hit him. He held me in his arms in his fatherly embrace. Or maybe I held him in my arms, in my daughterly embrace.

It was another weekend from hell. I had had so many of those weekends now that that expression seemed to mean very little. But language escapes me: I couldn't think of any expression that could come anywhere near how bad things actually felt. He continued to try to process what I had told him. *You went into the hospital for a week, all by yourself? Your boss knows all this, and it doesn't matter? If you don't do it now, will that mean you can never do it?* I told him I didn't know yet exactly when the surgery would happen, but I knew that the situation would be enormously complicated by mom's health. I knew that I had some more tests to do, and some more doctor's appointments. It was clear to me that I would do it, but it wasn't yet clear when. And then I told him the decision at which I had arrived: "I think we shouldn't tell mom about this yet, because of how it will make her feel, and whether she can deal with the implications."

We thought about that. It would be difficult for both of us to hold back something this serious from her. I had never done that with either of them. But we had the strongest reason possible—her present situation. He agreed. So we sat and thought a little bit about how in hell we could manage to do that thing. I had to go back to Los Angeles the next day, though. I left him some of the material on surgery I had gotten from the office at the hospital right before my EEG, and I kissed my mother goodbye and went back to work. My father looked stunned all the way to the airport and as I kissed him goodbye. "I'll call you when I know . . . ."

Following through, and continued anguish

When I got back to Los Angeles, I went to the pharmacy: Topomax© 25mg/100ct ($160.27) and Lamictal© 100mg/100ct ($222.84). I found out about some problems. Even though my physicians' staff had sent the appropriate information on the next upcoming in-patient test to my insurance company, and even though they had made the appropriate requests for coverage of this test, my company had not yet responded with "approval." And you don't want to do things like this—costing what they do—without your insurance company "approving" them. Of course, let me repeat what I said previously, it is still the case that even if they approve it, the approval itself clearly states that "approving" it doesn't guarantee that they will actually "cover" it: the Yes Maybe response. The surgeon's staff who had been trying hard to do this gave me the actual name of the person officially making the decision (but who hadn't yet responded). I ended up having to fax—twice—that person, explaining that the test had been planned for a specific time period in which it was likely that I might have a seizure, so if they did not immediately approve it, I would have to wait another month or so, which would of course delay everything else.

Finally, finally! The company faxed "approval" to the surgeon's staff.

So two days later, in the middle of July, I went in to Cedars Sinai to do another test: a SPECT (single photon emission computer tomography). This is another test in which you get wired up—electrodes on your scalp—and then "encouraged" to have a seizure. In this test they want you to be able to tell them just exactly when you are about to have one, so they can inject some radio-opaque liquid literally at that moment. Then they have some time in which to make the SPECT scan which gives them information about the effects of the seizure itself. So I checked in there for an overnight stay—planned for a time of the month in which I was most likely to have a seizure—got taken off my meds, and started on another of my favorite huge, long books: Thomas Mann's *The Magic Mountain*.

Whereas things had gone very well at UCLA, they seemed to screw up endlessly that time around. I seemed to have fallen through the cracks on the list of patients, and so no food was delivered at lunch. I filled out some forms for dinner, but they apparently didn't get to the kitchen on time. I had no dinner. Unlike the ward at UCLA, this ward seemed to keep no snacks, so all they could seem to do for me was get a small plastic cup of cranberry juice and a little yogurt out of the machine two floors down. But they kept me awake. The next morning I had to fast before the test, so no breakfast. I went down to the lab to get wired up again and to just sit there sit there sit there, waiting for a seizure.

This time, since they needed to inject some stuff right at the moment you are about to have a seizure, the radiology technician had to sit there sit there sit there. For an hour. For another two hours. Nothing. By then they couldn't give me lunch because of the pending injection of stuff. So I sat there another three hours. Close to the end of the day, though, I thought I had that strange feeling which shows up right before a seizure. I didn't wait until the seizure actually happened, but told them, as they had instructed, that it was on its way. They immediately gave me the shot of cold stuff in my elbow. But as luck would have it, I actually had just a slight glimmer. A few minutes went by. Nothing. Damn. The technician had flagged the neurologist in the next office, and she came in to look at the records. But there wasn't much to see.

She was about to leave the room, when I got the real event. So, I actually got the injection a little too early. They stood there looking right at the EEG show, knowing exactly what they were looking at, but unfortunately they still didn't get exactly what they had wanted. They scheduled the scan for that evening, took me back upstairs and tanked me up on my medications. Because of how late in the day—and into the evening by the time they did the scan—they decided that I needed to stay there another night. For this test the staff had given me careful instructions on how to drive my car there for the appointment, and exactly where to park it, but then the medical staff stood there and told me that patients undergoing this procedure were not allowed to drive themselves home. But it seems that the staff had put me on the list of patients checking out, so I wasn't on the list of the kitchen staff. So I went to bed disappointed *and* grumpy *and* hungry. I had to take a cab home the following morning—they needed to check someone else into my room by 10:00. My apartment roommate gave me a ride back the next day so that I could pick up the car which I should not have driven there in the first place. The total cost of this test listed on the preliminary bill from Cedars Sinai: $4,322.00 (I ended up paying about 10% of that, plus 20% of the bill for a specialist involved who wasn't in the group approved by my "PPO" insurance policy.)

And then I went to see Dr. Itzhak Fried, the neurosurgeon who would actually do the surgery (and assistant professor of Neurology at UCLA). He—Dr. F—and the team including Dr.

D-E—would review the findings from my EEG and my SPECT to make some decisions about the surgical procedures. This procedure tries to locate where in my brain I produce nouns and where in my brain my seizures originate in order to make some crucial decisions: will the removal of the seizure-causing tissue affect the production of language in my brain? And, furthermore, the general ability to map the naked brain with controlled testing of an awake patient contributes to knowledge of how the brain functions. (And that knowledge may prove invaluable for other human beings.) He seemed to be very interested in my case, and we talked for close to an hour about a number of things. He was certainly interested in my foreign languages—for I had studied a number of them, and I spoke—with some regularity—several. We listed all the ones I had studied, and categorized them.

And then he asked another question: "which ones are the most important to you?" It was possible that the surgery to remove the portions of my brain producing the seizures would also threaten a foreign language area. And in that case, we would have to make the decision as to what to do: protect the language and sacrifice the resection, or sacrifice the language abilities but resect the epileptic tissue. So I rank-ordered them, but then I sat there wondering what I would actually be willing to lose for this surgery. And of course I would have to make that decision before the surgery so that the surgeon could do the deed, if necessary, during the surgery itself.

I sat there considering what he had told me. It was a paradox that the surgery might threaten those languages that I knew the best—the ones I actually spoke—but perhaps leave the ones I only read untouched. And I found myself interested in several more intellectual issues which occurred to me. I asked a question: if my Russian, for example, was located in a certain part of my brain when I learned it—and spoke it—did it somehow move backwards when I stopped speaking it, but only read it? And how on earth does that actually happen? He smiled, and said that we know that it does (in most cases), but we don't know why, and we don't know how. We talked a little bit about some scientists who had done research on that—and I found myself interested in trying to find out more. I also found myself worried about what, exactly, would happen to my foreign languages. He said that that was exactly what they would try to find out before doing the resection. And then he told me how.

They would take a more or less circular portion of my skull out, and then put electrodes on the tissue of the brain itself—on my left temporal lobe. And then they would actually wake me up—with my brain exposed—with all those electrodes attached. Then they would have me talk to them in order to be able to locate—exactly—which part of my brain was involved in which part of my language abilities. This would involve some specific kinds of "conversation"—especially naming things, for they know that nouns are often produced in the part of the brain near where he and my neurologist think my seizures begin. And, for me, they need to find out where I produce the nouns in my primary spoken languages: my native English, and in Italian and French.

There is some evidence that foreign languages are "stored" and "performed" in parts of your brain different from the location of your native language. And, to make things easier, they have evidence that languages you only read are located farther "back" from the site they needed to test, and so would very likely remain unaffected by the surgery. He and his team would try to map where my Italian was and where my French was. And that would involve getting some native speakers in these languages to actually attend the surgery. They would ask me questions in those languages so that he—the surgeon—could map where my activity was taking place. "This will," he said, "take a while." Normal surgery of this kind, he said, would take about six hours, but for me, because of my multiple languages, it would probably take closer to nine hours.

They would do this in order to see whether the removal of the tissue producing the seizures was located precisely in a part of my brain producing language. For they would have to make the complicated decision about how much of my brain tissue to remove. And if my seizures were located in a part of my brain so crucial to linguistic abilities—that is more complicated than just the "location" of nouns—they wouldn't remove it. If they couldn't remove any portion of my brain because the seizures originate in that crucial spot, they would close my skull and stitch me up and that would be it. Dr. F is a very warm person—I liked him immediately. He knows that people are afraid of the very idea of surgery, and so he spent some more time trying to reassure me about the procedure.

We discussed, however, the possible effects of the surgery itself on the brain—technically, I suppose, referred to as "side effects." Somehow, though, it seemed to me to be part of the "price" for the surgery. After all, in most cases with medications, the side effects will go away when you stop taking the drugs— that is, change medications—but in brain surgery, some of the side effects will be permanent. But it is unclear *exactly* how any particular patient would respond. And the ultimate effects would depend on the portions of your brain they decide to remove— because, of course, they will test for seizure origins once they are in there in order to make that decision. But he was confident that he and Dr. D-E now knew enough about the location of the origins of the seizures that they wouldn't need to do that second "intracranial" EEG. *Thank God.* One domino had finally fallen on my side. He said we would move ahead and schedule the "resection."

We had talked initially about doing the surgery in October, but we had to work around his schedule. So we penciled in a date in the middle of October. Knowing that that was a likely date, I could actually plan to do something I had always wanted to do, but which had been on the back burner from scheduling the surgery. I could indeed go to Italy in September to see the opening of the exhibition that was directly related to the series of seminars I had produced. It was a kind of culmination of the previous three years of my work. I'm grateful that I was lucky enough to be able to attend.

The first weekend of August I went to Tucson. My mother was no better. In fact, she was worse. For eight months now she had been in excruciating pain. And while in excruciating pain she still had all of the difficulties she had had before with her breathing problems, so she had to get upright often to avoid having her lungs fill up with bodily fluids. And she was on a number of medications designed to treat the pain as well as possible. One of the side effects of all of this was that she felt no hunger at all, and so my dad had to try to feed her on some kind of schedule, even though she didn't want any food. She had lost weight to the point where she was very thin.

Her throat was dry—in part from the medications—and she had to work hard even to breathe, much less to talk. I stayed with her though, just to be there. I read to her from a book I knew she had enjoyed. I gave her a very gentle sponge bath, careful to stay away from the opiate patch on her shoulder. I kissed the palms of her hands, and I held one—gently—against my cheek. I tried for some small talk, but that was hard, too. But she was the kind of person who could stay with you in sweet silence, and so I stayed with her. I laid down next to her, wanting to hold her in my arms, but knowing that it would give her more pain than comfort. So we simply held hands, and laid next to each other. I laid there aching, and I cried very softly, not only for her pain, but for what she did not yet know.

That weekend my father and I decided that we finally had to tell her so that we—all three of us—could figure out how to handle taking care of me. From a practical point of view, we needed to discuss the dates and the question of whether dad could come to help me and arrange someone to be able to care for her. From the emotional point of view, we needed to be honest with her.

She sat on the edge of her bed, cringing with her now normal pain. dad told her the basics of the decision. I needed to tell her that if I were under any other circumstances with respect to my job, I would simply delay until she recovered. And I tried to express all of how I felt about it. For this would involve, of course, sheer practicality for her and for me. But it would also involve the emotional strength of my father to take care of both of us. And I knew that she would feel the tragedy of knowing that one of her children was about to go through an awesome medical ordeal, but she could not be there for her. My father and I felt the deepest sympathy for the pain of her present medical condition and for the pain she felt because she could not help me. She felt the sadness of something like this happening to one of her children at exactly the point in her life in which she could not be of help. So she sat there on the edge of the bed, in pain—her own pain—and looked at us in our pain. I will never forget that moment.

But at least she knew now what the next few months would require. And my father was grateful that there was no longer any need to keep this from her. Once again, I felt so moved that I could always be honest with my family about what was happening to me and why. I kissed my mother goodbye—she held my hand so firmly. I got on the plane on that Sunday to go back to work, stared out the window and cried, cried, cried in my deep despair.

That first week of August, I went to the pharmacy for another month's worth of meds: Lamictal© 100mg/100ct ($222.85) and Topomax© 25mg/120ct ($163.19). I had increased my dosage, and felt the full side effects of the Topomax©, and I hated them. I started to be scared to actually talk to people. I would sit in my office and wonder: is this the future? I was one of the most verbal people I had ever know, and there I sat, with a drug-induced speech defect. An expensive speech defect. One I was paying lots of money for. *God*.

My boss asked me to meet with him in mid-August, and told me the situation. He had spoken to the parent organization to ask whether they could provide some financial support for an employee for a brief time given this medical crisis—he had not named me. They said no. We both knew that it's not the case that they didn't have enough money to do it, but they would not do it. Because of that he had figured out a way to respond to my initial question: would he allow his institute to keep me on a little longer? Because, he said, the parent organization would provide nothing, he would arrange to extend my contract for a few months, but no longer. All I could do was be grateful for that. So I signed the new short-term contract extension.

At work I began the process of saying goodbye to my job career of the previous seven years. I had to do a number of things, some of which were directly related to the closure of the huge project I had done for three years. Some were directly related to organizing my files so that anybody who needed to look at my records of projects or research in the last seven years could easily understand them. I had to start to take some things home. I had kept a lot of my own books in that office, while filling up my bookcases at home as well, and so I had to start to take boxes home so that I wouldn't have to move them all at once. I had to start to write the project summary material to leave with my boss. I had to start to plan for possible surgery dates until my surgeon told me specific dates when the operation could be done. And I had to make another major decision: who to tell and what to tell.

I had all the same reservations I had had before, but now I had a new source of pain. I needed to continue to steel myself for what was to come, and I didn't want to now have to try to explain everything to my co-workers. Some of them—but not all of them—would be certainly sympathetic, but they would also want the whole story, and I didn't want to have to give the whole story. I didn't want to have to relive the whole thing. I didn't want to find myself talking about it in part because telling the story would threaten my emotional self-control. I've talked about this before. For some people, talking about the situation might have been necessary and comforting. For me, it was threatening.

And I didn't want to give lots of information about *why* I was having brain surgery because that would make some dangerous information public knowledge. I lost some sleep over that, too, for I was just about to do this horrendous, expensive medical event because I was just about to hit the job market—and I knew that that information might very well affect my future. In fact, as I have said before, based on what I had "learned" about other people's private affairs—because of gossip—I knew that actual privacy was unlikely. But I felt the imperative to, at the very least, *officially* keep it private so that there was a chance that I could find a job without having to deal with that. Of course, as we all know, the chances of other people all keeping information like this private are slim to none. But I didn't want to give "permission" for it to be public by making it public.

But I did need to tell some people. I certainly needed official help from the personnel coordinator who would handle the paperwork related to my job. I needed to tell her the whole truth. She was the direct source of another domino falling for me—not against me—for she was genuinely sympathetic, and started immediately to do all the necessary paperwork. And more than that, she immediately advised me how to file the kind of information actually required, but keep as much as possible private. She understood what my tenuous situation was. She gave me confidence from the start at her professional abilities for something like this, but above and beyond that professional expertise, she gave me genuine personal support. I imagine that that kind of job requires abilities with personal interaction much higher than most of us have—higher, certainly, than I have. I don't think that I could have done her job anywhere near as well as she did it for me.

I had to consider, now, who to tell. And when. I had made some good friends at my job there, and I could pick several right away to trust. Some were truly astonished when I told them the truth. One friend had to lean against my bookcase to steady herself from falling down. To their credit, not only were they immediately supportive of me and what I now had to do, but none of them seemed to be upset that I hadn't told them about this situation before. This was another event in which you find out who your friends really are. And I had some. Indeed, that very emotional conversation with some of my friends made them confident in trusting me as well, and we could talk to each other about the complicated nature of revealing medical problems to co-workers and about the issues of privacy. Those friends promised me that they wouldn't compromise mine. I believed them then—and I believe them now.

Most of them were astonished at my news—at the major effects of that disorder and at the awesome nature of approaching brain surgery. And some of them were immediately aware, without having to be told, of my fear of consequences on the job market. In fact, I got told a few stories of their friends who had paid that price with other medical issues. And I got a question or two about whether that had anything to do with my job ending. That question remained unanswered.

An ending

The dates for the surgery were narrowed down. Early November: Election Day, 1998. I called my dad. I knew that my mother wouldn't feel much better, but we knew we could move ahead trying to plan taking care of me in the month of November. I told my boss and the personnel coordinator when the countdown would begin, and began to studiously plan the details of my job to avoid breaking down in the face of what the future would now irrevocably be. But I had to face it anyway, and all I could do was to try to keep the door closed while I was at work, and to make sure to do the best performance of my job that I knew how to do—to try to be as professional as possible even in the face of professional apathy. That had been one of my mother's lessons, and part and parcel of my personal sense of the importance of ethics even in the face of catastrophe. She was closer to my thoughts now than she had ever been.

I packed for my planned Labor Day weekend with my parents. I went to the pharmacy: Lamictal© ($222.85) and Topomax© ($163.19). We would need to carefully discuss exactly what the plans were for the dealing with the fast-approaching events. My father called me a few days before I would come, though, to say that the morning before my mother seemed to be unable to stay awake, and he was concerned about the effects of the medications—for there are always side effects of medications. Her home-care nurse had come by to see her, and suggested that perhaps a medical examination would be needed to find out what the nature of the response was and maybe adjust the medications. I knew that she was still in pain, and I knew that she had been to the hospital now three times that year. I knew that my father was just trying to stay calm and supportive of her. I asked dad whether he thought I should come a few days early, but he didn't want to cause me to have to leave work before the holidays. He was sensitive to the fact that my job had allowed me a flexible schedule, but knew that I was going to ask for more privileges soon. And my mom looked as though she was resting well, so he said there was no need. I kept my original plans to go the next weekend.

On that Tuesday night, the first of September, 1998, my brother called me on the phone. "She's in the hospital. You better come. They said she probably won't make it through the night." *My God*.

I got a ride to the airport and got on the next available plane, and sat there in a sense of shock. We hadn't been ready for that. We had been told that her condition was not life threatening. I sat there *trying* for numb. I had to go through Las Vegas after midnight, and I got to Tucson about 3 am. My brother picked me up and drove me to the hospital. We literally ran down the hallway into the room where she was. We held her hand as gently as we could, and stroked her face as gently as we could. I kissed her: "I'm here, Mama. I'm here." But she never woke up. She died just before 6 am on September 2, 1998.

Goodbye, Mama.

7 Into the Storm

I stood there, remembering my mother standing beside my bed in intensive care five years before, holding my hand and telling me that she wouldn't leave my bedside, ever. I held her hand when she died.

My other brother had flown in, but arrived too late, and all we could do was hold him. All we could do was to try to comfort each other. We went to the funeral home where her body was. We stood and held each other, and then he said the only goodbye he could. We went home in shock. We all stared at each other, knowing that we were thinking about the fact that her doctors had diagnosed her with the "shingles"—*never* a life-threatening disease. So we all thought that she would pull through that—the only question was when. None of us had said goodbye to her until she was mostly gone, unconscious, sailing away. She could not say goodbye to us, either. The nurses told us that our sense of hearing can last until the very moment of death, so she might have heard our goodbye. We'll never know.

Looking back at everything, the medical opinion was that she had a cancer which originated in her abdomen and moved through her body very fast. It was difficult for anybody to know that because she was already suffering pain—and had been for eight months—from a diagnosed but not threatening disease. Her doctor told my father that it was possible that the liver scan they had planned in January—the one she had prepared for, the one that the hospital failed to perform for mechanical dysfunction problems—might have indicated that that was present along with the herpes zoster pain. But even if they had found out earlier, there would have been no treatment, in her condition, to cure that.

We all suffered from grief and shock, as anyone would. I sat there on a couch feeling as though I was also sailing away. I was close to the time when I might very well have breakthrough seizures, and I had had no sleep for the past 36 hours. So in the background of my mind, I was afraid that I would have strong ones because of the lack of sleep. In the foreground, I thought of all the medical catastrophes that my parents had lived through, and that my father was now emotionally underwater in. I felt very little, I think. I know that I was nearly totally numb at that point. I couldn't imagine what else might happen, but I was no longer trying to defend myself. My emotions had gone under. I put my arms around a teddy bear that my mother and I had bought together long, long ago, before all of these medical disasters had begun. I curled up in a fetal position on the couch on the back porch, and tried hard, very hard, to sail away into oblivion, to not feel anything anymore.

In the hospital, when it had finally become clear that my mother was dying, my father had been asked whether he wanted to support resuscitative efforts, or authorize that they not be tried. It had become clear that there was no cure for what she was suffering, and, my god, how she had suffered—intense pain for the previous eight months. He had decided, his own sense of loss intertwined with his deep empathy for her pain, that it was better not to. It was in any case his decision to make, but I felt exactly the same way. My brothers felt exactly that way. We made sure that he knew that. And we held each other, and remembered her.

I stayed a week with my family, and we all had the wake. We talked to each other about all the things we remembered of our lives with her. I know more, now, that I ever had before about my brothers' sense of their own lives: of growing up with her and of her constant and unconditional love. We talked about what we could have done, should have done, but had not done differently. We talked about what we had and had not known. We reassured each other that we could not have changed anything—except that we might have been able to say goodbye. And I knew that, for me, I would rather die fast—I would give everything myself to keep my loved ones from having to struggle with the Long Good-bye.

We talked about whether we could have changed anything at all, and about grief itself. We learned from each other what we would want from our family if we were in mortal danger, or if we were to drop dead, with no chance to say good-bye. We learned what we would want for ourselves. We talked about how brief life really is, and about how impossible it had been for us—all our lives—to know how and why and when catastrophe would happen. My mother and my father had talked about dying before, and my father knew exactly what she would want. We cremated her body, and put the container with her ashes in a trunk we had of her mother's, who had died only a year before. The important thing for us was not the burial or a ceremony, but the remembrance.

Dad and I talked about the near future. One brother said to me that if my grief changed the way I felt about the surgery, maybe I should consider postponing. He, and my father, were concerned about my ability to deal with the upcoming events. But I sat there, again, and contemplated the same issues I had before. The major factor in the timing of the surgery had not changed at all: my health insurance. And if I postponed, it would break my psychological stride—and my stride was my strength. One of the hardest aspects of treatment like this—for me—is the amount of time it takes to get everything set up. I'm the kind of person who considers things carefully, but when I make a decision like this one—a scary, personal one—I want to close the door and go do the deed. But the test, here, was endurance.

And when, exactly, would I be any more *ready* to do the deed? If I wanted to do it at all, I had to do it while my insurance would clearly cover it. Postponement would put that in danger. It was that date which determined the future. And when would I be any more numb?

We talked about how, because of mom's death, everything had changed. My dad wouldn't need to stay home to take care of her—he could come now to take care of me. I knew—I felt it then and I still feel it—what kind of fear he must have felt knowing that now his daughter would go into a hospital and go under the knife for a complicated and threatening surgery. For we had talked about the dangers—and there are some—of the surgery itself and about the possible effects. He would go again to another hospital, soon, and watch his daughter, as he had watched his wife, lie in bed with needles and cords and tubes, about to submit to a life-changing event. Many people might say that the fact that he could come to take care of me was, somehow, a "silver lining" of my mother's death. I can't arrive at that. I will live all my life with the sense of loss, the price we paid for him coming to be with me.

I flew home, and went back to work. Application material for our fellowships started to arrive, so I had to start to read some of them. I not only stayed mostly numb, but I actually *tried* to stay mostly numb. I went to see my cardiologist to do yet another EKG before the surgery, since the fact that I had had an infarction complicated the issue of whether I would have negative reactions to the stress of the surgery. The doctors had to make that call, too. Since they had no official cause for that attack, other than response to drugs I was no longer on, the decision was in support of the surgery.

Fifteen days after my mother's death, I had another appointment with the neurosurgeon, Dr. F. My father wanted to be there with me, and so he flew in the night before. Dr. F was as helpful as he could possibly have been. We talked again about the nature of the surgery, and exactly what they would do. We set the date: November 3, 1998. He knew that my mother had died, and expressed his sympathy. My father was there, but he was mostly silent. I knew why. He was trying to survive his horrible sense of loss and his fear for the future. He was recovering from the shock of his wife's death and so opening up both to all the potential consequences and to the bottomless sea of what would never happen again. I sat there numb still. I asked some questions, I'm sure, but I don't really remember what they were. I sat there actually thinking about my father standing there watching *me* go into the operating room.

I somehow listened to some of what Dr. F was telling me, but I saw the image of my mother standing next to me in the hospital long ago, holding my hand, stroking my face. I felt a phantom of that touch. I saw the image of her lying in her hospital bed. I watched myself, somehow from afar, listening, there in the office, again, to the repetition that there were some danger factors—but not many—and there would be some effects of the surgery. I remember my father's face. I will always remember how I saw both his and my mother's in that room. I wondered whether I should do this at all. I thought about dying on the operating table. I wasn't thinking about that as my own loss—for I was suppressing those feelings—I was thinking about how it would devastate my dad.

And then Dr. F told me about another possibility. There was a reporter for the *Los Angeles Times*, he said, who was doing a series of stories on medical issues, having particularly to do with brain surgery. This reporter was hoping to be allowed to actually be present at my surgery and to write his story about it and about me. And again, I barely processed that. He assured me that they had respected my privacy. They had given no information about me to this reporter. He knew nothing personal, not even my name. So his question to me was whether I would give permission for this writer to know about and write about my surgery. He suggested that I think about it, and said that his staff could arrange an appointment to speak to that writer about the events.

My dad and I went home. He told me that, knowing he needed to come to Los Angeles to be with me for this appointment, he had brought something from my mother. It was a watch that she had given him so long ago. He held it in his hand in his pocket all the while that we had spoken with the doctor, so that he could somehow feel that she was there with us. I knew that feeling.

I thought about the idea of a reporter, and about what would happen. I imagined what I thought would be his first inquiry to me: tell me about your case. And I thought again: *where do I start?* I didn't know whether his story would be about me as a patient in a complicated case, or just the operation. And I thought about what the story would have to be—epilepsy. I remembered—it flew quickly by me—that question put to me the last time I went to see a necessary medical doctor who didn't know all this stuff. I remembered how I had a hard time producing an answer—*where do I start?*

I want to be clearly understood here: I had no reason to think it would go badly, only deep suspicions that it might. I was in personal fear of the idea of being interviewed. And why? I was having more and more and more difficulty talking about my life. I was getting more and more detached from it just to make it through another day. Various members of my family, including my father, had had some negative experiences with reporters. Journalists had taken careful notes of what they had said about health issues, but then published a story in which those details—the complicated details—were omitted or just glossed over. I couldn't have told my story without complicated details.

In addition, I felt then, as I had felt before, the potential damage of going public with epilepsy. For if it went public to that extent, I could never take it back or control it or even complain about how many people knew about it. I felt that it would take all the strength, that my father and I had, just to actually survive this thing. I knew that he was also in pain, and I felt sure that he wasn't ready to give public answers about this situation either.

And there was another issue for me. I imagined that my circumstances at my job might be part of this story. I felt as angst-ridden as I had ever felt about talking about that. For one of the reasons that I was doing the surgery had to do directly with the personal effects of the loss of that job. I would have trouble talking about that without talking about the personal effects and the pain of having decided to do life-altering brain surgery. Even if I decided to go public by newspaper story, I would have to carefully structure what I would say about those issues. I didn't think I could do that. Not yet. I wasn't sure I would ever be able to arrive at a simple explanation, for the past seven years of my life had been a symphony of intertwined complex medical and personal issues—you are reading the umpteenth chapter right here right now.

I considered another scary option. Would I have to be legally careful about what I would say? Would I have to avoid saying anything about the job issue which was also the insurance issue? For my real answer to any question about why I was doing the surgery would have to address that. And any description about the surgery itself—what would be done and why—would have to do with both details of my condition and some account of the reason to choose surgery. So there was, for me, a conundrum. My condition was not life-threatening, so there would have to be some explanation of why I was doing the surgery. The technical, medical description of the surgery—even if there were no discussions of any of the personal issues—would have to talk about epilepsy. And I would want that explanation to cover the complexity of my epilepsy, which would be the reason why I did the operation, and the reality of the effects of the surgery. So I would want that explanation to be true, but to be true I would have to say some things which might have negative effects—not on the story—but on me. So I would have to decide—"right here right now"—what my official responses to those effects would be. Could I manage to emotionally control what I would say? For if I said something I would seriously regret, I knew that I could not control that—that is part of the nature of public coverage. And so I felt the need for some self-control. And I hadn't arrived there yet. Now, I know that I'm going around in circles here. That is exactly the problem: I sat there, unable to feel that I knew what was the *right* thing to do. So I wavered about whether I should do it, and I made no decision.

Can I do this?

I had spent the summer knowing that I couldn't depend on going to the last major events in the major project I had spent years on! That was because I had to do the necessary pre-surgical tests whenever they were scheduled. But because I knew now when the surgery was actually scheduled for, I could go see the exhibition in Italy. It would be the last big event for me, and the last trip to Italy I would make for my job—the last time I would ever be a representative of my institution. It was a beautiful fall in the city of Ferrara, and I was extremely impressed with the exhibition produced by a friend of mine. I enjoyed the people there, I loved seeing all the paintings which had been the subject of our seminars in the previous two years, and I loved the intriguing little city of Ferrara. It is surrounded by an old city wall, and you can walk along the top of part of it to see the city itself and to look out over the fields in the valley.

I walked along the wall and down a cobblestone street to one of the cemeteries in Ferrara, the old Judaic one. I spent some time just strolling around, looking at the old, eroded gravestones from hundreds of years ago and the plaques for citizens who had died in the battles of the world wars. I sat at the foot of an enormous tree and thought about the wild beauty of the place. The major cemetery in Ferrara was a huge, geometrically square and ordered space, but this smaller cemetery was a wilder, more beautiful place. I sat in the grass and thought about mortality, and remembrance. I sat remembering moments with my mother, laughing and crying, talking about the important things in life, holding her hand when I was young and holding her hand when she was old. I sat there, aching for her.

I sat and faced death. I have never felt like I could judge whether other people had or had not faced that. I know that we don't always recognize the truth in other people. But I know that very few of my friends and acquaintances felt that they had ever faced it. And I thought about the fact that facing death is another event which changes you forever. At least, it changed me.

I don't want to give the impression that I'm telling you that the brain surgery I was about to undergo is life-threatening. It's important to know that there are always cases in which a patient dies in surgery—for there are some known exceptional reactions to otherwise safe procedures, and, let's face it, there are some cases of human error. It's important also for me to make it clear that the surgery I was about to have was not at all itself dangerously life-threatening. My doctors had made that clear to me. I believed them. In fact, I had looked up some information on the statistics, and they supported that assertion. (Of course, I might be one of the very few who die on the table. Deciding to do surgery requires that you know and accept that.)

But I sat there, as I had sat a year before on the peak in Sequoia, and as I had stood four years ago on the slope of the Dolomites, and thought about my place in the world. I was in the .06% of the population who had epilepsy. I was in the fraction of the people with epilepsy who broke through every drug. I was in the fraction of those people who had a dangerous and semi-life-threatening blood-cell response to the drugs. I was in the fraction of those people who would do brain surgery. I understood why it would be difficult for anybody else to try to understand how I felt.

And I faced loss. I faced the fact that this kind of brain surgery is a cross-roads. If the seizures you have—particularly *gran mals*—actually disrupt everything, maybe it is easier to decide that surgery will in fact be a blessing. It's difficult to say. But my case was a different situation altogether. It was still a question of the damaging effects of continuing to have seizures and side effects of the drugs, but it was mainly a question of which path is—which *will be*—not the greater gain, but *the lesser loss*. And you can't know it, you have to guess it. The doctors can give you some of the information they have from previous cases, but they can't know how it will be ahead of time. Indeed, they can't know how it will be because they haven't had it done to them. In fact, none of my doctors had ever had a seizure (that I know about), or brain surgery; all they can tell you, based on extensive knowledge of other cases, all they can know is what is most likely to be the case, either way.

Some people would do better with lots of reassuring support—lots of assurance that things would be much better, and that they would be delighted with the results. Not me. I needed some acknowledgement that *there would be a cost, and that I had to accept that.* It would be silly denial, for me, to just look at the "bright side." Look at the dark side, too. But different patients have to try to do what they need to do. I have no advice for anybody.

Patients have to cope with whatever that reality is, and with the responses of other people, who perhaps assume that you need unconditional support and who avoid discussion of the negative. But I'm not telling anybody what he or she should do. I would advise, in so far as I am advising, that friends and relatives try to be sensitive to how the patient needs to cope. But, in life, we always make decisions to try to help people see things in a different perspective, especially frightening things. This is another aspect of coping with people who have no personal experience in all of this. People who haven't ever done this probably can't understand it or how you feel, but that is not criticism of them. They have to deal with you anyway, and you have to deal with that, somehow.

Here's what I sat there thinking about: what I had been told would happen. They cut open your skull and slice, with a knife, part of your "self" off the rest of your "self"—try to stop the seizures by removing the section of your brain where the abnormal neural activity starts. It's not the same as having some other part of your body interfered with. It is having your very "self" interfered with. Some people might in fact be more afraid of effects on other parts of their bodies. But for me, the brain is the location of my soul.

For many kinds of epilepsy, they can't actually "see" the damaged portion of your brain. It looks just like every other healthy part looks. So, unlike surgery for tumors or for visible scars, you have to trust the ability of the neurologist to test for, during the surgery itself, and so for the surgeon to know, as intelligently as possible, what exactly to take out. Those judgments are often made based largely on the EEG information. But in my case the doctors decided to do some complicated brain testing *during* the surgery, the testing Dr. F described in my last appointment with him.

For most people, you may recall, finding where language is "located" involves only one language—your native language. For me, though, since I had three spoken languages—and they would have to map all of them—my surgery would take longer. It might take nine hours.

And the difficulty of this case is that they agreed that it was important to take as little of the brain tissue as possible because of the possible effects of loss; on the other hand, you want to take as much as is likely to be effective in stopping, or at least reducing, the seizures. Brain surgery like mine is a case of complicated judgement with irreversible consequences. Your life, literally biologically and personally, is in their hands. You have to trust the decision of your doctors.

And I faced the other thing my doctors had told me: one of the possible effects of the surgery like mine would be effects on language itself—the ability to speak. Their careful, considered opinion was that it probably wouldn't affect my abilities in language, but it might affect the speed with which I produce it. Both my neurosurgeon—Dr. F—and my neurologist—Dr. D-E—were also careful to say that it takes a long time to recover from brain surgery, so it would take a long time to determine what was and what was not a permanent effect. Indeed, as they had said, the *more* linguistically skilled you are, the longer it would take.

So I had to face the fact that even when the surgery went as well as possible, it might change my life irrevocably. I would almost certainly live through the surgery, but my brain would be different forever after. *You can't go home again.*

I walked back on the ancient wall of Ferrara to my hotel,

trying to soak up as much as possible of the beauty of that Renaissance city, knowing that I wouldn't see it again—not with *this* brain—not in *this* life.

When I flew home, I found the letter from my insurance company, giving the surgery "pre-approval." The next day I went to the pharmacy and got my month's worth of meds ($386.04), and the following day I woke up with seizures. I went to work anyway, and faced, again, the tricky issue at work: who should I tell, and how much should I tell them? One evening I went with a friend, R—one who knew nothing about my situation—to see an interesting movie, *Pi*. Neither of us had known what the plot was, so we sat there while the story of brain malfunction unfolded. And I sat there recognizing many of the clues, and feeling not only sympathy, but empathy with the major character's experiences. Towards the end of that movie, the major character—suffering from brain abnormalities—gives himself a gruesome lobotomy with a power drill. It's a horrifying scene—it's supposed to be a horrifying scene. My friend couldn't watch it—she covered her eyes and cringed.

But me, I watched it. I knew from the plot that it was inevitable that he would do that. I knew why someone might be moved to do that. My friend sat there wondering how on earth anyone could stand even the idea of something like that. I sat there, detached from the horror, wondering whether his brain had actually felt anything. The end of the movie is grim. That character ends up severely brain-damaged, and unresponsive to things which had been so important to him before. I sat there surprised, not by the film itself, but by the fact that I could watch it and not be horrified. Once again, I think that was evidence of how detached I was *trying* to be.

That fall, just as every fall before, became intensely busy because we were involved in the selection of candidates for scholarships. I needed to spend long hours there, reading applications, doing research on publications, reading material in several foreign languages, and making documents with information for review by the directors. That process involved reading hundreds of articles and summaries and parts of dissertations.

We had to evaluate a lot of material, meet to review our files and decide what the next step would be. The decisions would be made by the Director, my boss, and the Assistant Directors. I did just as I had done before: I spent long hours for weeks trying to process the information. It was a bittersweet experience, for I had done it for the seven years of my job there, and I had done it well. But now I had to face both the fact that I needed to do it well one more time and that it wouldn't change anything. In a certain sense, that hard work distracted me from worrying about the impending crisis. But it also made me tired—physically tired. And I had to cope with the despair of it all. For even though I had always done my job this way—at the level and with the intensity required by my position, it didn't matter. Even though I had always been praised for that performance in my job reviews, it didn't matter. In the evenings, I would go to the coast and walk along the beach and think, again, about the futility of it all.

And I would think again about who I wanted to tell. And who I needed to tell.

My boss, of course, knew the entire story of what I was about to do. I had some colleagues—and some friends—at work who would certainly notice that I was out of the office. In addition to choosing who I would tell, I had to more or less "make up the story." And by that, I don't mean to invent information. I was in the same situation I had been before: I didn't want to lie about why I was doing this, because, obviously, it was a very serious medical thing to do. And I didn't want, as another difficult task, to have to remember exactly the "story" I had told.

You might have felt very differently in these circumstances. You might have felt the need to tell almost everybody—and to get some sympathy or support. If I had had a brain tumor, I think I might have felt differently about that situation, but I have to admit that I'm not the kind of person who tells everyone everything.

So I chose some friends, and opened the door. Every single

one of them was astonished, both by the fact that I had to do it, and by the fact that I would do it.

My good friend R—standing by my desk when I told her—was astonished. She literally steadied herself against my bookcase when she heard the words "brain surgery." She was the friend I had been with when we saw that movie about self-inflicted brain damage. She was close to speechless for a while, too. But she turned into a very good, very close, very supportive friend.

Several of my friends were immediately sympathetic. Several of them were supportive of the fact that I hadn't made this situation public. Once again, I got some confirmation that people who had never had these kinds of problems still understood—immediately—why I had kept them private. A few of my friends put two and two together, and figured out exactly why I didn't drink alcohol when we went out to party. One had told me—soon after I told her—about her own serious and emotionally scary medical problems, knowing that I would understand why she hadn't told me that before. She knew that she could trust me to protect her privacy. She told me as well that she would like to be able to come see me in the hospital and keep me company and comfort me. It was very kind of her, but I'm sure that part of the reason she felt that way was because she knew the seriousness of that event.

My father and I had discussed this situation in general, for it is often the case that some friends would be happy to come and visit you in the hospital. Some friends, however, might not like doing that. I know some people who are afraid of going into a hospital for any reason. And in my case, there were some other crucial factors. I had been told, by both my neurologist and by my neurosurgeon, that this kind of surgery will certainly produce several immediate effects. I will need to be very careful—as in any surgical case—about being exposed to anybody else's germs. In recovery from major surgery, I will need to sleep a lot. I will need to be on medications suppressing any infection problems. But the main difficulty in my case would be that my brain will swell up immediately after the surgery, and one of the effects of that is that I will have trouble, for a while, talking at all.

My dad and I had thought that it would actually be better—for me—if I didn't have to cope with visitors until I specifically felt better and able to deal with them. My friends were also sensitive to that, and they understood it. My father would call a few times to let them know how things were going. This particular friend—the one who was herself dealing with a serious medical event—was supportive of that. She told us that she knew that situation, and that she expected nothing from me, but just wanted to be able to sit and be with me a while. Furthermore, she told my dad that she would be happy to come and sit for a while, so he could certainly go get some dinner, or do some errands, or just go out and walk some. Indeed, it was very kind of her.

So very few people actually knew what I was about to do, and why I would be away from my job for a month, maybe more. I trusted them, but I was nervous about the fact that I trusted them. This is another aspect of having major medical problems—you worry about who your friends really are. And worse, you find yourself thinking about whether you really want to know that. I felt—again—some anxiety about that.

In the beginning of October I went to the pharmacy again . . . . I took the long Columbus Day weekend and went to New York City to meet with my closest and dearest friends, the ones who had seen me have that first *gran mal* Thanksgiving Day, 1992. I will always remember that weekend, too. They were to arrive very early on a Saturday on the red-eye flights. But I took the flight the afternoon of the day before everybody else arrived. I would pay for the hotel that night, because I knew the consequences for me of sleep-deprivation. As the plane started off the runway, into the sky, I felt the seizure coming on, and I sat there, staring out the window, thinking: maybe I will, at some point, be able to live without ever feeling this way again. But I wrote in my journal: *I feel most of the way dead now.*

I walked alone around New York City that evening, thinking about the future: will this ever actually look the same for me? I ate alone that night, took the drugs, and went to bed. But I didn't sleep. It was normal that I didn't sleep like other people—the medications I was on were the ones which interrupted my sleep—but that time around I didn't sleep much at all. My friends arrived the next morning, in little groups, and soon we were all there.

I felt again so alone, so very alone.

It's not the case—it was never the case—that those friends weren't aware that I felt alone, and didn't do the best anybody could do to comfort me. It is the case that I knew that nothing like this had ever happened to any of them. They *knew* that I was scared, but they didn't know how to comfort that in me. They were uneasy that I seemed distant, but they didn't want to push. How do you deal with somebody so intellectually detached? I did the best that I could to distract myself by having a good weekend with my dearest old friends. But I simply couldn't rise above that dread feeling, the feeling that everything I was now doing felt like the last time that I would ever do it.

I was trying to stay calm—almost numb. But that was paradoxically harder with those close friends than with any other friends, because I wasn't as good at controlling my responses to them. But I tried to just chat about life and enjoy whatever I could manage to enjoy.

In the back of my mind, though, I could hear the clock ticking.

We ended up just talking about Los Angeles, where I lived. I had always felt ambivalent about moving there, but the previous seven years had involved an excellent job, and so of course I had stayed. My friends were asking me whether I thought about leaving Los Angeles and moving closer to one of them. But the medical issues had connected me directly to a neurological specialist at UCLA. And then the complexity of my medical situation had involved a number of specialists and medical procedures at UCLA. And my file had, of course, gotten bigger and longer and more complicated. Then, as now, for me, the very thought of living somewhere else immediately prompts me to consider the medical consequences of that. It's not that I have no confidence that I could find good doctors elsewhere. It's that I had then, and still have, a sense of dread about the unavoidable consequences of changing doctors, of having to tell the whole story again.

A new doctor would have to, first of all, read my three-volume medical file and maybe go look up the most recent medications I've been on. And then I would have to start filling out forms about the medical stuff—*all* the stuff—which had happened to me in my adult life. Then I would have to go through a series of conversations with each doctor giving my "history." A new doctor would of course have questions to ask, and the answers would be long. And a new doctor would, as all doctors do, feel the need to re-examine and re-test me rather than to take for granted all of my previous doctors' opinions and diagnoses. This isn't a complaint. On the contrary: I have nothing but respect for that. But the very idea, for me, of starting over again, to find a doctor, to get a doctor, to describe everything, to do all the tests again, to start, essentially, back down at the bottom of an extremely painful climb, was the major factor now, for me, for any consideration at all about where I should live, and what I should do—indeed, where I could live, and what I could do.

So I hadn't even considered actually leaving Los Angeles for quite some time now. When one of my dear friends remarked to me that I seemed much happier there—in Los Angeles—than I had been in the past, I snapped.

Happier? Much *happier?* Jesus. You think that I am *happier?*

My dam broke. I ended up rigid with the amount of self-control it took for me to keep from *screaming* that at her. She forgave me—instantly—with nothing but sympathy. For those friends—my oldest friends—saw the awesome paradox. I had somehow been able to stay in control—detached and intellectual—and to actually talk about this horrendous event with my colleagues and my acquaintances and some of my friends. But here I was almost yelling—viciously—at one of my closest and dearest friends, who was sitting there trying for sweet comfort because *I* wasn't talking about this horrendous event. *God.*

I didn't forgive myself for that, though. I withdrew. Literally. I found myself crouched down in the bathroom, staring at the floor, living one breath at a time. My dear friends didn't know exactly what to do for me. My closest friend—M—came to find me and to hold me until I could face it all again. All I can do is apologize for that lack of self-control, but those friends have seen it all—and they have forgiven it all. I don't think they have understood it all, but they have supported it all. Once again: it's hard to know—and wrong to judge—the depth of what other people may have suffered in their lives. What I do know is that they did for me all they could—all I would let them do.

I had the sense, then, as I had had in 1992, that one part of my life was ending, and I had to say goodbye. We all went home on different flights, so I got on the plane and stared out the window, and said another goodbye.

I remembered reading somewhere that one of the negative symptoms of my kind of epilepsy is "affective flattening" of emotion—numbness of feeling—and I felt the deepest sense of irony. Me? I was *trying* for numb.

Down to the starting line

On the 19th I saw Dr. D-E again, and he talked a little bit more, in detail, about what he would do during the surgery. Dr. F, of course, would do the cutting, but he would do the testing, and make some decisions about how to proceed—how much to cut, and where.

And the associate From Dr. F's office called me again. They had hoped that I would choose to participate in that proposed *Los Angeles Times* article on my surgery, but I sat there, almost speechless again, remembering how defeated I felt by the position of a public presentation. I thought about whether I could talk about my mother's death, which had everything to do with how I felt about what was about to happen, but which would, very likely, have nothing to do with the focus of the story on my surgery itself. I wondered if I would sit there, with the journalist, numb, or whether I would sit there, with the journalist, crying and speechless. I had no confidence that I could "present" my case, and I had some fear about how somebody else would present it. I can say to you now that it has taken me a while to be able to give *this* account.

I decided then, because of the way I felt—or failed to feel—that I didn't want to deal with that. It would be another crossroads: you can never go back from making something public. Letting your friends and acquaintances know is one thing—letting the one million plus readers of the *Los Angeles Times* know is another. I said no. I think that the woman calling might have been disappointed. But she also asked me if I would care to participate in an ongoing neurological research project. She was careful to say that this wouldn't be public. It wasn't medically required, but neither would I be charged for any services related to it. My response to that issue was 180 degrees opposite to the issue of the newspaper story: I said "of course." I would be happy—or at least willing—to try to provide research information on these medical issues, because it's true that even if it wouldn't contribute to my case, it might to someone else's. That is what research is all about. In fact, I felt better that I could at least do that, even if I wouldn't do the newspaper interview project.

I went back to work and read some more dissertations and articles, and took some more notes on all of them to give to the directors. I went to several meetings to provide recommendations for scholarships, which were major factors in our choice of awards. I reflected on the irony of that, as well, for this time I wouldn't be there to meet them.

On the 21st, I stopped taking the prescribed one aspirin a day—following Dr. F's advice—so that I wouldn't bleed profusely on the operating table. On the 22nd, I went to see the anesthesiologist, Dr. V. She wanted to describe to me, in careful detail, what the process of the surgery would actually be. As I had been told before, anesthetizing me would be somewhat complicated for this kind of surgery. She would need to "put me under" in order for the surgeon to open my skull, but then she would have to wake me up—*during* the surgery—in order for the team to be able to test my brain for the location of aspects of language. And then she would put me under again to finish the surgery. She reassured me that the actual surgery would not be painful—there are no nerves in your brain—but that I would certainly have a headache when I woke up because of the pressure on the tissue and the skull itself. She wanted me to know that in advance. I asked how bad the headache would be, and she smiled. "You know, I can't actually tell you because I haven't done this myself." I smiled back at her.

Some patients find that it just hurts too much. One of her surgical patients had asked, after about a half-hour of being awake, to be put back under because of the headache pain and the fatigue of doing the tests, and so they did that. Some of the patients had actually panicked when she woke them up, and asked immediately to be put back under. Since Dr. V was the anesthetist, she was the one who would stay in touch with me the entire time. She reminded me: "I'm the only doctor you'll actually see." I told her exactly how I felt: that they should do everything they can to map my brain before removing any tissue, so I won't ask them to stop. I'll stay there, awake, with a headache for however long it takes to map me. In fact, I said to her: "if I ask you to put me under, don't do it. Keep mapping!" I got ready for a whopping headache.

On the 25th of October I went in to give a liter of my own blood, in case I would need it during the surgery. Brain surgery actually causes very little bleeding, but I followed the advice to make sure that my blood was available to me in case it was needed. (If it was not needed, it would be put "on the pile" of blood available to other patients.) The following day I tried to call another friend—a good friend who still didn't know what was about to happen to me. He was one I would have told sooner, but he was the one who had been in charge of the exhibition in Ferrara. I certainly didn't want to distract him in any way from that endeavor. Ever since we had both come back from Italy, he had been up to his eyeballs in more events in that project, so I just hadn't found a time to tell him what was about to happen to me. But I thought I should, and, because he was a good friend, I thought he would want me to. So I went over to his office to see if he had a moment to speak to me.

He proved to be the best of friends: he wasn't irritated that I hadn't told him this before, and he was entirely sympathetic to issues having to do with public knowledge. In fact, he told me that he wasn't at all surprised that I had kept my situation private, and he understood exactly why. He knew some people who had done the same, though not with my disorder. He would have done the same. So he gave me a big hug, and told me to call if I needed anything, and assured me that he wouldn't say anything to anybody about this. I knew, I had always known, that he would be discrete.

On the 27th, I went to a brand new laboratory at UCLA, not yet actually "open," called the Ahmanson-Lovelace Brain Mapping Center. I went to do the new research procedure, Brain Mapping. This is a project supervised by Dr. B. It uses an fMRI—a functional Magnetic Resonance Imaging test—to try to measure and map the functions of the brain. (UCLA is one of only two institutions in the United States which do this procedure.) In my case in particular, because of general interest in the topics but also because of my upcoming surgery, she wanted to try to map the multiple languages in my brain—a relatively new procedure.

I was then, and I am now, happy to provide information about brain function to those studying it, for you never know what kinds of information we will at some point need to know. The processes of my surgery would be directly related to what the doctors had learned about the brain from other patients before me. And it was clear, in my case, that they wanted to know as well as possible where in my brain the different languages were located. I was, and am still, impressed with that project. I had done MRI's before, so I knew some of the ropes, but this one had some slightly different aspects. The fMRI machine is huge. It is loud. It is powerful—60 thousand times the magnetic field of the earth! Dr. B told me: this machine is strong enough to erase credit cards! You have to pretty much strip yourself of metal objects of almost any kind. The procedure for me was an attempt to map which parts of my brain are involved in which kinds of language production. And because they were particularly interested in my multiple foreign languages, they had managed to locate two assistants who spoke Italian and French so that they could map which parts of my brain operated in those languages.

Furthermore, they wanted to try to locate some different aspects of language. For the research we now have seems to indicate that nouns are located (or produced) for most people in a certain part of your left temporal lobe. But actual grammar—language ability—seems to be located in another. And, as Dr. B explained to me, there seems to be some evidence that nouns might be stored in more than one location, but grammar ability seems to be found in only one. So, if surgery damages, in any way, that part of your brain which produces grammar, the effects are seriously negative. Their research indicates, though, that because nouns—the names of things—can be located in more than one place, if a certain location is damaged, then your brain might be able to use another location. The neurosurgeons, then, want to know as precisely as possible where different language functions operate in order to make decisions about the surgical procedures for the brain.

Dr. B was to try to map those aspects, and then, because my brain could also be tested in the surgery, she could measure how well the fMRI itself can do that. For it's not the case that everybody will have the kind of surgery which can actually test the naked brain itself. This is also an interesting aspect of this medical problem. It's hard to know what is "normal" in the brain, since this kind of surgery isn't done on anybody who's not *abnormal* in brain function.

So I got wired up, including with some small visual "glasses"—that little machine that's an old "toy," a small stereo viewfinder. Then we went through a long and complicated series of processes. In the fMRI I had to be taped down to the table in order to keep my head as still as possible so that the MRI machine can map some of my brain functions. But if you move too much, the image won't be clear or useful, so they don't want you to move your jaw in order to speak. So how do we test language if you're not allowed to talk?

I lay in a huge metal tube. Dr. B taped the viewfinder to me, and me to the table, and gave me some earphones so that she could tell me what was going on and what she wanted me to do. The fMRI makes a lot of noise, so you need earphones, both to muffle that noise, and to allow you to hear the instructions they will give you.

Dr. B and the assistants tested, then, for a few aspects of language. They would show me, through the viewfinder, some objects, and then ask me to think of—not say—the names of those objects in the different languages they were trying to measure. They had the multi-lingual participants speak to me in both Italian and French, so that she could try to map which part of my brain was paying attention to that, or doing something during that. The procedure was first to ask me to think about a certain image in one language. That's not hard to do. But then they asked me to try for a few moments, if I could, to stop thinking, in any language. That would provide a kind of intermission between the operations of one language and of another, and so it might make the "mapping" process easier and clearer.

I have to say that when I started to purposely think in different languages, I also started doing something that I had not been asked to do—in fact, it might have had negative effects. For example, while looking at an image, and thinking about the Italian noun for it, I would seem to wander off to—to "remember"—

the original source of the name, often Latin. And I knew, because my neurosurgeon had told me, that languages not actually spoken—such as Latin—are normally located in parts of your left temporal lobe farther back from those spoken. Because of that, he wasn't worried about any possible damage to that group of languages in the surgery. So it ocurred to me that I shouldn't be mucking around with a language other than the one being tested, much less a non-spoken language from a different part of my brain. And I would try to stop myself doing that, or, what might be more effective in the long run, to silently order myself—*in* Italian—"bisogna non pensare in latino": "don't go thinking in Latin!"

And sometimes, when I would be visually shown an image to name in French, it would be an image of something I couldn't immediately remember the French name for—for example, an umbrella. It would immediately occur to me to ask (myself) what the name was in Italian, because French and Italian can be very similar. I even started to think if I knew the noun in Latin, because both Italian and French are close to Latin. But then I had to stop myself from doing that, for two reasons: the first is that, because we are trying to measure the locations of my brain activity in French, if I start thinking in Italian or Latin, the fMRI might end up measuring the activity of two or even three languages at once. The second reason is that the intellectual process of trying to identify the relationship between two words might actually represent logic, or something, anyway, other than ordinary "simple" production of French nouns. This is a larger problem. In fact, I would start to think about *that* problem, and I had to stifle that kind of thinking as well. All I was supposed to be doing was thinking: *parapluie*.

So I understood the problem. I was extremely interested in how they could measure that stuff, and whether I could do anything for them which would help. And I tried hard to suppress my thinking about those issues while they were imaging my brain. It was hard work. The fact that it was hard work suggests, to me, that it is hard to exactly map the distinction in brain function between language and logic. But I know that Dr. B is trying to map those functions in part to contribute to the problems of brain surgery.

This test—or set of tests—takes several hours. In many ways, the worst of it is the discomfort—bordering on pain—of lying still, on your back, for hours. I'm glad that I could do that set of experiments. I'll be happy if I contribute to information which would help other people in the future. But I was also glad to be able to focus my attention on some scientific questions about how the brain and language work. It gave me a refuge from imagining the moment the scalpel would slice into me. And I knew something about myself. I had always, all my life, been interested in trying to understand how things work, so the fact that I was interested in these scientific issues involved in my case was not a surprise.

But it was also true, and I clearly knew this too, that it was easier for me to think about it that way than to think about it emotionally, or to try to tell other people how I felt about it emotionally.

This was part of my defense against the panic looming up at the edges of my thinking about the surgery and its effects. A few close friends have told me that they were astonished that I would talk about this upcoming surgery as a kind of scientific event—they were sure they could not possibly have felt that detached, or talked in such a matter-of-fact way. I believe it, for people are different in how they respond to things like this, but I wonder sometimes if other people facing something like this might also be able to cope that way. I don't know, because I don't know anybody who had to deal with anything like this.

I made it back to work that day just in time for the Halloween party. The few friends I had there who knew that that was my last day before the surgery gave me silent support. None of them tried to make me talk about it, especially because we were in a huge group of people. I talked a little bit with R—now a close friend—away from the rest of the group. She tells me now that I was talking, in a more or less detached way, about the fact that they had warned me that I might actually lose some abilities in my foreign languages. In fact I had made a joke: saying that if I had to lose a language, let it be German! (I don't really use German—I just know some terms.) I told her about the fact that in the surgery someone would have to come to speak to me in Italian. We joked that it ought to be her, since she *was* Italian! It was only a half-joke. I know that she would have done it for me, but I also knew that she had never been involved in anything remotely like the kind of personal experience that would be for her. In fact, I know from personal experience that she can barely stand to see any violence—slicing open any part of the body—even in a film. How could she have survived standing there talking to a friend whose skull was sawn open? I was grateful that she would try to do it for me, but I am grateful that she didn't have to do that for me.

As the party went on, I wandered a little, and stood a while thinking about how few people I had actually told, wondering whether I should have told more. But I didn't want to. Once again, I didn't really want to explain everything. And of course it's true that the longer you live with something like this, and the longer you wait to tell somebody about it, the longer the story about it becomes. And I have always been one of those people who pays attention to details, so my story about some experience like this is long and complicated.

One of my newer friends who didn't know what the situation was came over to me to say that he had heard from a friend of mine that I was about to go on a month's vacation, and to ask where I might be going. I just looked at him, wondering what to say. I found myself in an extremely uncomfortable position in circumstances like that. For when somebody asks me a direct question—where are you going?—I know that I have to lie, or avoid the question, or try to give a quick account of things—all those things. I stood there, stunned, wondering what to say. He was a new friend, but for some reason I trusted him. I don't know why—I just felt that way. And so I told him the truth. I spoke quietly, so that people would not overhear it. He didn't express surprise. I think maybe he felt it, but he asked for only a few details, and just wished me well.

And then another colleague came up to me, to whom I had never spoken about the disorder, much less the upcoming surgery. One whom I seldom saw. Who had nothing directly to do with my work. He came up to say, quietly, that he knew what I would be doing, and that he certainly hoped that all would go well for me and that I would recover soon. I stood there, stunned, wondering what to say. I don't think I said anything other than "thank you." It was kind of him to wish me well, but it gave me more evidence that I had no control over who actually knew the situation. I looked around, wondering how many people there actually did know—without my knowledge—what I was about to do.

I stood there on the terrace, surrounded by all these people. I looked around me, and off the hill out to the ocean, and thought: "this will be the last time the *I* that I now am will see that." So I silently said a kind of goodbye. And then I just went around to say happy Halloween to my colleagues and friends.

I had this wild desire—the way people sometimes do when they face a moment like this—to go over to a friend I knew only slightly, take him by the hand, pull him over into the stairwell, and kiss him like there was no tomorrow. But I didn't have the nerve. I held that image in my brain, and left alone.

That Friday night R took me out to see an Italian movie we had talked about. It was *La vita è bella*, about the holocaust. It's a complicated movie because it involves both positive aspects of human kindness and the horrible aspects of that time in World War II. I remember that I felt detached from the whole thing. In fact, I didn't seem to be able to respond to the positive at all—I was trying hard to stay detached from the horrendous event *I* was about to actually do. I was trying hard to stay numb.

7 INTO THE STORM

Here we go, into the storm

That weekend my apartment roommate—P—had arranged to go stay at her boyfriend's place. My father would arrive the next afternoon, and she did that so that he could be there for me. It was very kind of her to do. It would give me and my father not only enough space, but also some emotional privacy, so that we didn't have to try to behave in a friendly way. We could feel totally comfortable, as we always have, with each other. I will always remember that.

On the morning of November 1, 1998, I got out the Power of Attorney form I had done in 1995. The first name on the list of executors was my mother's. I crossed it out, and dated my initials. Then I sat down and wrote my will. I had gotten the right forms to do that myself—in my own handwriting. I followed the right format so that it would be as clear and as valid as possible. It was one, simple, page. Then I wrote a letter which went into the same envelope, and put it on my bookcase where my other personal stuff was stored. My father would know where to find it.

He arrived that afternoon. We held each other and spent some time together not talking at all. Then we went over the schedule, and the paperwork, and the names of important contacts. I gave him an envelope with some stuff in it: the names and phone numbers of doctors involved in my case and the same for the few friends of mine who knew what would happen. They had already organized a plan so that he would just call a very few of them to tell them how the surgery was going, and they would call the others. He would call my dear friend—the one who had been with me on Thanksgiving 1992—who had stayed with me until I woke up from the seizure—who had told me that it had been a seizure—and she would call my other old friends. He would call one of my close friends at work, one who knew who else she should tell.

I had photocopied my credit cards and made a list of that kind of stuff. I copied my car title, my insurance card, my social security card, and the information on my bank accounts. He took the envelope, silently, and put it in his bag. He knew why I had done all that. And then I gave him the copy of my will. He didn't read it—he put it away. We stood there, looking at each other. We both knew that it would be highly unusual if I were to die in this kind of surgery, but we both knew it was possible. And I had also considered the possibility—unlikely, but still possible—that something even worse would happen. I might survive the surgery but with some kind of brain damage which might affect my mental status and therefore my legal status. I know that he was thinking about the very image of his daughter lying, like her mother—eight weeks before—unconscious, in a hospital bed.

One of my brothers came, the next day. He couldn't stay long, because he had to take care of his own family, but he came to go with me into the hospital. He was the one who lived far away, the one who could not get to Tucson in time to say goodbye to our mother. But he could come to say, not goodbye, but good luck, to me. And there's another reason why he came, a reason which makes me love him even more. He came for my father. Dad had done nothing but take care of his family for so long, now. He was always strong, he had always been strong. My brother came to be strong for him.

He arrived the afternoon before I went in. We went to the pharmacy to get another $326.10 of my medications I certainly wanted to take my meds in with me so that the hospital wouldn't need to provide them for me (you may remember that I had been told that to get that medication from the hospital itself would cost more than to bring my own).

Another almost unbelievable thing occurred. In the late afternoon, we had to go by Dr. D-E's office to get another set of signatures on another set of documents. This was a bunch of papers, not for my insurance company—we had already done a bunch of those. These were for the State Disability Insurance office. These forms would be sent to SDI in order to make sure that they would provide me with insurance coverage of my salary.

7 INTO THE STORM 235

I needed to mail them in the next few days to make sure that they get to the office on time to try to get the paperwork done on time to try to get my file set up on time to try to get a check in the mail before (I hoped) the end of the millennium.

Dr. D-E's staff had filled them out, and he had signed them, and left the office. But, and it was a big but, someone—maybe him—had somehow left one little line blank: the official medical name and location of my surgery. *Jesus.* Obviously, the information was required, and we needed to have it, to do it, to put it on the form, *now!* I stood there looking at that stuff wondering what to put down. Is just "brain" a technical name? Do I need to tell the SDI staff where in my brain? *Exactly* where? Do I need to draw a picture for the form? One of the nurse practitioners affiliated with my neurosurgeon—Ms. P—was there, and was kind enough to help me try to get the information right.

So she and I sat there and looked at the form. She had seen some before. She gave me the valuable advice: we better get the exact name right here, or who knows how long it will be before they send it back to you, by mail, telling you that it's the wrong name and so the wrong medical procedure and so not valid for their coverage. My dad and my brother were sitting outside in the car, waiting for me, thinking I had just run down to that office to pick up some stuff. My friend the nurse and I started to go through some medical encyclopedias to get exactly the right anatomical surgical description. I will remember that all my life.

My nurse friend had a lot of medical training, but she wasn't a neurosurgeon. So she would find some terms in this dictionary that might be appropriate, and I would stand there and translate them from the Latin (or the Greek) to see if we thought they actually had anything to do with what we needed to write down. (But just because I could read the Latin, that didn't mean that I could know exactly what the medical terminology meant.) It took a little while. We went through several books. We finally made finally made an educated guess, got a pen, and did the deed. I'm grateful to her for helping me do that. My dad would put those papers in the mail on a specific date—not that day—in order to meet the requirements: you can't mail it before *this* day or after *that* day.

And then the three of us, my father, my brother and me, went to one of my very favorite restaurants for dinner. I don't remember what I actually ate, but I will always remember, for some reason, what my brother ate. We actually chatted a little bit about the place where we were, and about the restaurant, and about some other random stuff. My brother assured me that he would be here all of the following day, but then he needed to fly back home for his family. Tomorrow, he would be right here for me.

We went home and stood and looked at each other and somehow said "good night" (as though it could possibly be *good*). We went to bed early because I needed to be standing there at the admissions office at 4:30 am the next morning.

I took my rings off—the ones I never take off. One was a gorgeous aquamarine—the gem is from the peak of the mountain in the backyard of my mother's beloved house in Colorado. It was her gift to me. The second was a ruby—the "engagement" ring my father had given my mother long after they were married, to make up for the fact that he couldn't possibly afford it when he had proposed, long before then. The third was a plain gold band of my great grandmother's. I put them in a safe place, and stood there and wondered: if the surgery went really wrong, maybe I wouldn't be able to remember where I put them. Maybe I wouldn't remember them at all. So I kissed them, and closed the box.

I went to bed, but I didn't go to sleep. I just lay there.

Can you imagine what it would be like to *imagine* brain surgery? I lay there, in bed, talking to myself—silently—but talking. In English, in Italian, in French. I started making some sentences in languages I never actually speak in: Russian, Latin. I lay there a while trying to remember some of the tiny amount of

Japanese I spoke—badly—long ago. I had some random thoughts for no real reason—I lay there for a while thinking—in Italian—about the differences between French and Old French. I made a few sentences about what I was doing—very long and complicated sentences. I lay there for a while and named things in as many languages as I could.

I lay there for a while thinking about language itself. I was thinking about what Dr. B. had told me about research on the actual location of different kinds of language ability. I asked myself a question I had asked the neurosurgeon: is it possible that my surgery would affect my native language but not my foreign languages? His answer was, yes, it's possible. But we don't know that yet. We have to carefully map the locations of all of those language abilities. In his opinion, though, my abilities with languages I normally only read (but seldom spoke) would not be affected. They are located a ways away from the planned location of the resection. Another question: if you resect part of my brain which is involved in a foreign language, does that mean I'll wake up as though I had never studied it? His answer was: we don't really know.

I recited to myself some texts—in foreign languages—I knew by heart, ones I had learned long ago, from a professor I had admired long ago. I wondered if I would wake up after the surgery, not only not remembering them, but not even being able to read them. I distracted myself by wondering whether I might remember how they sound, but not what they mean. I should have, I said to myself, asked my surgeon about that possibility. Has that ever happened to anybody? I think I was thinking in Italian when I fell asleep. I don't remember dreaming.

I woke up before dawn. I didn't need my alarm clock at all.

8 Brain Surgery

UCLA Medical Center

OPERATIVE REPORT

MORRIS, AMY S

Date of Operation: 11/3/98

Preop Diagnosis: 1. Intractable seizure disorder
Postop Diagnosis: 1. Intractable seizure disorder

Operation: 1. Left frontotemporal craniotomy, left anteromedial temporal lobectomy and hippocampectomy with intraoperative surgical microscope and intraoperative frameless stereotactic guidance.
2. Intraoperative awake language mapping.
3. Intraoperative electrocorticography.
4. Leibinger miniplate cranioplasty.

Surgeon: Itzhak Fried, M.D.
1st Asst Surgeon: Langston Holly, M.D.

Indications: The patient is a woman with a longstanding history of intractable seizures. She underwent extensive workup pointing to the left temporal lobe as original procedures. She now comes to the operating room for left anteromedial temporal lobe resection with electrocorticography and with awake language mapping.

Procedure: The patient was brought into the operating room and placed supine on the operating table. A venous line was established. The patient was then placed in a comfortable position lying in a semilateral position with the right side down. In this comfortable position she underwent fiberoptic nasal intubation and then an induction of general anesthesia. An arterial line was placed. A Foley catheter was then inserted sterilely. The patient had pulsatile sleeves and TED stockings applied to the lower extremities. All pressure points were well padded. She was then stabilized with 3-point Mayfield fixation with the head about 20 degrees from horizontal. Of note is that the right hand and the shoulder were over the edge of the bed lying comfortably on a special padded plane. Registration to the frameless stereotactic Brain Lab system was then carried out. The head was shaved in the region of the planned incision and then prepped and Draped in the usual sterile fashion. Of note is that 40 cc. of Marcaine, 0.25%, and 20 cc. of Xylocaine, 1% with 1:200,000 parts of epinephrine, were infiltrated for local anesthesia at the pin sites, over the planned incision in the supraorbital region on the left above the zygoma on the left as well as in the posterior auricular region.

A question mark incision had been previously outlined in the left frontotemporal region and now the incision was carried out and taken to the level of the temporalis muscle. 1gm./kg. of mannitol was given in the incision. The incision was then continued through the temporalis muscle and a scalp flap including the temporalis muscle was then elevated and reflected anteriorly. The root of the zygoma was then exposed. Bur holes were then placed using the Midas Rex drill in the temporal squama, near the keyhole and further posteriorly. The dura was then carefully freed and the Midas Rex craniotome was used to complete the craniotomy. The bone flap was then elevated and kept in bacitracin soaked gauze for the duration of the case. The dura was then freed anteriorly as well as inferiorly and further craniectomy allowed for good exposure. Multiple dural tackups were then placed in the periphery for hemostasis using #4-0 Nurolon and the bone edges were waxed with bone wax.

The area was then redraped with gauze and the dura was then opened sharply using a #15 blade. The dura was then opened in a C-shaped flap based anteriorly. The cortical surface was then carefully inspected and the frameless stereotactic system was then used to verify localization and to correlate with the preoperative magnetic resonance imaging.

Electrocorticography was then carried out with a 20 contact grid over the lateral temporal lobe surface as well as strips which were introduced over the basal part of the temporal lobe ending mesially. Overall, the record did not show much spiking activity except over the most anterior basal strip where spiking activity was noted.

The patient was then brought out of general anesthesia and when fully awake she was then extubated leaving a small guide between the vocal cords. With the patient now awake, electrical stimulation language mapping took place. This was performed in three languages, English, Italian and French. This was done in view of the patient's high linguistic abilities and her multilingual background. With electrical stimulation mapping the area of the tongue over the somatosensory strip was identified as well as the area representing the mouth and throat. Stimulation there evoked sensation in these regions. An area just in front, compatible with definition of Broca's area, was also identified with electrical stimulation, and speech arrest was elicited there in all three languages. In addition, there was at least one site where anomic errors and language difficulties were elicited more posteriorly, posterior to the area of planned resection. The anterior 5 cm. Of the temporal lobe was completely free of sites with evoked errors.

With the language mapping now completed and electro-corticography accomplished, the patient was placed back under general anesthesia after having undergone reintubation.

Now, attention was directed to the cortical surface. At a distance about 3 cm. from the temporal tip an incision was then started over the pia over the middle temporal gyrus. This was done with bipolar cautery. The pia was incised and the incision was then carried out inferiorly over the inferior temporal gyrus as well, and then continued anteriorly over the superior aspect of the middle temporal gyrus, further anteriorly to encompass the temporal tip. The ultrasonic aspirator was then used to proceed with the resection to a depth of about 2.5 cm. in the white matter. The ultrasonic aspirator was then used to undermine an anterior temporal block consisting of the anterior 3cm. of middle and inferior temporal gyri. This block was finally delivered and sent to pathology. Full hemostasis was then achieved.

The Greenberg retractors were then brought into the field and placed over Telfa protection over the posterior margin of the resection bed as well as over the inferior aspect of the superior temporal gyrus. The Brain Lab system was then used to choose an optimal entry point into the temporal horn and dissection was carried down in the white matter to enter the temporal horn. The temporal horn was then opened anteriorly to expose the head of the hippocampus as well as the region of the amygdala.

Dissection was then carried out anteriorly and inferiorly to remove part of the fusiform gyrus as well as further temporal tissue and specimen was sent to pathology. Dissection was then carried out over the tentorial edge in a subpial fashion to remove tissue of the uncus. Here, the tissue was firm in consistency and the dissection then continued on this fashion in a subpial manner to undermine the head of the hippocampus and the various feeders from the posterior cerebral artery and the anterior choroidal artery weres then coagulated with bipolar cautery and sectioned with micro scissors using microdissection technique. Under the surgical microscope the dissection continued over the fibers emanating from the anterior commissure and the dissection then alternated from the medial to the lateral aspect of the hippocampus.

Attention was then directed to the posterior exposure of the hippocampus about 2-1/2 to 3 cm. from the anterior part of the hippocampus. Here, the hippocampus was transected and dissection then continued lateral to the hippocampus, medial to the hippocampus, as well as anteriorly and posteriorly and working over all these aspects of the hippocampal region under the surgical microscope the hippocampal specimen was freed and submitted for pathology and studies. It appeared that the anterior region of the parahippocampus was somewhat abnormal in consistency, but the hippocampus itself was not particularly firm.

Using the ultrasonic Cavitron further resection was carried out in the region of the uncus where the pia over the tentorial edge was kept intact. Further resection was also carried in the region over the amygdala as well as more posterior regions of the parahippocampal gyrus.

Electrocorticography was then carried out. This showed no significant spiking activity posterior to the resection cavity both laterally and mesially. However, there was still some persistent spiking activity present over the anterior part of the superior temporal gyrus near the tip. Therefore, additional resection was now carried out with bipolar cautery and the ultrasonic Cavitron to remove additional tissue in the area of the anterior part of the superior temporal gyrus. This completed the resection and now full hemostasis was achieved in the resection bed. The dura was then closed primarily using #4-0 Nurolon. Of note is that the walls of the resection cavity had been line with Surgicel. After dural closure, full hemostasis was achieved in the epidural compartment and the bone flap was placed back into position using Leibinger bur hole covers and central dural tackups were used as well. The wound was copiously irrigated with bacitracin in salinesolution. The temporalis muscle was then closed with #3-0 Vicryl. The scalp was then closed with #3-0 Vicryl and the skin was closed in the usual fashion. The patient was then released from 3-point fixation and a head dressing applied. The patient was then extubated and taken to the recovery room in satisfactory condition.

Estimated blood loss was about 200 cc. Needle and sponge count was correct.

Specimens: Anterior left temporal lobe block, fusiform gyrus specimen, hippocampal specimen, and temporal tip specimen.

Estimated Blood Loss: 200 cc.

Dictated by: Itzhak Fried, M.D.

Electronically Reviewed and Signed by: Itzhak Fried, M.D. at 11/07/1998 10:48.

November 3, 1998: 4:15 A.M.

I think my dad woke up before me.

I had no breakfast, because I had been told not to. I took my meds, though.

Nobody wanted any breakfast.

We were standing at the admissions office door at 4:45, as we had been told to do. The office, though, was dark, so we sat and waited. We didn't talk much. When the office finally opened up, I sat and signed forms. Then I got the patient ID tag strapped on.

So, here we go . . .

They sent me off, "downstairs," to do another MRI right before the surgery. We went looking, in a huge hospital, for the right suite. We took the elevator down. We followed the signs. We found an office. There was nobody there. We waited. Nobody showed up. The office was just a corner "cubicle" of sorts—there was no closed door and only half-height counters, behind which was an office with computers and lots of paper stacks and some blinking telephone message lights and not a single human being. The corridors were mostly empty. The people who did walk by didn't look at us as though they knew we were there for some reason. We *were* there for some reason, so we waited. Nobody came.

My father had worked in a hospital—a big, prestigious one—for 30 years. He was a little dumbfounded that we would be sent to an office with absolutely nobody there, and that any three people could wander into an office at the hospital—not a waiting room, but an office itself—and look around for information. We looked at each other. We looked at the office desks. We waited.

I don't remember how long. I finally gave up and went back to Admissions, in exasperation, telling them the situation downstairs. The person there advised me to go to another lab. My father continued to be deeply puzzled, dismayed and shocked, at the confusion, and at the terrible delay imposed on a patient who was scheduled for *brain surgery* in one hour! My brother, miraculously, remained calm and relatively cheerful throughout all this.

So, we got back in the elevator and went looking for another lab on a different floor, and signed in. And so the preparations got under way. The technician shaved a few little spots on my skull and attached electrodes and cords for a test—an Angio-Wada. He almost apologized for having to shave small sections of my scalp for the electrodes. I told him it didn't bother me. I knew that it didn't matter at all because the Big Shave was coming up. One of the nurses in the Neurology ward had previously given me very good advice. Because I had long hair, I could request that the surgical team would shave only the left side of my head. I would be able to part the remaining hair on the right and cover the shaved side while the hair grew back.

They didn't actually do the Angio-Wada in that office; they sent me to another. So down the hall we went, me with wires stuck to my head, draping down to my waist. I looked and felt like an alien from some 1960's outerspace movie. When we got to that office, there were a few people sitting there, waiting for some procedure. None of them, though, had wires attached to their heads. We sat across from a little boy, and he stared at me open-mouthed. We sat for a little while, but I don't think we talked much. I don't really remember whether we did.

They did the test, and then pulled off the electrodes and sent us down the hall, around the corner, to another bunch of elevators and down another couple of floors—to "pre-op." It was time to get ready for the thing itself. I had another wild idea—the pre-op reminded me immediately of some kind of barracks I had seen in movies about WW II. There was a row of beds down one wall and up another, and people in them, getting ready for something. The staff there were very sweet. They smiled. One of them, a woman, stroked my arm and handed me the gown to put on. She sent me down the hall to the little bathroom to change. I came back, walking down the long line of people doing the same thing, and gave my few personal items to my father. I had left my jewelry and my watch and everything else back home. I stood there in just a gown, feeling like I was standing there, close to naked, saying goodbye to my previous life.

And then they tube you up. My father and my brother stood back to let the prep technician do the deed. My father looked like he was about to pass out. I felt more sympathy for him than I did fear for myself. That was probably more of my own self-defense. The guy who put the tubes in me was very nice and very cheerful. He tried to assure me that it might hurt, but for just a moment. I had no fear of that, and I told him that I had had countless needles in my arms in the previous six years, and it didn't worry me in the slightest. He said that some people never got used to it. He was a pro, though. It didn't hurt at all.

I looked up, and my father was gone. I knew instantly why. I knew it was painful and frightening for him to see this image again. It was the moment when the surgery was no longer abstractly in the future, but happening right there, right at that moment. And I knew that he was looking at his daughter, lying in bed with tubes in her arm, the very image of his wife who had died that way only eight weeks before. He was strong—he always had been, both for my mother and for me, but I felt for him. My brother turned to look beyond the curtain, and then came up to hold my hand. At that moment, I felt more for those two than I did for myself. I told him to go to my dad. He kissed me and went to his father.

In fact, I didn't feel much at all. I didn't want to feel much, and I certainly didn't want to feel fear. I asked myself the question whether I had achieved some Zen status. I knew that my life was about to change forever, and I said a kind of goodbye to myself. The nurse standing right there put her hand on my leg and rubbed it a little. "Are you ready?"

"I'm ready."

Two technicians took me down the hallway, chatting the whole way. I stared at the ceiling, with the wild and silly thought that in that hospital you couldn't tell one hallway from another to save your life. I suddenly remembered the experience of intensive care some years before—you can't tell one *hospital* from another. I knew I was down a few floors, underground, headed to a closed room with no windows. It felt like I was sliding down some kind of hole, and I randomly wondered if people don't feel a kind of claustrophobia about that. I've never been claustrophobic. I had no fear.

In the operating room, there is almost a glare of suffused light. The entire room is equally bright—a big white box with stacks and piles of steel arms and smaller boxes and cords of machines, and people all dressed the same, playing with the stacks and piles and boxes and cords. I saw Dr. V, the anesthesiologist, sitting there, waiting for me. I knew what was about to happen—she had explained it all to me before. I sat upright on the surgical table, ready to go. In this room full of people doing complicated things, though, one of the nurses did nothing but hold me. She supported me because I was sitting up in a bed with no backrest, and because I was about to lie down and sail away. Her holding me was a necessary medical procedure, but, more importantly, it was a hug. For that moment, I lay back in my beloved mother's arms and felt safety. I'll never forget it.

Then I began my close encounter with the anesthesia tubes.

Dr. V put a small, narrow tube up into my nasal passage. I remember her asking me which nasal passage was bigger, and I remember a wild and brief thought: it isn't like I have measured the interior architecture of my own nose . . . . I said I felt like it was the right, and so she started to put the tube in.

Your nose is odd in the sense that you don't feel pain in your nostrils, but you do feel a kind of scary blockage and the motion of the tube. I had been warned, so I wasn't afraid.

But I was wrong about my nose. The tube got literally stuck. She pushed a little, and wiggled a little, but no go. So she tried the left nostril. Bingo. The tube slides in with no pain. It reminded me of the cardiac catheter experience. When they had done that, years before, I had felt at certain moments—or thought I was feeling—another tube sliding up my artery, looping around a corner, and entering my ventricle. It didn't exactly hurt, but it was eerie. Dr. V had done a good job of prepping me for the insertion of that tube in my nose. Then she told me what she was about to do. She would spray some anesthesia into my throat to suppress my gag instinct. That would then make it much easier to insert the shunt and the tube into my nose and down my throat. So she told me not to worry—and not to gag—but to just breathe in and swallow. It feels odd. I wonder whether some people find that very hard to do. I had felt a *lot* of odd things by then in my life, so I thought: here comes another one. And I took deep breaths.

I will remember all my life the feeling of leaning against the nurse who held me. And then, I guess, Dr. V injected the right stuff into my arm, and I sailed away.

@ @ @ @ @

"Amy. Amy, can you hear me? Can you hear me?"
Who is that? I felt groggy. I didn't know where I was. I could hear some other voices. I could hear some electronic beeps. I could hear an odd sounding swoosh of air. I felt a hand on my leg, and on my arm. I couldn't feel my right side much at all. But I did feel an annoying dull headache.
"Wake up. Are you awake?"
Who is that?
It was a woman's voice. She patted my hip a little. "Wake up. Talk to me."
And then I knew.
I was in a tent. So was she, Dr. V. I could see some slight movement above the tent, and see diffused light shining above it, like the mid-day sun. But I felt *odd*. My right side, the side I was lying on, was almost numb—the tingle was telling me that. My throat was dry, so I was croaking a little. I came fully awake,

enough to feel my right side falling asleep. I knew exactly where I was. I was lying on the operating table with my skull sawn open.

I knew there were people poking around up there—I had been told what would happen—but I didn't feel that poking around. I could hear things—machines, the swoosh of cloth, the clicking of metal. I heard Dr. F's voice in a sort of disembodied way. I could hear some babbling. I felt some more gentle rubs on my legs, and I was glad of that! And then I started to pay attention to some pain—not serious, frightening pain, but dull ache. I had been lying on my right side, motionless, for hours. My hip was sore and my shoulder was throbbing a little. I had this deep desire to roll over! But Dr. V was warning me not to move much. And my head felt like it was strapped down.

It was. But that didn't scare me. I felt no actual pain—just some annoying aches, just as they had told me I would. And I felt a hand on my leg, gently rubbing. I was comforted by that. Indeed, I will remember that simple feeling all my life. I had an image in my mind about what my naked brain might look like. I had seen some photographs of other brains before. In fact, I remember having the odd experience of imagining what all of this would look like from "above"—as though I were looking down from the ceiling.

I need to move my right leg. Dr. V let me move that leg very slightly, and very carefully.

And then I heard another voice. I recognized it. It was Dr. B, the specialist who had done the fMRI on me a week before, studying language function and location in the brain. "Amy, are you ready?"

What I didn't do was feel any fear.

So we began those tests. They were almost identical to the procedures we had done for the fMRI. You may recall that the fMRI had required that I lie very still because any kind of motion disturbed the imaging which was the tool for the experiment itself. I couldn't speak because the motion of my jaw would ruin the imaging of my brain. But now, under these circumstances, that problem had disappeared. It was no longer the case that there was just a machine mapping activity on the other side of my skull—there was a human being. In fact, there was a team of human beings. And in this case they didn't need an image produced from electrical activity—they were looking directly *at* the real thing—my brain—in order to directly measure the neural activity itself.

This kind of test provides an enormous amount of information which the non-intrusive fMRI simply cannot measure. The testing they do on the naked brain itself might be closer to reality than the testing in the fMRI, but the evidence they get from the surgery might give them crucial information on the accuracy of the fMRI. I remember lying there, in my own surgery, thinking about the scientific value of this awesome thing we were all doing. My friends tell me now that they are totally amazed that I could lie there and consider the technical features of my own sawn-open skull. But I could.

So I was familiar with the tests and I was ready to do whatever they wanted me to do. I remember wondering if the two foreign-language speakers involved in this procedure were having fun doing it. I couldn't actually see either of them. I could see, from under the tent, what I thought might be torsos in surgical garb, but I wasn't sure of that either. I could hear their voices quite clearly. Indeed, that entire experience was like one of those ghost stories seen in movies—I was hearing disembodied voices. And then I had the wild thought that this was like the experience I sometimes had during seizures—and I felt the irony of that. But I had known then that those voices weren't real, and I knew now that these were.

So, here came the flashcards. They showed me images of objects, and asked me to name them. We started in English. Dr. F and the team had placed electrodes on my naked brain, and so could actually measure the electrical activity in my brain cells as I produced certain language activities—primarily naming objects. Because he and Dr. B could map my actual brain tissue, they could make some crucial decisions. They could map multiple locations where I produced nouns in all three languages. As I said before, one of the problems with surgery for epilepsy is that the parts of the brain which produce seizures can look entirely normal. It is much easier for a surgeon to remove a tumor or damaged brain tissue than it is to know which part of the brain is producing seizures and therefore should be removed.

And so Dr. B would show me a picture—a little flash card—and ask me to name the object. Because Dr. F had electrodes carefully placed, he could map down to fractions of centimeters which cells in my brain were "firing" when I named an object. I had to name the object three or four times—but that was so that the team could be sure they had precisely located "ground zero." Then Dr. F could use the electrodes to temporarily "deactivate"—numb—a specific location and Dr. B would ask me again. When they did that, I wouldn't be able to name the object. I still knew what it was, but I couldn't name it. That confirmed those brain cells were active in producing nouns. They were mapping the centimeters of my brain which name things!

We went through the stack of flash cards in English. And then we began the same thing, with the same cards, in Italian. Just as I had done in the fMRI, I began to make myself think in Italian.

Looking back now, I remember the imagery of some of the cards they showed me. There is one in particular I remember so well because I couldn't remember the name for it, neither in Italian nor in French. It was a drawing of an object I very seldom saw, and I close to never used the name in a sentence, in any language. In Italian, I couldn't name it. I began to do the same thing I had done before, during the fMRI, which was to look at the object abstractly and see if what it resembled provoked the memory of what it was called. Then I started in on asking myself whether the Italian name was a simple, literal translation of the English. But here's one of the most amazing experiences in that surgery: it took me *seconds*—not even that long—to ask myself that question, and to try for the answer. It takes much longer to read this sentence itself.

And here's another example of that wild experience: directly after I asked myself that, I sarcastically said to myself—silently—that just because I can make a literal translation from English into Italian doesn't mean that that is the right name for the object! And—I remembered!—I had to immediately suppress myself from thinking in yet another language because they were mapping *this* one. So, I did something else. I said out loud—in Italian—that I knew exactly what the object was, but I couldn't remember the name of it in Italian.

Of course, this was not a quiz. They weren't talking with me at all, so, at first, nobody was giving me information or clues about what the object was named. I remember, too, vaguely thinking that this was itself slightly frustrating, since, looking at the thing but not remembering what it was called, I actually wanted someone to tell me. I was mildly annoyed that I couldn't remember. But I understood the situation. I also remember it crossed briefly through my mind that I didn't know whether my making my sentence—saying that I didn't remember the name—was helping the situation, since what they were trying to map was the location of the nouns themselves. And I remembered Dr. B having said—during the fMRI—that naming things and making sentences were neural activities located in separate parts of the brain.

These are some examples of what happens when you are awake in brain surgery. Your brain starts to wander around and ask itself questions. I was awake—fully awake—but I don't think I was totally "on the ball." I was exerting some effort to keep my mind from wandering around.

And then the second assistant began to speak to me in French. She showed me the images, and asked me to name them in French. I speak it, but not as often as English or Italian, so I know fewer nouns in French. The same card showed up, and the same thing happened to me in French. I looked at that object, thinking that I had probably never named that thing in any French conversation I had ever had. I thought: *the French might be extremely close to the Italian . . . . Okay, Latin? "Astrum"? That's neuter . . . .* Then I would say to myself: *Stop that!*

I also had another wild thought—whether there was any significance to showing me objects which were, in fact, not everyday ones, but more arcane ones. Do I stack those somewhere else in my brain? That question occurred to me, but once again, I shoved away that thought, knowing that I needed to stay on The Noun Path. And all of this was happening—my brain was doing it—in a second or two, even though it takes me a paragraph to actually describe it. But I didn't have all day to try to think through the etymology. I couldn't name that thing, and so we moved on . . . .

Here's a description of the image on the card they showed me: the object is a centrally conjoined group of five slightly-wiggled triangular "arms," against the backdrop image of a beach. *Stella del mare. Etoile de mer.* Starfish.

So there I lay, naming things. I could hear Dr. F, recognizing his voice. He was talking, not to me, but to the other members of the surgical team. He seemed to be naming things as well, but none of them were starfish!

I vaguely remember another series of quizzes in which I would read short descriptions of things—a series of nouns—and then name the object described. Dr. B would show me a flash card with "tall, pink bird" written on it, and I would say, "flamingo," or "teacher's red fruit," and I would say, "apple." Doing that meant I was understanding the verbal descriptions and so processing language itself, not just naming visual images. But now I remember the series of images much better than I do the verbal noun quizzes.

I don't remember with any precision how long all of that took. I couldn't see the clock on the wall, and nobody wears their watch into their own surgery! It lasted a while, though. And I had a headache—remember I told you that Dr. V, the anesthesiologist, had told me one of the patients had requested to be put back to sleep because of the headache. I thought of *that* noun—headache—all by myself.

It took a while—it seemed like hours—to finish the quizzes. When they had mapped what they needed to map in all three languages, they were ready to send me under again. Dr. B sat there in a diffuse glow of white light, and said "goodnight" to me. I don't remember saying "goodnight" to her. Dr. V told me later that she then slid the anesthesia tube back in, but I don't remember that. I somehow just sailed away.

@ @ @ @ @ @

(Do you remember that my surgeon had told me that a typical brain surgery of the kind I would have would take about 6 hours? And that he told me that, because I had so many languages, and because they would need to map them, my surgery would take longer—probably 9 hours?

Mine took 14.

It's rare to do this kind of surgery on a person with two spoken languages. Dr. B told me later that my case was unique. I was the only patient they had ever done this kind of surgery on in which they had to map *three* spoken languages.

A patient would normally be awake for about an hour. I was awake—talking—for about two and a half hours. The medical team also maps other functions of your brain located in the same area as the languages they are about to map—some kinds of "motor activity"—during the surgery, but they can do that without waking you up.

My dad told me that he and my brother remained in the waiting room, and in the hallway, and wandered around in the hospital for a long time, taking some breaks, waiting to hear about how my surgery was going—well into the evening of that day. The staff and sometimes a nurse would come out to tell them that things were going well, but that my surgery was taking longer than they had expected. Don't worry. Go get some dinner. Take a walk. No hurry.

It was well after 9:00 that night before they told my dad and my brother that I had come out of surgery and was in recovery.

They could finally go home. It was nearly 10:30 that night when the surgeon—Dr. F—called my dad to assure him that things had gone well, even though they had taken so much longer than originally thought.)

@ @ @ @ @ @

I remember, only very vaguely, waking up again to see one of the doctors, standing in front of me. I was lying on my back rather than my side, so I think I wondered if it was over. I couldn't see very well because my head was wrapped in gauze bandages. And I couldn't open my eyes any wider. She asked me, "Do you know who I am?" I couldn't talk at all. My dad was there and told me later that I just sort of nodded.

I remember a lot of details from the surgery and the recovery, but I'm not at all sure that I remember them correctly. My memory of the recovery might be faulty about what other people were doing with me or for me. And furthermore, I sincerely doubt whether I remember the order in which they happened. Part of that experience was that I was paying no attention at all to the "real time" of those experiences or, I think, of anything happening to me. Maybe it's important information about the effects of the surgery or the general anesthetic that I wasn't processing "reality" much at all. But I can tell you that some of these experiences are still very vivid to me.

Dr. F came to see me—I think it was soon after the surgery. He asked me questions, too, but I don't remember what they were. I remembered his voice, though. I think that when I heard his voice—before I opened my eyes—actually, my eye—I thought for a moment that I was still on the table. I think I was used to hearing him talking, but not to *me*. Dr. D-E came to see me then (whenever the "then" was—I had no idea what time it was), in the post-op ward. He would show me something, and then ask me if I could name it. He held out the tip of his tie to ask me what it was. I knew what it was, but I couldn't name it. He held up his pen—I couldn't name that either.

This time, though, I didn't lie there trying to remember the Latin root, or match it with a noun in some other language. This time, I wasn't thinking in any language. I don't think I was thinking at all. I was just lying there, looking at the face talking to me, watching some "things" appear before my eyes. I remember the question, though, so I was processing some aspect of language. It was kind of similar to my experience during a seizure: I could hear—and understand—the question, but I couldn't give the answer. During the seizures, though, I had started to hear slightly odd voices, and I would start to feel that overwhelming *deja vu*. But this wasn't the same experience. Just as in the surgery itself, everybody sounded normal. I didn't feel any *deja vu*. (Neither was I lying there thinking: what is the German for "*deja vu*?") I remember, though, how I felt.

Dr. D-E said things had "gone well." He repeated what he had told me before the surgery: I would have trouble talking while my brain was swollen and recovering from the surgery. They kept me there to make sure I was recovering from the surgery itself. And then they let me fall back asleep. I was happy to do that.

My dad was there in the hospital to watch over me while I recovered. He told me—afterwards when I had recovered some—what had happened.

I slept that night after surgery, and the entirety of the next day, my father tells me. I remember some fragments. I remember my brother's touch, and his voice. He had to go back home, but he kissed me goodbye before he left. I'm not sure I really saw him—maybe I just remember his voice. I remember some fragments extremely well, in fact, I'll never forget them. But I don't know—and I'll never know—how exactly those fragments were organized.

I wandered back and forth between sleep and dozing. I was talking to myself, silently. I became aware of that. But something was slightly odd. I wasn't lucid enough to pay rational attention to that, only to *feel* that it was odd. I wasn't making a coherent story, I was just randomly thinking of disjointed phrases and of images of things and the names for them. And I would then "see" some images of the words themselves kind of sailing past me, as though they were written on an invisible ticker tape at different angles. And when I saw the words, I knew what was odd. *Ya dumala po-russki.* I was thinking to myself in Russian.

I studied Russian long ago. I spoke it then, but in the previous ten years I had stopped speaking it, and only read it occasionally. And here I was, *thinking* in Russian!!! I didn't ask myself why, but I noticed that it was odd. I would wander around a while in fractured Russian. I thought of the names of some things. I think I wandered around a little bit in the grammatical cases in Russian (nominative, generative, dative, etc.), and I think I conjugated a verb or two. Then I would sail away.

Then I would slowly come back, almost awake. Almost. The name of something in Italian would "occur." Just some random thing. I was remembering places I had visited in Italy, both very recently and many years ago. I would "see" the image of a beautiful Jewish cemetery I had visited in Ferrara two months before—an enormous old tree and some gravestones—one of them with the family name Fink. I was sort of wandering around even in my half-dreams, looking at things. I wondered where I was.

I sort of knew I wasn't actually seeing all this stuff. I would open one eye, slightly. It was my right eye—my left eye was somehow difficult to open—and see the edge of the pillow under my head, the arm brace of the bed, and the face of my father, sitting next to the bed, reading something. And then I would close that eye and sail away again. I remember going from some Italian rambling phrases to some French rambling, and then back again. I saw the written text of an Italian poem I know so well: *Nel mezzo del cammin di nostra vita . . . ."* Some Greek words would somehow come to me: *plethora, zeugma, hamartia.* I remember seeing the characters π (pi) and Δ (delta). But I don't *speak* Greek at all. I would see images of people I knew for whatever reason. I think I heard some snatches of songs, but I don't know now what songs they were. I would doze again.

I would wake up, or at least feel as though I had somehow woken up, and I would vaguely wonder where I was. I would think of a word for no reason, and I don't think that I knew at that point *which* language I was thinking in. Again, I would open one eye, and see my dad. I knew that if my dad was there, all was well. Even though I was "seeing" visions of climbing up the *klettersteig* on a mountain named *Rosengarten*, I knew I was just hallucinating somehow. And that was just fine with me. It was in fact some kind of comfort. I would hear some soft voices, but pay no attention to what they were actually saying.

At some point in there I was either remembering or just imagining a lighthouse. I think I was just imagining it, because I didn't have that feeling of familiarity. I don't know why. Maybe there was no why. And images of people walking past me would recur. I would "recognize" some of them, but others I would not. I remember one moment very clearly: I was standing on a shore and a small figure wandered by me. But he was at a funny angle, as though he were walking on some spatial plane other than the one I was standing on. It was extremely vivid—I will remember the image itself all my life. And then I would go back all the way under.

Sometimes, interspersed with these experiences, I would "see" circles and triangles moving—rolling. I remember the images, but I don't think I remember the sequence of them. One of those triangles started out one-dimensional, and then rolled into a pyramid. I remember watching a drawn spiral seeming to unfurl in front of me, like watching a carpet roll open. But it was rolling on a line angled towards where I would be if I walked straight forward—that is, in a kind of three-dimensional space. I remember a figure of a rectangle "opening up" and becoming a pentagon. I remember a set of small squares expanding into a larger set. There were lines and colors on them. I felt like I was moving backwards from them, and so beginning to see the "larger picture."

The "larger picture" was edges of fabric—lapis blue and deep green and blood red—and some feet literally standing one on top of another. I saw a row of bent arms in striking colors making a kind of chain. I saw a face I recognized—sort of. Then I saw the image (of the set of images) get smaller, as though I were backing up away from it. Again, I "recognized" it, but didn't think about what it was. Much later, remembering that experience, I knew what it was: a mosaic in a church outside of Venice, Italy.

I saw some symbols which looked slightly like algebra. Those I recognized when I "saw" them—they're from two paintings that I know. It isn't that I clearly remember, now, the actual symbols. I couldn't write them down now without looking them up. What I remember now is the impression of recognizing what they were. It was only after I recovered from the surgery that I had an idea of which paintings I remembered, and I looked them up. They were ones I had recently seen in my trip to an exhibition in Italy. Another striking image hit me: two figures on either side of a vase full of tall, white flowers, against a background of gold. I recognized it instantly. I *felt* familiar with it, but I don't think I "named" it at all, or thought of what the image actually was. Later, after I had recovered from the surgery, when I remembered having "seen" that image, I knew exactly what it was: a painting I had last seen long ago. It was the *Annunciazione* by Simone Martini (c. 1344). I remember seeing patterns in the color of red-orange, with small plants and flowers, some strangely symbolic flags, and a unicorn! It felt familiar, but I didn't "know" what it was until later. It was mixed-up imagery from a set of 15th-century tapestries: *La Dame à la Licorne* (c. 1500).

I don't remember thinking in English. I don't remember naming things, or telling myself stories in English. But I don't know whether it would be true to say that I wasn't thinking in English just because I don't remember it. I have often had the experience of thinking in a foreign language, on purpose, training myself to use the language well. I have also spent time thinking in one foreign language about another, teaching myself both of them and repeating the process of tracing some of them back to Latin. I might have done something like that. Maybe my mind was literally staying back in the largely unaffected portions of my brain—staying out of the site of the surgery, where my native language was affected.

I sort of woke up late on Day 3. My dad told me that it was Day 3—I didn't "know" that. They brought me some food and some oral medications. For me, the experience was like looking through a long-distance lens. I don't remember seeing the room, or all the people in it, or the entirety of the tray with food on it. I remember my father's face and feeling his touch. He tells me that I hadn't eaten anything since the day before surgery, but even on Day 3 I refused the food. Somebody's hand gave me a small carton of milk. I drank a little bit, took the pills they gave me, and went back under. The next morning I think I ate a little bit. I wasn't hungry at all. As they had warned me would happen, my left temporo-mandibular joint—my jaw—was swollen and ached. I couldn't open my mouth wide at all, and I couldn't chew. All I could do, essentially, was slurp. Slurp, and sleep.

I remember the sense of touch, too. My father's touch. A nurse's touch. I wouldn't even open my eye—my right eye—to see who it was. I knew, or I thought I knew, and I felt comforted by that. I remember the feel of that touch, just as I remember that nurse's hug in the operating room as they put me under, and that touch on my leg as I was waking up during the surgery itself.

Dr. D-E came by to see me twice a day, every day that I was there, even (my dad tells me) when I was still "under." I don't remember much of what he did those first few days. After I was "awake," he would stop by to talk, and to see if I could talk. He would pick up a small, clear container with water in it and ask me if I could name it. I could not. I could not think of the name of that thing to save my life. Furthermore, I couldn't do what I had done while awake during the surgery itself, which was to sort through the names of that object in other languages to see if that was a clue. I couldn't intentionally think in *any* language at that moment. He was talking to me in English, and I was trying to think in English. All I could do was sit there, look at the thing, feel that I knew exactly what it was, but have no idea what it was called.

He would hold out the end of a slim piece of cloth hanging down from his collar and ask me what it was called. I would remember that he had done that before. I knew exactly what it was, but I couldn't name it. He would hold out a short narrow tube-like thing and ask me what it was. I couldn't name it. All I could do was watch him use it to scribble on a flat thing, tell me not to worry, that things looked good, that he would be back the next day, wish me good night and leave.

I couldn't talk much at all. I couldn't move my jaw much, but neither could I produce much in the way of sentences. I'm not sure I was making sentences at all. My father would talk to me, but he knew better than to ask me lots of questions. He would ask "yes or no" questions. I could nod or shake my head. I could (sort of) say "yes" or "no." But I couldn't name anything.

On Day 4, I had a visitor. A good friend of mine wanted to come to visit me and just make sure that I was okay. She had talked to me about it before the surgery, so I knew that she would come. It was very kind of her. She knew what the reality would be, and wasn't expecting me to talk to her, to tell the story. And that was crucial, since I couldn't have told the story. In fact, my father had been very careful to make sure that most of my friends did not come to visit me precisely because I wouldn't be able to talk.

Before the surgery, he and I had set up a networking plan with my friends. He would call a few close friends to personally let them know how things were going. And then those friends would call a few of my other friends to let them know how things were going. They all understood that I wouldn't be able to chat with anybody for a while. My dad didn't want me to feel frustrated with that. And, of course, I was just barely operational at all. I had to sleep. It was hard for me to stay awake or to pay attention very long. And, on Day 4, I still could barely, barely talk.

In fact, just as dad had thought might be the case, I wasn't really awake or operational when my friend came to see me. dad tells me that it was on Day 4. I remember her being there, but only just. I remember seeing her face in a kind of fog. I wasn't sure when I saw that face whether I was imagining it or actually seeing it. I vaguely remember her voice, too. But I wasn't awake enough even to try to talk.

The next day another three good friends came to see me. This time I was more or less awake, but I still couldn't talk much at all. I could understand what they were saying to me, but I couldn't even think of a response, much less say one. They knew it would be the case, so nobody was surprised. They were only trying to cheer me up, and that was sweet. One of those friends had had his own medical problems. In fact, in that Christmas vacation of 1993 in which I had had my cardiac infarction, he had also had a heart attack at his home. We had joked about it, saying he had had a sympathetic attack. Another of those friends was a colleague at work. Since he worked directly with my boss, I had been forced by circumstances to tell him as well about the medical problems. He had always been kind and supportive, so he also knew the story. He came just to give support, not to make me talk about what was happening.

The third person was also a colleague from work. She was Italian. I managed to ask her to speak to me in Italian, and she did. All of a sudden my brain snapped to attention. I understood her Italian perfectly, and I answered her question right away. I had to be careful with my jaw, but I didn't even have to search for nouns. They just appeared. I sat there in wonder! My Italian was not only undamaged, but it was more operational at that moment than my *native* language! This wasn't a total surprise, since Dr. F had told me that foreign languages are often located away from native language. But at that moment, a few days after surgery, when I could barely think in English, I could chat in Italian.

These good friends knew better than to exhaust me, though. They stayed only a little while, then left me to rest.

That night, as an added distraction, my menstrual cramps arrived. I remember lying there with my attention distracted from the ache in my head by a new set of aches in my abdomen. I always took ibuprofen for those, because it was the only over-the-counter painkiller which worked. So I had a couple of them in a paper cup on my bedside table, ready for the next cramp shift. But the nurse brought in a doctor—the resident—who told me I couldn't take them. He authorized only acetaminophen. I tried to think how to explain that it had never worked as a painkiller for me, but I couldn't construct the explanation. So the ibuprofen disappeared, and the useless acetaminophen arrived and just sat there. I didn't sleep much that night. I lay there kind of sailing around in the sea of dull ache with random abdominal pain spasms. I didn't actually think much, but I remembered the infarction, and laid there trying to ignore *this* set of pains.

On Day 6 Dr. D-E said that I was healing well. That I was looking good. That I could go home the next day. I slept some more.

On Day 7, I got in the "check-out" lane. They took off the iv set, unwired me, and a nurse took me down to get a shower. My head was still bandaged, so she wrapped it in plastic to keep it dry—and therefore unwashed—in the shower. And I had to leave it bandaged close to another five days. You can perhaps imagine the way my scalp felt. The left side was largely numb, but the rest, last shampooed six days before, itched like crazy. I came back to get dressed again, in most of the same clothes I had worn six days ago. We signed a wad of paperwork, and then my father went down to get the car and drive it up to the exit. There I sat, in the wheelchair right before the open room door, waiting for my dad to show up again.

Suddenly a face appeared in the door. It was a familiar one. It was a woman I knew—but only casually—from work. It was a woman with whom I had never spoken about any of my medical issues, much less about surgery, and under no circumstances about where the surgery would happen and what room number I would be in.

I sat there in shock. Literally. My father and I had carefully constructed our plan about making sure to keep people from visiting me in the hospital for two reasons, both of substantial importance. The first was just to keep me from having to try to talk when I virtually could not. To give me the most rest and the least stress possible. My friends had understood that immediately.

The second reason was that I didn't want everybody to know where I was and what I was doing. I was trying to preserve as much privacy about all of these issues as possible. I didn't want to have to see people not close to me, and I didn't want to have to just be polite, and for God's Sake, I certainly didn't want to have to answer questions about my medical condition! Like: What had happened? Why did you have surgery? How did it go? Why didn't you tell us you were going to do this? I didn't want information about my condition and my medical procedures to be public knowledge.

So I sat there, quadruple dumbfounded. Why was she there? How did she know? What did she know? And, the most difficult question at that particular moment: *What is her name?* It isn't the case that I had never known her name. It was the case that I couldn't remember names much at all, certainly not the names of people I knew only slightly. Most of my close friends who knew everything about what was happening didn't know which room I was in. How did she know that? I knew that my dad had never spoken to her.

And there she stood, in the doorway, smiling. Asking me how I felt. How things had gone. When I would be back at work. I don't even remember exactly what I said, because, even under the best circumstances, I couldn't really talk. And I don't really remember what I said also because I remember very well what I was thinking: *what is her name? How did she know?*

She was very kind to me, and she had always been a kind and friendly person. She wasn't being intrusive, she was just visiting briefly to say "hi." But she told me how she had known I was there. She had seen her boss in her department—not mine—who told her that I was at the UCLA hospital, and told her basically what I was there for, so she could find out which floor and which room to visit.

I would like to say that I almost had a heart attack when I

found that out, but, because I *have* had a heart attack, and because I don't tend to joke about them anymore, I won't put it that way. I was jolted. And I was silenced, I think. I mean, I was having trouble talking at all, to anyone, but I also had to sit there and imagine what that meant—that a person at my job had simply casually remarked to another person who only slightly knew me where I was and *why*. I stared at her. I asked myself: *who else knows?* I remember looking past her down the hallway, terrified that more of my "colleagues" were about to show up.

I want to say that I'm not criticizing her at all. She just said a few cheerful things, and asked me how long I would take to recover, and then wished me well. But from the moment I saw her right up to the moment that she said goodbye, I still couldn't have said her name if my life depended on it.

I will remember, all my life, the terror—the sense of constriction of my heart—I felt at that moment. I had recovered to the point where I could kind of think rationally: how many people know? How much do they know? How did they find out? Would I ever know how they knew? Would I ever know how many people knew? And the answer to that last was clearly: no.

After she left, my father showed up, ready to take me home. I asked him about that visitor, and he confirmed what I had been sure of—he hadn't spoken to her, or to anyone outside my circle, about me.

So the week of immediate recovery from the surgery was over. I got in the car to go home and begin the long haul.

My apartment roommate—P—had gone to stay with her boyfriend for a week so that my dad could stay in her room. K, the very first person at work—other than my boss—that I had told about having to do the surgery, came to help us out. Right after the surgery she had done something sweet for me and for my dad. She had cooked some meals—some good ones!—to bring to my apartment so that my father wouldn't have to worry about that. She stayed a little while with us to see how I was, and to offer my father whatever help he might need. She offered to take me back to the hospital a few days later for my scheduled suture removal. We arranged that, and then she kindly sent me back to bed and left us alone, to rest.

I had to sort of set my bed up differently. Ever since the surgery, they had kept my hospital bed angled so that my head was higher than the rest of my body, making sure that the swollen blood and fluid would run down and reduce the pressure. So I had to pack my bed with pillows to do a similar arrangement. But my back was sore, precisely because it had been angled for so long. I had walked very little, and lain in only either of two positions for so long that I was stiff and sore. I needed to start to move again, but every night I had to hunch back up and get stiff again. They had warned me about that. Slowly, slowly, slowly I tried to wiggle my pillows a little so as to very gradually angle back down to level.

I had gone through the antibiotics they had given me for the immediate post-surgery recovery, but I was still on the acetaminophen (big deal!) and on the dexamethazone. But I also had enormous trouble remembering the names of the drugs I was taking. And the effect of that was that I couldn't remember when I had or had not taken this one or that one. My father had to keep careful track of what, how much and when. I remembered that he had had to do that very same thing for my mother up to the moment when she died, just nine weeks before.

I don't know that I have anything to say about how we felt that week. For the weeks between my mother's death and my surgery, he and I had simply strapped ourselves in, in our own ways, to do the deed. My dad had been able to go to a support group back in Tucson, right up to the day he came to Los Angeles, to be strong for me. I had just gone numb from erupting catastrophes sometime in the spring of 1998. And I had just stayed mostly that way, a defense, I suppose, against feeling itself. Given what I knew I had to do, feeling would just be a distraction at best. Just after the surgery I simply had scrambled brains, and had thought—in any serious sense—very little about any one thing. I had just wandered around through a bunch of different languages, remembering things learned long ago but not the least bit relevant to my life. If I were writing a novel about this, I might suggest that that fact is enormously significant. My brain was purposely repressing the actual reality in order to defend itself against the emotional pain. Maybe that's true. But maybe my mental processes were more physiological than that—maybe they had to do with swollen brain tissue and hence just neurons diverted into the backwaters—literally the backwaters—of my memory, bopping around.

I had moments during those weeks in which I remembered good times with my mother, and I wept. I had been buffered from thinking about my mom's life by my own pain and physical shock. But now, it all flowed back. I was recovering, in a sense, from having spent so much time sleeping, but I continued to feel, not only the need to sleep, but the *desire* to sleep. To keep from thinking about the actual present now. The sense of crisis was receding, but the reality of it all—of all the other problems still clearly there—was coming back in quiet but relentless waves.

I certainly didn't want to talk to my colleagues yet because it was difficult and frustrating to talk. My friends called me at home to wish me well, but they knew better than to try to make me talk much. But I felt the strongest need to make one call myself. I called that colleague, the one I knew only slightly, who had just shown up at my hospital room that last day. It was, for me, an extremely painful experience. Since I had trouble talking, I couldn't be anywhere nearly as smooth as I would want in order to express my thanks for her kind thoughts. And I wanted urgently to tell her that I didn't want my situation to be made public—to ask her not to talk about it. I don't know if she understood how or why I felt that way, but she kindly said she would respect that. I hung up with the persistent uneasiness only slightly appeased. I knew that between the time she had seen me, and my phone call to her, she might very well have already mentioned it at work.

And of course I knew that the way she found out meant that *she* wasn't in control of who knew.

(She told me much later, when we talked about that, that she had heard from the "grapevine" that I was there for brain surgery. She was at the hospital visiting another friend, and so just stopped by to say hello to me, too. She could see right away that I looked awful and couldn't respond, and so she felt bad about having "violated my privacy." I've tried to reassure her that I didn't then and won't ever hold it against her personally.)

On the Wednesday of that week, my good friend K took me back to the hospital to have the sutures removed. The nurse slowly pulled off the mummy-wrap bandages and cleaned off that side of my head. It was covered with all the now-dried liquid gook from the surgery—my blood was only one kind of gook. My scalp on the left side was mostly numb. I could feel some pressure, and, in fact, a little itch, but no pain. It took a while for her to clean it up, but I still couldn't wash my hair yet. She was kind but forceful: "Don't do it. Leave it as long as you can possibly stand it, so that the skull can heal without any additional stress." I stood there contemplating the exquisite itch on my scalp, at a level which I had never felt before. It was Wednesday. Of week two. I hadn't washed my hair now for going on nine days, much less brushed it

The hair on the right side had just been wadded up in order to get stuffed into the bandage wrap, so it was sort of hairsprayed with crusty disinfectant and blood into a truly weird multiplex bird's nest ledge. When they cleaned the left side gook all off, for the first time I got to see my own ground zero, still close to naked. The hair had only just begun to grow back, but the scar, a big curving white bumpy road, was naked of hair. It still had a few scabby spots, and I was told to leave them alone.

I asked, sarcastically, if I could possibly wash my hair before the year 2000. The nurse smiled and said, "Absolutely not." Then she said: "Hold out until Friday?" I said: "Can do." She gave me a little packet of very light stocking caps to wear all the time. My naked scalp would sunburn in just a few moments. The combination of the side effects of my meds—extreme sensitivity to sunlight—and the vulnerability of the naked, sutured scalp was actual danger.

Early that Friday morning my dad drove with me to the airport to pick up my oldest friend, M, flying down from Oakland to spend the weekend with me. She was the one who had been there holding me when I woke up from that first *gran mal* in Tucson (back in Chapter One). She could tell immediately that I wasn't able to talk much, but she didn't care. She had just come to be with me and to hold me, and to just give me whatever she could. When we got back from the airport, I did the deed. I took that first post-operative complete shower. That first one in eleven days. It was on Friday, the 13th.

It was hard. I pulled all the bandages off, slowly. And then I stood there, naked, looking at myself. Looking at the mudpie hair on one side of my head and the desert fault-line ridge on the other. Looking at the little slashes where the stitches had been, and the little ridges, here and there, of remaining scab, still holding on. I looked at the still-bruised eye socket and the oddly angled jawbone. I got in the shower, and, with a handful of shampoo, I started on the bird's nest. It wasn't just a question of clean—it was a question of unwind and untwist and untangle and untie big long wads of hair. And I had to be careful to keep the shower-pressured water off the left side of my head, for the tender scalp would otherwise be torpedoed. And even though I was careful and gentle, big hunks of my hair detached themselves, slid down to the floor of the tub and clogged up the drain. But the scalp on the right was overjoyed. It preferred to cast off hair and take the twinges of pain in order to get the scrub of shampoo.

I stood there essentially massaging half of my scalp. The right side was happy; the left side was not. A huge sector of the left side of my scalp was just numb. The network of nerves had been severed, so it was just a kind of cast-off fishing net lying on the ground of the top of my head. But the fault line was very tender. It wasn't in pain, but it was standing there getting ready to wrack under any kind of scrape. My jaw hurt, and the skin there at the edge of the incision was extremely sensitive. That shower took a while . . . .

When I toweled off, and carefully dried the remaining hair, I stood there again and looked at myself. The distraction of that deep desire for clean was gone, and the reality of how weird I looked settled in. I stood there and broke down and wept. My friend heard that, and came to just hold me. She didn't need any explanations.

That week had been the process of coming back to reality. That weekend we drove up the coast, the three of us, to a beach I knew well and walked along the ocean some. I could sort of talk, but I could in no way actually express the complexity of how I felt, and how I was starting to feel. I sat in the car, staring out to sea, listening to my dad and my friend talk. In fact, I was listening to the sound of them talking, not the content of their phrases. I was thinking about my mother. No, I don't think that's really true. I was *feeling* about her. I felt the desire—the intense desire—knowing it was beyond my reach—to feel her touch. I was wearing my sunglasses—the old ones large enough to fit my swollen temples—and looking out the window. Nobody saw the tears rolling down.

We stopped to have our picnic, and to enjoy the ocean. I wasn't really processing conversation—in part because I still had trouble making conversation. I was just staring out to sea. I sent my father and my friend off to wander the beach and play some. Sitting there alone, carefully in the shade of a palm tree, lots of pain came washing in. That was a beach where I had been years before with my lover. I remembered an afternoon when my parents had been there with him and me, and my mother and I made guacamole in a styrofoam take-out container, laughing, wondering just how much mashing we could achieve with a short, wide-pronged plastic fork. I saw the laughing face of my mother, and tears were rolling down my cheeks.

I remembered a night that my lover and I had camped at that beach. The sky was clear and the moon was full. We had stood there, looking at the moon, in an embrace. He had stood behind me, holding me, his chin resting on the top of my head, swaying gently, silently, sweetly. I cried for that, too. Half of the top of my head remembered the sensation of that touch. The other half was essentially dead now, and now wouldn't even feel that. I thought maybe my scalp would never feel that the same way again. I felt two senses of loss woven together: I wouldn't be able to feel it now, but it would never happen again anyway. And I wept for that simple sense of loss of feeling woven into the memory of a deep, abiding feeling of loss.

I sat there, staring out to sea, and considered: numbness. It was physically, biologically, a loss of feeling. And for me it was an emotional state. That last year had been an endless, imploding cascade of loss and fear. Loss of past hopes for the future, realization of the futility of my own efforts, and fear for the medical voyage of no return. I don't remember exactly when—the day, or the hour or the moment at which—my sense of feeling had just gone under, but it had, I guess, in naked self-defense.

I had more or less roboted my way through most of that year. I remember my friends saying to me that they were literally astonished at how detached I had seemed when I told them about the brain surgery I was about to do. It looked like calm. There were days in which it was a kind of calm. I have always been an intellectual person, and I had spent the last 15 years of my life studying, doing research, and thinking about intellectual stuff. My training and my self-defense let me keep myself interested in the complicated issues about the function of the brain. There were other days in which it was the only way I could find to talk at all about what was about to happen to me. My sense of fear did not make itself known in words. It wasn't an "idea" to talk about—it was a rising surge.

And now, in a sense, the feared "event" was over. But I had never been afraid of the surgery itself. In fact, I had been able to think, in a detached way, about the surgery as a new experience. Lots of people might want to forget the whole thing. I know that many people are absolutely horrified at the very idea of "waking up" in the middle of brain surgery, but not me. On the contrary—I had never been horrified by that. In some kind of perverse way, it had given me the sense that I would actually participate in this, rather than have this horrendous thing done to me. It gave me a way to refocus my very existence. That surgery itself gave me an experience I will actually always cherish. I know that that is weird, but it's true.

The fear was for the consequences of the surgery.

They had told me from the start that it would take awhile for my head to heal from the biological stress of the surgery. And it would take even longer for my intellectual brain to heal from The Big Scramble.

But would I—my *self*—ever heal?

9 The Aftermath

Two weeks after the operation dad took me in again to see Dr. D-E for a follow-up. He thought things were looking good, and told me—reminded me—to give myself lots of time to recover. He told me some details about the surgery itself, and so I got more fragments of that Big Picture. They had originally intended to resect as little brain tissue as possible, but after the neurosurgeon had done that, Dr. D-E had tested my neural activity again and found that some other portions of my brain were also producing seizure activity. So they removed a little more of my brain than they had originally planned.

Take it easy, he said, and don't worry.

Three days after that I got on a plane—with my doctor's approval—and flew north to spend Thanksgiving with my brother and his family. It was important to do that because my father needed to go see a number of his friends and professional acquaintances at a yearly conference in Austin, Texas. Yet he didn't want to leave me alone, so my brother invited me to come and spend the holiday with his family. In fact, he offered to fly down to Los Angeles and then fly back with me, but I didn't think I would need that kind of help.

I wanted to be sure that my father felt secure going to see his friends. He had been so strong for me, and for my mother. I had no doubt that he would himself need some emotional support for what he had been through in the last two months. My flight went fine. There were no surprises. Well, there were one or two, since I had kind of stopped paying attention to the fact that I looked odd—my jaw was still swollen and I still had the remnants of a black eye and I was wearing that odd stocking cap. Some would stare, but everybody was nice.

My brother picked me up at the airport and drove me towards home on the scenic route. We stopped in beautiful state park, deep in the Oregon woods, with a series of gorgeous waterfalls, and strolled around the kid's path—level and easy to walk. For me it felt *so* good to move around. I felt like I hadn't really walked in years, and yet my last trip to the gym had been only 16 days before. So we walked and walked. And talked about things. My doctor had warned me that it would take quite a while before I could go back to the gym to do the kind of hard aerobic exercise I had always done before. But I needed to walk, and my brother took me on a tour of that lovely park.

I had wondered how the kids would react to seeing me looking as though I had been beaten up. I have to say that they were a little bit shy of me at first, but after a little while, after I explained things, after I showed them the actual scar, they were fine. My brother told me not to worry—once they thought everything was fine, everything would be fine. When I showed them the scar, they were a little freaked out, but, as my brother had assured me, once they knew about it, it was okay.

It was a quiet vacation. I still had to sleep a lot, especially in the early afternoon. I began to dream about my mother—I would wake up, not knowing where I was, with the strongest possible feeling that she was with me. I began to think about the "dreams" I had had right after the surgery, because I don't remember strong, emotional ones then. They were creeping back.

I was happy to be with my family. After Thanksgiving, both my father and I flew back to Los Angeles on the same day, so that we could meet in the airport and come back home together. We spent that last weekend in November driving up the coast and taking some walks in the parks. I was feeling better, but I still had to sleep a lot. I remember fractured moments from my dreams, but I don't remember them the way I remember "dreaming" right after the surgery. That weekend we stood out on a ridge overlooking the Pacific, knowing I had to cope with the next big event: to return to work.

I didn't want to. It isn't that I didn't want to do my work. In fact, as my dad noticed, I was getting a little bored with my life the way it was, so it would probably be good for me to get distracted by some work. But I was thinking about The Spotlight Problem. I had to think through, one more time, what would be my "story." The advice I was given by some of my friends, who had dealt with similar things, was to just gloss over the fact that you'd had some medical stuff done—but give no details. Most people, they said, were polite enough that they wouldn't push you for details.

One more time around this very uncomfortable merry-go-round. This time, it would be visibly clear—maybe not from down the hall, but certainly from close up—that something had happened. I had a swollen face and some huge stitches. I'm sure that my dad felt again, as he had many times in the past, that I should just feel free to tell people what had happened. He would never have tried to keep private something as huge as all of this.

The nurse who had advised me, before the surgery, to keep my hair long so that I could part it on the right and use it to cover the left side was a genius—not only because she knew that, but because she gave me the emotional comfort of knowing it before I went into the operating room. She understood, I'm sure, that the emotional effect of having a shaved head is usually hard for women (and maybe for some men). I'm sure that my father would say that that is another reason to let people—not just your friends—know what will happen to you, so that they won't be "shocked" to see you. Your friends would make the effort to comfort you about the way you looked—as well as what you had just experienced—as soon as they could. I remembered having stood there after my first shower, finding myself shocked—even though I had been prepared—at how I really looked. I knew it would be a shock to everybody else. I knew that lots of my colleagues at work would join the strangers at the airport—to look at me with surprise, to say the least.

I'm not criticizing anybody for that, either—it's human nature. I think most human beings would be a little bit shocked to see, on the street, another human being who looked like she had been beaten up and Frankensteined—with stitches on her head. Part of the recovery process is to know that it will happen, and to get ready. I remember thinking to myself that many of the women I knew would be terrified to go out of the house looking the way I did—in fact, I think they might refuse. I considered whether that might be an enormous difference between male and female patients. I wondered if your average man might worry, not that he was ugly, but that he looked like he had lost the last fist fight, whereas the average woman might feel that she was now unbelievably ugly. Me, I was less concerned about how I looked than most of the woman I know, but even I was gritting my teeth. It was going to be a double whammy: people would be shocked at how I looked and incredibly curious as to why.

The left side of my head had begun to grow back its hair, so it wasn't entirely naked. But the huge jagged scar was still entirely visible. If I combed my long hair over the left side, that scar area wasn't immediately visible—that is, most of it was not. But the stitches stuck out from above my ear angling down to my jaw joint, on a big welt. There was no way to cover them, short of wearing a bandana in the bank-robber mode. Even a hat wouldn't have done it. And my face was still swollen. The place where my left jaw joined my skull had been altered—it angled out more than my right—enough so that it also made my face look odd. So I got ready for the responses to that, and went back to work.

I wasn't driving so soon after surgery, so my father would give me a ride to work. I had arranged for short days, and so he would pick me up at a certain time. Just as I had done before, I showed up about 7 am, before virtually anybody else was there. But then my colleagues started rolling in. Most of them were surprised to see me. Some of them were genuinely surprised that I had been gone, and had no idea where I had been. And some of them—colleagues, not friends—clearly knew where I had been. But since my hair covered most of the scar, many people didn't really notice that anything medical had happened—or at least they didn't act as though they had. But, of course, if they got up close on my left side, they could see the sutures.

Some stopped me in the hallway to ask where I'd been. I gave my (kind of) rehearsed response: that I'd had some medical difficulties, but I was back, and things were fine. As had been predicted, most people didn't ask for more information. A few did. But I said that it was "surgery." For most of those people, the fact that I didn't give more details gave them the clue, and they didn't ask for more. In two cases, though, I stood there getting a series of highly personal questions about "what kind of surgery," right there in the hallway. I had to, at some point, say: "The details about this are personal." It was a situation I knew would happen. And, furthermore, I knew that my declining to give details would make it clear that I didn't want people to know. That would make it likely that people would immediately try to find out because I had given the impression that the details would be interesting because they are secret.

But what can you do? Once again, I had to face the situation I knew I would face. It is extremely hard to hide this kind of brain surgery—with a month's absence and a large, swollen stitch welt on the side of your head. But there you are. You have only a few choices. 1) You can tell the truth. You can clearly, voluntarily, put that information out in public, and deal with the consequences. And there will be some consequences. 2) You can make up an incomplete, evasive response, which, because it's evasive, will provoke people to try to find out—to gossip. 3) You can lie. You can make up a story and then try to look like you are telling the truth. That, of course, requires that you rehearse your account, and, what is perhaps worse, to carefully remember the "official" story. 4) You can try extremely hard to avoid being asked the question.

Back at work

A few days after I came back to work, I went to the seminar I had always been attending which took place once a week. The participants in that seminar had noticed that I had not been to the last four sessions. As I sat down at the table with the 10 or 12 people in the room, one of those participants, sitting across this big table from me, said: "Amy, you're back! My goodness. Brain surgery! How did it go?" One of the others turned to me and said, "Brain surgery? My god. What happened to you?"

I wasn't prepared for the inquisition in a room full of people. I stared at the person who had asked me that first question. I couldn't immediately think of the appropriate answer in a room full of people. I don't remember exactly what I had said, but I think I said: "I'm okay. I'm . . . ," and I paused, trying to think of the right adjective . . . "getting better."

There was another factor as well. It was barely a month after the surgery, and I still had some trouble talking. I wasn't any good at the "come-back." Even under normal circumstances, it usually took me a little while to compose my sentences. And sitting there, at the round table, being asked for an account, was close to paralyzing to me. To give some credit, though, the scholar who had first asked me that saw that I was not ready to talk about it, and gave the kind of apology you can give with a look, avoiding talking even more about the situation.

And again, I want to be clear. I'm not slamming her. She was being kind. She didn't know that my situation wasn't public. She had clearly gotten the information about me from somebody else who had presented it as openly public. She was another example of someone who got the information—but not from me—and whose response was a case of kindness, expressing concern. So I'm back into an extremely difficult aspect of this kind of medical situation. There is no way you can actually keep something like this private—because not only did other people know a lot about my situation, they knew it *as* public knowledge.

It was certainly a major factor that they could see that something had certainly happened. The story—the "brain surgery" story—was out, and might have gone absolutely anywhere already. I didn't know whether everyone knew the whole story. I got some clues from some, and some flat statements from others, telling me they did know.

That seminar was a fairly intimate group of people. Several of them, seeing that I was back, waited for a break in the seminar and then came up to ask me how things were. Several of them, standing on the other side of the room, waved and smiled at me. One tapped another on the shoulder to turn him around, and pointed to me. I got another smile and wave. Everybody was kind. But I got, again and again, the questions about how it had gone. And one flatly said that he hadn't realized that I had seizures.

Of course, everybody, even the ones who knew I had had surgery but hadn't known why, now knew why. So, at that moment, my situation had flipped 180 degrees—now virtually everybody who knew me knew the "why." And I want to be clear here: the fact that I had done the surgery was "visible," so the fact that people knew that something had happened is no surprise. But the fact that the information as to why was already known by people I hadn't yet spoken to was a surprise. The fact that they openly asked me—in the presence of others—how I was was a surprise. A scary one. My personal, private, medical circumstances were clearly, simply, open public knowledge. And there was no going back. You can never take public knowledge back.

I stood there, quiet, afraid to try to address that at all, and distracted from the conversation itself. I was contemplating the effects of that. I was thinking through the problems. I was telling myself that I had been right in fearing that it would happen. I suppressed some immediate thoughts about what that would mean for my next job search. I didn't want to talk anymore about it, so right after that seminar was over, I went to my office, called my dad to come pick me up, went to the parking lot to wait for him, and went home. I went to bed, curled up, and got myself unconscious.

9 THE AFTERMATH 281

That first week I got another surprise. I found out that the forms sent from the office of Dr. D-E to my insurance company were "insufficient." So they had not processed my "case." So they had not sent any checks. My employer's policy was to help its employees file with the California Employment Development Department (EED), but then to pay only the amount necessary to cover the difference between what EDD pays you and your normal salary. Since I was officially working only part time—my doctor's instructions—I was getting paid only a portion of my salary. So I had to get on the phone and get some confusing information from my insurance company, and then wrangle with the EDD. Here's their story:

They had received the package of forms from the various medical offices involved in my case, but they had received "insufficient" information. When I got through to somebody on the phone (after the obligatory 15 minutes on hold), I got referred to somebody else. I spend another 8 minutes on hold, and then got the explanation that they had faxed a request to my doctor's office for additional information late in the afternoon of November 25. Wednesday. The day before Thanksgiving. And, EDD told me, they had gotten no response. So, my file had gone into the "insufficient information" pile, and they had not processed my request, and had not put me in the system for coverage. They had not "covered" any of the time I was absent from my job.

My question: what was their question to my doctor's office? Their answer: more information about my diagnosis. So I hung up there, and called his office. I sat on hold there for three minutes. I got the staff member there who processes such stuff. They had not received a fax request. So, I hung up there and called EDD again. I was on hold 11 minutes. I got a staff member there. I told *them* that my doctor's office had not received that fax. I asked them to call his office. They said that policy was to fax. I asked them to fax again. Fortunately! I had written down Dr. D-E's office's fax number. I hung up, and again called Dr. D-E's office. I got right through to the staff member. I told him that the fax was on the way. It would ask for information from my doctor. He told me Dr. D-E was out of town. I told him the situation. If the request didn't get to my doctor in less than a week, and if it would take a week for EDD to process, I wouldn't get any funds in less than three weeks. He understood the mess. He was very kind. He went right to work on this problem. (It took only two weeks.) I hung up the phone and went to nap for a while.

I had also begun to go back to the insurance-form maze, for I had had so many medical events, most of which were billed separately, that the amount of paperwork and computer activity was awesome. In fact (can you believe it?), now, a year and a half after the surgery itself, my insurance company is still processing some of the services and bills and calculations of what I owe. It ain't over yet. And, of course, I'm still processing the claims for services since November 1998.

And then I got another twist of fate—one that I had suppressed in my memory until I went through my files to write this book. Right after I returned part-time to my job, my boss's administrative assistant brought me my performance review to read and sign. The official date on that review: November 3, 1998. I couldn't have read it, much less signed it, that day because, on November 3, 1998 I was lying on an operating table with my brain sawed open.

Furthermore, for the first time in the years that I had done that job, my review contained an inaccurate report of projects I had worked on and achievements I had made. I knew at the time that that had to do with other administrative changes that had recently happened, but I wasn't going to sign that review. I sat there, feeling one more time, the sharp pain that my boss, who had always been supportive of me, and who had given me nothing but "Excellent" performance reviews, had now handed me a middling one, downplaying the work that I had done and its significance to larger institutional projects. He didn't rate me as less than "Excellent," but neither did he praise the intellectual content of what I had done for him and for the institution.

So, for the first time, I did not sign that review. I sat down and presented my "response," not officially to the review, but to my boss, asking why this review did not include the following achievements, and I listed them. You have already read about most of them, in my previous reviews. Those achievements were aspects of the various projects—and *ongoing* research tasks—I had been doing for years now. It was a clear signal to me that I would have to fight, for the first time in that institution, for the official description of both the nature of my job and my performance of it. So I started that process, of a series of my memos to him, and his to me, about what ought to be put in the description of my achievements there. I sat there close to tears at a) the fact that it was happening at all, and b) that I had to sit there in recovery from the major brain surgery I was having *while* he was sitting there writing this review. The difficulty of doing that little task so soon after surgery, and of suppressing the personal pain of it, was even more exhausting.

That afternoon I went home and went to bed and I sailed away—*hoping* for a little unconsciousness.

This series of evaluations, going from "excellent" to middling, gives cause to wonder about underlying factors. As is apparent, the less favorable review came about only after the decision against renewing my contract. It is of course possible that the quality of my work declined after that decision, but I swear it did not. An alternative interpretation of the events is that there had been instructions that *this* last review must not be so glowing, else what was the justification for letting me go?

So, this little event raised the question again. No, that's wrong. It didn't "raise the question"—the question had been there for a while now. It presented another episode of it. It looked like an attempt to "justify" why my position—with me in it—had *not* been made permanent. And I wasn't going to sign the review. That began a series of "conversations"—mostly on memos—with my boss about what kind of accomplishments should be stated in that review.

A month after my surgery, I went to the pharmacy . . . .

More follow-up after surgery

Six weeks after the surgery, I went back to see Dr. F. I wanted to get some more detailed information from him about my surgery itself. But, as fate would have it, when I saw him that afternoon, my file had gotten mixed up—again—with someone else's. It isn't that he didn't remember me. He certainly did, and he certainly remembered my surgery! But he was careful about giving me very much information without looking at my file. And again, I understood his situation. A doctor wouldn't want to screw up somehow and tell you something other than what was recorded in your file. He was being careful. I knew that. I wasn't angry, but I was enormously disappointed at not getting those details. (It wasn't the first time—and it wouldn't be the last—that I would have a medical appointment in the UCLA system without my medical file! And that problem was in no way the fault of the physician. Can you imagine what that's like for somebody with a complicated history?) My skull, though, and the healing from the surgery itself, looked good to him. Don't mess with it, he said. There was still—six weeks after the surgery—some scabbing. Don't mess with it!

I have to repeat an important point here: I was still suffering from difficulty expressing myself, even six weeks after the surgery. It isn't that I seemed to be unable to speak or to make serious mistakes, but I wasn't good at remembering questions I wanted to ask, or to express the questions the way I wanted to. So even the ones I asked didn't really get me the information I wanted. I made another follow-up appointment with him, and left feeling that, at least in the healing sense, things were going well.

I don't remember much about the time between Thanksgiving and Christmas. My father continued to stay in Los Angeles, though I had begun to be entirely operational again. I slept a lot. I was not back to "normal" yet. But, once again, "normal" was not going to be possible for me, because I had to get ready to walk away from the last seven years of my work.

This was just another chorus in the Opera of the Abnormal for me. I had done, in the previous few months alone: in-patient EEG, two MRIs, two PET scans, 8 or 9 blood tests, one death of my mother, and one brain surgery, and I was about to have my office prepped for the job-ectomy.

Preparing to leave my job

I would go through files for various projects in the seven years I had spent there, and the sense of loss would well up. I would do my mantra, chanting: *numb, numb, numb.*

Some colleagues hadn't known me well enough to know that my job was a contract job. They hadn't known that it would expire. Some colleagues had trouble believing the rumor I was leaving because I had been there so long. Some who had only just heard about my brain surgery would come to stand there in a sort of stupor and ask me what I was going to do next.

I would have the wild thought: what next? Car crash? Leukemia? Hit by a meteorite in the 7-Eleven parking lot? I didn't really have a good answer to that because the issue of what my next career move would be had slid so far down my Things To Do list that I truly couldn't manage to care, or even to fake caring. What was I going to do next? Well, in about an hour I would go home and sort out medical bills and insurance forms around my dining room table and then down both sides of the hallway, to the kitchen and back again. Then I'll take a nap. Sleep is what I'm looking forward to. But I didn't say that. I would shoot for some more amorphous response. "Well, I'll take some time off. I'll decide what I want to do next." Pause. "I'll be here another month or two."

I started to take a few of my books home each day, to reduce the number of boxes full of books I would have to cart out to my car on the last day there. And I started to clean up my computer, making sure to leave everything having to do with my job there, organized for easy access for anybody else. And I had a lot of files from seven years of projects as well as research notes on possible candidates for scholarships. I made careful lists of what was necessary to accomplish for my projects before I left. I received another draft of my performance review in mid-December, only slightly altered, and still not acceptable to me. I wrote another memo about that, and sent that stuff back to my boss.

But what did I do for myself? I tried to map the effects of the surgery on my brain. I was certainly told that I might have trouble remembering the names of things. But it wasn't clear to my doctors exactly how my use of nouns would be affected. And, since they discovered that my nouns in all of my languages were located in multiple spots, it was unknown how I would be affected. To repeat, there is evidence that brains can "store" a noun in more than one location. In that case, your brain might have to relearn where the "back-up" nouns, as it were, were located, and get better at finding them swiftly. But it might take a little bit of time for your brain to do that. I started to test myself and to keep some records.

At Christmas, my father and I went back to see the Oregon family. We both had to deal with some more pain, for this was the first Christmas without my mother. We had both been suppressing some of our feelings in order to make it through each stressful day, but now, on vacation, with the family, we knew, even without talking about it, everybody's pain. She was not there with us, and she would never be with us again. We tried to celebrate Christmas, but it was full of pain. My father gave a present to his granddaughter, a tiny tea set that my mother had had from her family. My niece had played tea parties with my mother—I sat there remembering so clearly the last party, at Christmas in our house in Colorado. My niece was still too young to really process the reality of death, but she was moved by that. We all were.

We tried not to ruin the joy of Christmas for the kids, but I couldn't suppress my grief. My father and I stood in the kitchen, holding each other, remembering the last Christmas, my mother's pain, and her trip to the hospital—the beginning, although we hadn't known it, of the end. We both had to somehow deal with a deep and abiding emotional pain. I am even now at a loss to describe that Christmas. Anybody who has lost a wife or mother might feel as deeply as we had. And yet, the magnitude of our loss was off the charts. I needed to sleep a lot, but I also *wanted* to sleep a lot. I wanted oblivion.

If I hadn't pushed my boss—hard—to extend my contract, the end of that year would have been the end of my job as well.

Happy New Year.

@ @ @ @ @ @

The Personal Domain

That's the basic account of my recovery period. Now let me tell you how things were with me—with my actual, physical head.

Because many of the nerves in my scalp had been severed, Dr. F warned me that I might get twinges and some pain as the nerves grow back. Just after surgery, the section of my scalp above the line of sutures—above the removed plate of my skull—was simply numb. I literally felt nothing there at all. The section of my temporo-mandibula was sore for a long, long time. (It remains, not sore, but extremely sensitive—I suspect it will always be that way.)

They removed the stitches about two weeks after the surgery, but I discovered, as I went along, a few little suture fibers, sticking up from my scalp. I had to pull a few of those out. Right around the scar itself the skin on the other side was extremely sensitive. The hair began to grow back. I was glad that I had kept my hair on the right side. If I had not—if my entire scalp have been shaved—I would have had to have worn a little stocking cap, which would have rubbed my skin. I would have had to wear it anyway, out in the sun. I probably would have worn it indoors as well, since the scar was, for a long time, entirely visible. And under those circumstances I would have gotten some more shocked reactions from others. Of course, right after the surgery, while I was still bandaged, I got some shocked reactions anyway.

And it took a little while for the bruises to heal. It was quite a while before I could open my jaw to the same extent as I had before. And the angle of my jaw where it joins the skull was different—swollen, sticking "out" a little. That subtle change in the shape of my skull—and hence my face—was one of the effects of the surgery which is still the case. It's permanent. You may recall that one of the side effects of one of my medications—Dilantin©—is a "coarsening of the facial features." That had happened to me already, years before. But it was also a side effect, in a sense, of the surgery. It's one of the aspects of this part of my life which has very little medical significance, but an unavoidable personal significance. People tell me that they don't really notice it. But I do. My glasses, a pair that I bought before the surgery, are now a little bit too narrow for the width of my face. Now they leave a kind of crease in the skin at my temples. Again, I don't know whether other people notice that, but I do, every day. I'm not telling you that this kind of thing only happens with this kind of surgery. I'm telling you that it didn't happen before, but now it is permanent—an effect on my face of the surgery. I don't know how men would feel about things like this, but I believe I know how women would feel.

Because the angle of my jaw was permanently changed, I have another little problem. I'm embarrassed to tell you, but here it is: I drool sometimes. Always on the left. Once again, that's not such a serious or dangerous problem, but it is embarrassing and a little scary. It gives me the sense that I am losing my self-control. I have some swallowing problems I never had before—I inhale my own saliva sometimes. I have to be very careful now—for the first time in my life—*how* I eat.

And then there are some surprising little, tiny things. They don't feel—to me—like a "loss." They are just weird overnight changes. I used to like chocolate. I didn't love it, or feel as though I needed it, I just liked it. Now chocolate just doesn't move me. Now, after brain surgery, I feel a new, deep desire—figure this out!—for *oatmeal*. I was never much of a meat-eater before surgery. It wasn't a political stance, it was simply a lack of desire for meat. But after surgery I started to crave hamburgers. Not cheap burgers from chain restaurants with a pile of other stuff on them, but a large, medium-rare hamburger, with very little on it. I didn't mind eating naked burgers. It wasn't the entire experience—it was the meat all by itself.

Dr. F had told me that, as my scalp "regenerated," I would get some slight itch or twinges, like little pin-pricks. He had told me not to worry. It's not a problem—it was the nerves which had been severed growing back again, growing into a new network. So on the left side, on the edges of the suture, I began to get pin-pricks. But they weren't all little pricks. Some of them were sharp, fast, deep stabs. It would make me literally twitch in pain, but I knew it was *good* pain. And I never knew when they would come again—it was random. Sometimes I would have a series of them so sharp that tears would swell up in my eyes. But I knew that it was actually a good sign. My scalp—parts of it completely numb—was coming alive again.

As it came back alive, I began to have one of the weirdest sensations in my life. As the nerves on my scalp grew back, they seemed to be networking with some other nerves from afar. The slightest touch just above my eyebrow on the left would produce a ghostly sense of touch in the scalp at the top of my head above the scar. If I traced, with my fingertip, along my brow towards the left temple, I felt that eerie, ghostly, tippy-toe sensation creep along the top of my sutured skull.

But parts of my sense of *myself* were still numb. I began to kind of quiz myself as to what I could actually remember immediately. For example, I did my Ph.D. in literature, so I carried a "permanent" memory of literature I had specialized in, and, especially, literature I had loved. But some things had changed. The writings of Dante I had studied—in Italian—I remembered instantly—just exactly the way I remembered it before. In fact, I had thought of snippets of it very soon after the surgery itself. Soon, I could sit and recite to myself poems I had studied years before. But other poems I had memorized before, and known perfectly, I now couldn't recall. For example, there are several poems written by John Donne that I have always loved—but written in English. Before the surgery, I could recite parts of them by memory. But now I could only recall some fractured bits, but not the phrases. I could recall the "content" of a "quotation"—a kind of image of what the phrase was about—but not the actual quotation itself.

And there was another really weird aspect of this. I could easily think of odd, arcane words, ones I seldom used. It's normal words that are the problem. I did an experiment on myself. I just sat there and said to myself: think of some words and list them. And then I looked away from my list, and tried to remember what I had put on that list. And it was hard for me to remember the list I had only just made. I tried that on images as well, and that was easier. I got interested in repeating that test for myself, as part of my recovery. Once or twice a day I would give myself quizzes.

I had some "passwords" for some locks and for my computer. I had written myself notes before the surgery so that I could find out what they were if I didn't remember them. Some of the passwords are in Italian. Some of them are numbers. Fortunately, those came to me immediately, which is good, because I couldn't remember where I had put that memo to myself. And I hadn't hidden the memo, either.

In the first month after the surgery, I remember being on the bus to go see Dr. D-E trying to remember the last name of my roommate of the last four years! And I couldn't! I couldn't even think that this name was "like" this or that, or "sounded like" this or that. I drew a total blank on something I had known as everyday background information for years. I had to think about that for the next 20 minutes before it came to me.

When I had done the in-patient EEG the preceding June, I had read some interesting articles written by physicians on aspects of cases like mine. There were a few phrases that I instantly liked, and instantly learned, and talked about even to my doctors before the surgery. But now, I couldn't remember them. I could sort of remember some parts of them. I could sort of form an image of some of the processes they describe, but I couldn't get the actual expressions. I began to test myself. I would look back in my notebook for notes I had taken while in that earlier in-patient EEG session, and "learn" those phrases again. Then I would start on a blank page and try to write about my experiences of the surgery. Then I would pause, and ask myself: what were those terms? But I couldn't produce them. I would sit there in fear, because, not only had I known them well—by heart—but they were names of things which related directly to my condition and my surgery. And yet I sat there, unable to name those things related directly to my sitting there!

That was a common experience. I had always—many years before this experience—kept a kind of diary. It had notes of things I had read, or things I was thinking about, or citations I wanted to look up. You may recall that I had done some research on cognitive processes—the way that people think and remember— for my job in the years preceding my surgery. So I would read my notes about something I had done or read, and then turn the pages and try to write a sentence about exactly what I was doing— that is, about trying to remember words. But when I got to the point in the sentence in which I was going to name the words I was trying to remember, I wouldn't remember them. We're talking about not being able to remember words I had read five seconds before. Ones I had read for the express purpose of remembering them. So, it was hard for me to "find" or "produce" names of things I wanted to talk about, but it was also hard—at that point nearly impossible—to "remember" words I had only just thought of, and only just *seen*.

I would go find a book with poems or phrases I had known by heart. I would start to read the sentence. In some cases then the rest of the sentence would "find me"—and I could look away and finish the quotation. But in some cases, I would have to read the whole thing (a phrase, or a short quotation). Then I would look away and try to repeat it, but fail. I would remember some words, but not the actual expression.

Sometimes I would sit and try to make a list of the phrases—or titles—I could recall from this author or that author. And I would think of one, but with the feeling that I might not have it exactly correct—and that was true.

I wouldn't want to make a huge list for you of all the kinds of things I did. But my point is that I knew that right after my surgery I had a lot of trouble with those things I had known by heart before.

I had trouble remembering people's names. I usually knew instantly the names of some very close friends, and of my family, but I would have a little delay remembering the names of other good friends. I would have trouble immediately remembering the names of people I worked with, people I had known for many years.

And I had to cope with being "stunned" that I couldn't remember things I had known so well before. I had to cope with the fact that my mental procedures—*how* I was remembering names and things—were very different from how I had done it before. The very fact that I had to consciously work hard at names and nouns was frightening, in part, because it slowed me down. I couldn't say much of anything at a normal talk speed, much less perform what I had been easily able to do before: have a quick and complicated discussion about complicated things with lots of intellectual terms.

I constantly quizzed myself. I constantly felt dread that I would never make it back to anything resembling my pre-surgery norm. I would constantly consider, on purpose, the "scientific" and "medical" descriptions of these procedures in order to make my performance a kind of "thing" for me to examine. Some people tell me that that is a kind of defense against facing up, emotionally, to the fear and to the sense of loss. But, in my opinion, it wasn't an avoidance of admitting those feelings, it was an attempt to not feel that. It was another case, for me, in a long line of attempts to not feel. But it was also a sense of recovery itself for me, because I had always been able to think that way. I was glad that those intellectual abilities—to think that way—had survived. I spend some time—I still spend some time on this—thinking about how my brain thinks about my brain.

My good friends were as encouraging as they could possibly be. As time went on, as I was "recovering" from the surgery itself, my co-workers and even my close friends would tell me that I sounded "normal." But I would sit there, trying to think of the noun I was trying to use, unable to "get" it. I would have to do what I sometimes did in my foreign languages, which was to give some information about the "thing" I was trying to "name" and hope that the other person could guess it. But, in my native language, I was close to silent in many circumstances in which I would formerly have spoken, easily and in complicated detail.

Again, I am not criticizing my friends. They were doing the best they could. I'm not telling them—or you—that they should have done x instead of y. But I felt the enormous loss of being unable to express myself. A friend would ask me how I was doing. I would answer that I was having some scary problems with language. She would tell me that I sounded fine. I would tell her that I had problems remembering the names of 19th-century authors. She would tell me that *she* couldn't remember the names of 19th-century authors. She would "assure" me that that was normal. I would stand there, thinking: *just because it's normal for you, doesn't mean it's normal for me*. I felt painful frustration that I had trouble expressing how I felt, knowing that when I tried to do that, I would be told that my sense of how I was was wrong. I sounded "normal." I was doing well. I was fine. I shouldn't worry.

But I would stand there and think: *you can't know what this is like. You can't know what's happening in my brain. You can't know that I can't find the right word to express how I feel.* I would sometimes say that: I couldn't find the *right* word. My friend would think that I thought I had said a *wrong* word, and would assure me, again, that I sounded fine. I would stand there and think that before the surgery, I almost never had a problem naming or describing things. A pile of adjectives or nouns would occur to me instantly, and it would take a nanosecond for me to choose one, to be sophisticated about what I said. Now, I would stand there and try to think—in fact I would sometimes stand there just frozen—until a word—*one word*—arrived. And sometimes it wouldn't arrive soon enough for me to continue the sentence. I would stop dead. A friend would add in a noun, or ask me if I meant this noun or that noun. I had to just nod, or make that person sit there while I tried to find a different one. I knew that my friends were simply trying to encourage me—and that's the good side. I knew that I couldn't express how difficult that situation was, and that was the bad side.

But there was one marvelous effect of the surgery that I had never expected, and it was a surprise to my doctors as well. I have always had a fairly nice voice, and some ability at singing. (But that's not the same thing as an ability at music itself—that I didn't have much of.) But after the surgery—almost *right* after the surgery—I instantly became three or four times better at *harmony*. Before the surgery I had trouble singing harmony, because I would seem to slide back into the melody. And I had trouble hearing harmony as distinct from melody. But after the surgery I heard music differently. I could hear what felt like all of the different aspects, including the complex sets of rhythm, distinctly. And I subconsciously tap my fingers now. It isn't that I never did it before, but I would do it consciously. Now I do it a lot, without really thinking about it. I wasn't very good at those rhythm distinctions before, either. I could kind of work at paying attention to this or that aspect, but it didn't come naturally. But after the resection music became an entirely different *experience* for me. Now when I drive around with friends, we have the radio on—they all sing along with the melody. Me, I sail around in the harmony.

@ @ @ @ @ @

On January, 4, 1999, I got draft #3 of my substantially altered job performance review—still officially dated November 3, 1998. Its description of my job and my performance was much better than the previous drafts had been, but not what I had argued for. This one "admitted" to the list of projects I was involved in—including ongoing ones. This one admitted that I "was the primary reviewer of [Fellowship] applications in several languages." That review, like the previous ones, had no "Plans for Improvement." This time, though, I wouldn't be there to improve anything. "Overall performance rating: *Excellent*." I held that in my hands and felt another wave of despair. I was emotionally exhausted at that battle and at how I felt about it. It had been grueling to do it and to *try* not to feel much about it. I considered another try at correcting it.

On January 12, 1999, my boss asked to meet with me, and informed me that he would announce the following day his resignation four days later—on January 15! It wasn't public knowledge yet, but it wasn't a total surprise to me. The consequences of major administrative changes at high levels were substantially affecting many aspects of the parent organization. I went back to my office and sat there trying to think about what I had to do because he was leaving. I signed my review, for the ante was raised now. I had to get it filed while he was still the director. I also needed his personal letter of recommendation for me, and I needed him to do it—on the right stationery—*before* he resigned as a director. I needed it before the end of the day that Friday. It would be on a HUGE list of things an executive like that would have to do in the next few days, and I would have to push hard on that. I laid my head down on my desk, thinking I would probably cry. But I didn't. I just felt heartache. I grit my teeth. I pushed. I got that personal letter of recommendation late in the afternoon on his last day as Director. That letter states that I was a "highly valuable colleague." It was praise of my performance in all of my projects—including the ongoing ones—and a statement of confidence that I "could manage any kind of project that a research institute would undertake."

My contract would expire the end of April. As soon as my former boss resigned, and left the institute for his own projects, I found myself in No Man's Land. I did some research for an associate director on material related to research on scholars, the kind of work I had done all along. I closed out the files on a number of projects, and I wrote some descriptions of information available in my files.

On January 14 I went to the pharmacy: Lamictal© 200mg/60ct @ $149.99; Topomax© 25mg/120ct @ $163.19; Diazepam 5gm/30ct @ $12.92. A total of $326.10 for a month's meds.

On January 19, I did another follow-up EEG: $492.

But: at the end of January, 1999, I had gone 16 weeks without a single seizure.

I saw Dr. D-E, who told me that the EEG was looking good. I told him about the Topomax© side effects, and said: *Please take me off this horrible stuff!!!!* But no. "We don't want you to have side effects from the withdrawal as you recover from the surgery." But I could start *very slowly* to reduce the amount. I sat and thought about the reality of that: I was recovering from surgery which had stunned my language abilities while taking drugs which reduced my language abilities. Then he told me about a conference which was coming up: a symposium on the question whether a well-known 19th-century artist—Vincent Van Gogh—had suffered from temporal lobe epilepsy. I wrote that down in my calendar, not knowing whether I could attend it, but enjoying the irony.

What to do next?

My father and I began to talk about what I would do after the end of my contract. We spent some time talking about our emotional feelings about all of this. We started to talk some more about my mother's death, and how that changed things. My parents had moved in January, 1998 from their Colorado house down to Tucson for the express purpose of my mother's health. She had such a hard time breathing living at 8000 feet. It was clear that they had to move lower down. They had bought the house in Tucson, and so the Colorado house sat empty. They had left some stuff there, though, with the idea that they might go back in the summer to enjoy the mountains.

But now that we had (somehow) made it through these crises, we had begun to feel again—deeply and strongly—about our sense of loss. About our sense of doors to the past now being closed, and locked. I was with my parents that summer long ago when they went to Colorado looking for a house. I was with them when they decided to buy it. I had visited them there as often as I could, loving the place itself and the fact that my mother loved it as she had never before loved a place. I felt a deep need to go to a place that reminded me so powerfully of my moments with her—of her joy at life. And of that day in the truck when I broke down, and she had given me the most moving comfort in all my life. And of her unwavering, unconditional, abiding support of me all my life. My dad and I talked about the possibility of my choosing to live there for a while, recovering from the effects of the surgery, and from the personal loss of my long-time job and my trust for my boss, and from the personal loss of my mother herself. And, perhaps even more important, recovering from my suppression of the feeling of loss. Being able to mourn, and to heal from that.

I felt some of that, but I also felt the desire to flee—to go back to a place I loved. One which required no actual accomplishments or performance or even complicated explanations of the last year of my life. My parents had very good friends there, and I knew that. They would accept my presence immediately, and be kind. So we made the plans. I would go spend some time in the Colorado house.

But we also tried to address how my father felt. For him, as well as for me, that house was a living reminder of deep personal feelings with my mother. It was a symbol of her, and of the last years of her life. Every part of the house, every view out every window, every mountain you could see from the back porch, would be her touch. It became clear to me that he wouldn't—he couldn't—move back to that house. He wasn't even sure that he could go back to that house and feel the presence of the past. I came to the realization that he needed to close the door. To sell the house and try to find a way to start a new life. I wanted to do for him what I could. We decided that I would put the house on the market, and do the job of selling it, so that my father didn't have to cope with all of that. We decided I would have that Colorado summer, no matter what happened in the fall.

At the end of March I went to do the follow-up tests: another MRI and another PET—about $1500 worth. I went to the pharmacy: Lamictal© 200mg/60ct @ $155.68, Topomax© 25mg/120ct @ $170.77, Diazepam 5gm/30ct @ $12.92. The prices of the medications had gone up: $339.37.

Medical costs for the month of March, 1999: $1,839.37.

April 16: I went to see Dr. D-E: six months post-op with no seizures. Looking good. I told him, again, about how much I hated the effects of the Topomax©. He told me that I could start down very, very slowly.

Three days later I went to see Dr. F for a follow-up. He said things were looking good. I asked him if he had ever read some of the research I was doing on brain functions—particularly visual perception. He himself had an M.D. and a Ph.D., and was of course familiar with some of that work, and so I could sit and talk to my brain surgeon about the research project I was doing. I had gotten a crash course on brain function. Actually, I had topped my crash course with an *infracranial* course.

My last weeks at that job were painful. There were lots of complicated things going on, but there is no reason for me to try to discuss them all here. I would sit there in my office looking out over Los Angeles, thinking about the futility of it all. I was trying not to let the loss seep in and break down into tears in a fetal position hiding under my desk. A good friend there undertook to have a staff party for me, but I didn't want one. I didn't want to have a "party" with a group of people who didn't know me well—and whose names I would have a lot of trouble remembering. They would ask me to explain why I was leaving—it's not like it was my idea—and what I was going to do next. What I was going to do was try to sail away.

Even the higher-level directors of that institution, after my former boss had left, seemed to stay away from the issues involved in my "leaving." I got a last minute invitation from one of them to meet briefly at a bar or a restaurant somewhere as a kind of "closing interview." I had a kind of "good-bye" lunch with some of the people I knew the best, and told them I was going to Colorado that summer and that I wouldn't know what I was going to do in the fall until the fall. They were all friendly. "Keep in touch."

That last week of April: 28 weeks without a seizure.

The exhibition directly related to the project I had spent the last four years working on opened at the building next door two days before my last day at that institution.

As a fitting gesture, one of the events which happened that spring was a seminar on some aspects of the topic of "Visual Perception." Some of the scholars invited, by a department head, to that seminar had been on my list of those whose work was directly pertinent to our interests, and who should be considered if we decided to do some kind of event. You may recall that I told you that I had done several years of research on "Visual Perception," for my only-just-resigned boss. Much of that work also involved some work on what is called "Cognitive Science"—on how the brain actually works. In fact, I had met several times with a scientist who was directly involved in research on art and biological processes—and on possible seminars we might produce on those topics. I knew that material very well. I had produced a lot of notes and various versions of proposals for seminars, and I was very familiar, not only with the work of several of the scholars involved in this upcoming event, but also with the larger issues involved in a discussion about the relationship between this kind of research—much of which was scientific or medical—and the issues of our institute's research interests. As my boss had previously asked me to do, I had provided this information to the director who was in charge of this upcoming seminar.

My last day at that institution was April 30. That seminar began on May 5. But had I been invited to attend it? Guess.

There I was, after seven years of work at that institution, after three years of research on the topic of visual perception, after a crash course on other issues and other work on cognitive science, after personal knowledge of brain function, after brain surgery, there I stood, uninvited. I'm telling you this because it is directly related to the general atmosphere of that place, and to my responses to the incredibly interlaced personal experience with professional interests. Overnight, I was an outsider.

I had to officially and procedurally request that I be able to attend that seminar. I wasn't pushing to be invited as a speaker, or as a representative of the institution, but as an only-just-made-former employee who had worked extensively on those topics and who knew the work of several of the participants. Let me give you the short version: I pushed hard in a tactical way and, at the last minute, I got in. Here's *why* I am telling you this:

One of the participants in that seminar was a professor of Neurology, Radiology and Pharmacology at UCLA. He was the director of a new institute there, the Ahmanson-Lovelace Brain Mapping Center, which uses the complex machinery recently developed to produce information on the brain. That institute had only just opened—officially. But I knew right away that I was one of the patients who had been there the previous fall, before they had even got the right signs on the door.

Do you recall my description of the "functional MRI" that I had done that fall, right before my surgery? I had done it in the UCLA Brain Mapping Center. I had done it as part of the research conducted by one of the faculty at that center, Dr. B of Psychiatry and Biobehavioral Sciences. I had done it for the express purpose of providing direct data on some cognitive processes (and on how to test those processes). Then Dr. B had been part of the team for my brain surgery. And here I was now, in a seminar, at a table, sitting next to the Director of that institution—whom I had never met—Dr. John C. Mazziotta.

I liked him enormously. Many of the conversations in that seminar involved both scholars in the humanities and specialists in medical and scientific research. Of course, Dr. M didn't know me personally—or what I had done down the hall from his office—but I asked him some questions directly related to how we can know about brain processes. I had tried to understand the aspects of brain imaging, and I was able to ask him some questions about the more complicated issues—without telling him why I knew about those more complicated and detailed issues. He was intrigued, I think, by that, but gave me good explanations about the processes.

I had been informed that the structure of this seminar did not include questions from the "audience"—and I was considered part of the very tiny "audience." So my direct discussions with the participants took place in coffee breaks, in hallways, and in the ladies' room! But I enjoyed it enormously, because I learned a lot about the topics I had done research on—and a few I had actually been involved in. One of my friends told me that that would be nearly the best possible event for me to participate in because of what I had been through. She was right. That seminar experience was one of the most positive events in my recovery from the surgery. But I was circumspect. I didn't want to push my personal case into the limelight.

Dr. M, at the end of the seminar, had invited the participants to visit the Brain Mapping Center for a tour, and so we all got on a bus. He stood at the head of the bus to mention that some of the machines at the imaging center involved magnetic fields and radio waves, so he asked whether anybody had some kind of electronic mechanisms in their bodies—for example, pacemakers. Nobody in that group did, but the question started a number of jokes about the kinds of things people might have which would be affected by the magnetism. Some people asked: "How about pocket knives?" "How about teeth fillings?" Then the jokes began: "How about nose rings?" I smiled. Of course, my question was slightly different, and a little cryptic: "How about titanium?" Dr. M paused just a moment—less than a second—and then answered my question: "That's not a problem."

He gave us a very interesting tour of the Center. As we walked down some of the corridors, we saw some photographs on the wall of MRIs and of PET scans. They are gorgeous images—in black and white or in vivid bright colors, of the brain and its functions. Most of the participants found those very interesting. And then we saw some photographs of brain surgery, in fact, actual resection. Most people, of course, have never seen a naked brain, and so most of those participants had the same reaction that most people would have—they were a little grossed out. I remember standing there in the hallway with a bunch of people making sarcastic remarks about the surgery being done, and expressing just how grotesque it looked: "My god, how could anybody do that? My god, how could anybody let them do that?" Dr. M pointed out how amazing the surgery was, and what kinds of problems it could solve.

We went to the big fMRI suite—that's where they had done that long, multi-language fMRI on me. There were too many of us to fit inside the "observation deck," so I just stood back. I got an invitation or two from other members who saw me out in the hallway, and who offered to let me have their spot to see the suite, but I smiled, and said "It's okay. I've already seen it."

When we finished our tour, we got back on the bus to go back to our institute, but Dr. M would remained at his office building. He stood at the doorway of the bus, shaking hands, telling people that it was very "nice to have met them." When he shook my hand, he gave me a look of recognition and said: "Nice to see you again." I had not met him before the seminar, but he might have seen "me"—my brain—before. The following week I emailed him "the story." He emailed me back that yes, he had gotten the clues, but had of course said nothing to anyone about it—respecting a patient's privacy. I asked if I could come back and visit that institution again—I wanted to pay more attention to the imagery and the mechanics of how to study the brain. "Come back and visit," he said, "anytime you want."

I am glad to have made some of the connections I made in that seminar. It was one of the very few positive moments at that point of my life. But once again I contemplated the irony of it all. What are the odds that there would be anybody—*anybody*—at my (now former) institution who had both extensive scholarly knowledge and extensive personal knowledge of this kind of research and the issues involved? And yet I had had to literally push my way in to that event.

I had another complicated experience coming up. My very best friend—my oldest friend—and I had planned (long before my surgery) to take a trip to Italy that May. I had always enjoyed Italy, and she and I had had a fantastic vacation there almost exactly ten years before my brain surgery. I contemplated the irony of that. It was in 1988 that I came home from Italy with some funny bumps on my arm. It was then that I went to student health to have it checked out. It was that fall that I met my soon-to-be lover. It was that moment which began the dominos, because the doctors in student health were the ones to tell me that I had a form of epilepsy. I look back now at the significance of those moments: of how much joy she and I had felt in the freedom and the pleasure of that trip. It was a moment at the very peak of my enjoyment of life, right there at the edge of the cliff.

She and I went to the west coast of Italy, to hike along a section of the coast I had loved. But the last time I had been there was the summer of 1993. I had been so tired that summer, from the medications—which had resulted in the bone marrow biopsy—and from dealing with the diagnosis, the medications, and the personal effects. I had hiked along the coast. I had sat, many times, on a high ridge, looking out over the Mediterranean, crying. I had felt so alone. I had called my mother and just cried over the trans-continental phone line. It was a gorgeous place with painful memories. But we went to see the place, not the memories.

We went on our own—we didn't need to take a tourist tour because I was fluent in Italian and I knew the area well. But I dealt with the effects of the surgery in new ways. I still tired very easily. Because I had not been to the gym very much—on my doctor's instructions—I couldn't hike as well or as long as had been normal for me (and was normal with my friend). I had to cope with the memories. I had to cope with the fact that my job was now in the past, and with a part of my life there.

I stood on the top of a promontory looking out over the Mediterranean, thinking about how my graduate studies had gone, for I came home from that first year in Italy to graduate school at UCLA. If I had started the meds before I went to Italy, I would never have managed to work hard enough to learn Italian. I wouldn't have been able to complete my intense scholarship to get the degree. If I had had the surgery done before I got the Ph.D., I would never have been able to pass my qualifying exams. They require an extraordinary ability to recall details—to name things. Given the damage, from the surgery, to my short-term memory, I wouldn't have been able to get that degree. Thinking about what would have happened—or would not have happened—if I had been diagnosed sooner, is part of why it was hard for me to write this book. And the issue of advice remains—for me—unsolved. Should you get this diagnosis made as soon as possible? Should you get on these meds as soon as possible? Would you want to get this diagnosis *before* you finish your degree? I stay on the razor's edge: I don't have any advice about that.

My friend was nothing but supportive of me—she let me talk but never pushed me to talk. For I still—six months after surgery—had trouble just talking. I could make normal sentences, but I couldn't express myself well at all. I felt a fierce frustration about that, and I was sensitive to any difficulties, and I needed more sleep, and I got tired faster, and I tried to fight the depression of facing the present and the future. And of course she had to deal with all of that. And she had to deal with my outbursts of anger—not at her, but at the challenges of life in general.

We went to visit the city of Florence as well. I knew Florence well because, long ago, I had gone to the University there for a year. It represented a part of my life which seemed so far away now. And I couldn't do what I would ordinarily have done—take her to as many of the sights there as we could visit. I was constantly tired. I had to sleep sometimes in the afternoon. I had to send her out to go see something, and plunge into sadness that I couldn't take her there. I would lie in bed and remember that long-ago year in Florence, when I chose to live in a foreign language, not being able to express myself fully, but working to be able to live in it. Now I lay there, only just "operational" in my "native" language, but not able to fully live in it as I had before the surgery. It no longer *felt* like home. I lay there thinking: I don't have a native language anymore.

And here's the great paradox for both me and my friend: my Italian was smooth, largely unaffected by the surgery. I retreated sometimes to just think in Italian so that I didn't have to feel the sense of loss of language itself. But my friend didn't speak Italian, so I had to speak English to her, and to translate. We stood in the Piazza della Signoria, in the center of Florence, looking at the gorgeous buildings there. I was explaining the their architectural aspects, but I would hit the problem again and again and again. I could name all the various aspects, the design, the motifs, the imagery—but only in Italian. I had studied this kind of stuff for many years, but I couldn't name the things I had studied for all those years. I couldn't name them in my native language. I felt distance, for the first time in my life, between me and the language I had formerly lived in. I had lost something deeply personal, which would never return.

Again, my friend was nothing but supportive, because she

knew how I felt. But I felt despair, and she had to deal with that. It was hard. It is hard. And, because I knew it was hard, I had to deal with my depression about my depression and about her having to deal with my depression. Once again, I was in the emotional whirlpool. And I would lay awake at night and face the fact that I might be looking at the future. And I would consider whether I could ever actually feel better. My friends and my father had told me, though, that it was the right thing for me to do to get some distance from my job having ended. To be patient, and to try to do some things so that I didn't just sit at home and be morbid.

I got on the plane home alone—different from the one my friend flew on—and wondered if I would be ever again be excited about travel. When I got home from Italy, I did my laundry, packed up my car, and drove away, heading for the Rocky Mountains.

I wanted to be in my mother's arms.

10 The View from 14,000 Feet

1999

Driving back to Colorado took me back to the past. To lots of summers long ago when I went camping, and hiking, and visiting relatives, and enjoying the beauty of life. To taking my grandmother up into the mountains in her ancient 1952 Ford to go fishing. To take a wild trip with a friend of mine just driving wherever in Colorado we had the urge to go. We camped one night in Rocky Mountain National Park, at the foot of Long's Peak, in the constant rain, trenching around the tent to direct the flood away from our tent. It was hopeless. Utterly hopeless. I ended up standing under the porch roof of a picnic area with the guy in the tent downhill from us, both of us laughing at my having sluiced a river down into his sleeping bag.

I remembered having gone up to Trail Ridge in Rocky Mountain National Park with my parents, and hearing the story about a hike they had done long ago—a crazy one. It was a little stupid and a little dangerous—it turned out grueling and even scary towards the end. My dad had said that he was, his friends were, a little afraid, but my mother had never faltered. Keep on keepin' on.

I remembered my brother's wedding long ago. He and his

wife got married at the top of the First Flatiron outside of Boulder—a cliff promontory. It was a simple hike up to a certain point and then a rock climb to the top. I was the only member of his family to "attend" the actual wedding. It was a little crazy and a lot of fun.

I remembered a story my dad had told me about when he and mom went camping up in the Big Horns in Wyoming. They had done a hike a little more strenuous than they should have, and that night he started to suffer from exhaustion and altitude apoxia. My mother knew what was happening, and got her weak and confused husband out of the tent that night, into the car, and drove him down the mountain.

Then there was that summer a few years back when I went to the Arkansas valley with my folks and they bought their house at the foot of a "14er"—a mountain above 14,000 feet—one of the tallest peaks in the 48 states. I loved that house, and the fact that my mother loved it. I also remembered my father's story about that fateful last day there. They left for Tucson, with the storm clouds moving in. She turned to look at that backyard peak—Mt. Antero—through the back windshield of the car for as long as she could hold it in sight. I remembered standing there in January of 1998, packing, crying, feeling another "end" approaching.

Now, my father needed to sell that house. He knew that he couldn't go back there to live alone, even though they had had good friends there. He was torn, because he knew that I felt the need to go there, and that I was considering literally moving there, but he was also afraid that that might move me even deeper into solitude. I remembered that my mom had talked about keeping the house in the family so that her children and grandchildren could come to vacation in the Rocky Mountains. I cherished that idea because I loved that place. I loved the peaks themselves, but I loved even more the fact that that house was a living reminder of her and of her deepest pleasures in life. Dad and I talked about the differences between how he felt about that house and how I felt. Each of us understood the other. I understood his need to close a door and try to move on, and he understood my need to hold on to what was best in my life.

We had decided together that the best thing to do was for me to go back there and put the house on the market, hoping that it would not sell right away so that I could seriously consider whether I wanted to stay. And, hoping that it would not sell right away so that I could at least have that summer in my mother's house.

I had gotten off the plane home from Italy and into my car. I had to drive to the UCLA pharmacy and get my meds—three months worth because I didn't know whether this kind of medication would actually be available in the little town where I was going. I had to pay directly for my meds, and then hand-write a note to go with the receipt to my insurance company. I had bought more than one month's worth of meds in the past because of my multiple travel jobs, and had recently gotten notices from my insurance company that they would not cover the purchase of more than one month's medications at a time. So I had to get three-months' worth, give a short description of my summer plans, and mail the receipt forms—that one was over $500—that afternoon. I put a big bottle of water in my car, got on the highway, and sailed away.

My dad was going to drive up from Tucson and meet me there so that we could make some decisions about the furniture and stuff still in the house. And he needed to visit some friends as well. He told me he thought he would get there on the first Sunday in June, and would be waiting for me there. But I knew how hard it would be for him to walk in the front door of that house. So I drove directly there, through northern Arizona and southern Colorado. I came up over Wolf Creek Pass on June 5. It was snowing at the top of the pass—I will always remember that. I drove up to the house with memories flowing of my mother and my time there and our travels and the incredible sunrise and sunset there. I had been there—in January 1998—after my parents had left for Tucson, but my dad had not been there since. I spent the first night there, enjoying the awesome darkness of the mountains, thinking about the past. He drove up the next day, got out of his car, looked at the house right there at the foot of three 14ers, and paused. I knew it would be hard. It took a little time before he could do it. Then he walked in the front door of that house, of his past, of his life now gone.

You don't need all the details about that house. As luck would have it, it sold right away. But, as luck would have it, the buyers didn't want possession until the middle of September. It was bittersweet for me. It meant that I could have a worry-free summer—because the deal was done—but it also meant that I knew I would have to say goodbye. *Again. One more time.* I tried to stay resigned to that.

My father and I had to begin the end. We began to deal with disposing of the stuff still in the house, deciding what to keep, deciding how to move it, deciding what to put in a yard sale, deciding what to give to some local charities—in essence, sorting out and reliving the past now gone, trying to solve some practical problems and to say some good-byes. We went through boxes of old stuff from our family and my mother's family, laughing at how ridiculous it is to save so much crap. We would sit in the basement and go through boxes of stuff we had never even seen before—many of the boxes of my grandmother's stuff had been moved there by the two of us—unopened.

We would open a box and laugh, and then pick up something from my mother's childhood, and cry. We would tell each other stories about the past, and moments we remembered. We were having another wake there—sharing memories and love. He and I were very similar in our feelings about "stuff"—we didn't have a lot and we didn't care very much about knick-knacks. So we would joke that we were the very best people possible to clear out a house because we could pick up a knick-knack, remember the past, share the memory, and then say goodbye to the thing.

My mother had left a basket full of dried rose petals on the table at her house in the mountains. They were exactly the kind of thing she loved—simple, natural, full of beauty. I stood and remembered what she had said to me that painful day four years before, when I had talked about suicide: *Remember the flowers on Waunita Pass.* My father and I scattered her rose petals in the backyard, at the foot of her mountain.

We solved some problems that week, and then he left. He had a number of planned trips that summer—he was free now to go visit people he had not seen in years. We all knew it would be good for him to do. He would come back to the house again that summer to deal with the problems of the move, but he took off to go see some other friends, and to let me take care of the rest of the stuff, hash out the specific details of the deal, cope with some property maintenance problems, and climb 14,000-ft. peaks.

And write. I began to try to write about some of the complicated issues having to do with how the brain works—related to the research I had done on visual perception and my crash course on cognitive science. It was a kind of tactic of my coping with the effects of the surgery and the recent painful events in my life.

And I began to write this book. I began to tell the story I had felt I couldn't tell back when I had been asked to contribute to that *Los Angles Times* article. I would go back and forth between those two projects, letting myself write for a while about scholarly and intellectual stuff and then making myself tell a simple story about those aspects of my life which might provide information to other people. Which might tell the truth about a case like mine. My father and some friends of mine told me that writing this book might give me a chance to relive all of it, to "get it out." And to put the surgery itself in the past—to move on. But it also involves dredging up things I had suppressed, or wanted to forget. So I would often feel more attracted to the more scholarly, detached, intellectual stuff. Or I would hit the description of moments in my life still painful to think about, and I would stop typing and start hiking. It's hard to face up to a painful past, and it's hard to write simply and clearly about it.

I enjoyed the freedom I had to think and to hike. Hiking requires some physical abilities and some experience—especially in the Rockies. They are high enough that they remain, if not dangerous, at least more difficult than they look. I did everything I could think of doing up there in the Rockies. My dad had left his Dodge Ram in Colorado when he and mom drove down to Tucson, and so, that summer, I had it. Tough, powerful, and with 4-wheel drive. I got out my atlas of the state of Colorado, packed a lunch, and headed out. I drove up some crazy four-wheel drive "roads" to get up high in the peaks. I would park the truck wherever it could go no further and hike up to the ridges and the snowfields. In June the Colorado high country is often full of snow or snowmelt-stream overflows, or both.

I noticed that I was in the same groove as I had been in other mountains in other states and in other countries. I seemed to have no fear. One day I drove up into a snow-filled valley and decided to keep going up a sort of road that led along a stream bed. It was bumpy, but do-able. I hit a kind of corner, though, around a tree stump, and I turned at a sharp angle, went down slope a little, hit a hidden deep whirlpool in the stream, and got stuck there. I do mean stuck, 4-wheel drive notwithstanding. So I rerouted a little, but no go. I did the back-and-forth wiggle to try to get the tires out of the mud and onto some gravel in the stream bed, but no go. There was nobody else up there. I contemplated the problem. I did what I knew I would have to do. I got out of the truck into a foot and a half of creek water—its temperature was only just above freezing. I waded over to one bank, and got some rocks. I waded back and put those rocks under wheel #1. I went back to the bank, and got some more. When I had stacked up some behind #1, I went back to the bank for wheel #2. Etc. It took a while. I remember standing there, looking at the truck, looking at the gorgeous sky, looking at the total absence of any other human beings. If I couldn't get my truck out of the flood, I would have to stay up there for a very cold night, or walk down through the snow, looking for help. I thought about that, and *noticed* that I felt no fear. It took a while, but I managed to back out.

I did stuff like that a lot. I drove up another ridge one day, in and out of smaller creek beds, up and down some hills, through some trees on a muddy road (which is, truth to tell, not a road but a trail). I went to find a little ancient crater in the Mosquito range. The sky was clouding over. I was alone. I knew—I had always known—how stupid it is to go out into the wild country alone with nobody even knowing where you had gone, but I did it anyway. It began to storm, not just rain, and to lightning. I knew I had to try to get back to the actual gravel "road" before the worst part of the storm hit me, but I got stuck going up a very sharp hill. I tried that approach a few times as well, but to no avail. I stood there, under the clouds, looking at the lightning, contemplating what the next try should be. I vaguely wondered how many people came up that trail in the course of a summer. I laughed at myself. I got back into the truck and tried a different tactic. I turned around and backed up that hill, through the rock piles and mud holes. It worked. I made it back down to the big valley. I laughed at myself, but knew that I would do something like that again.

July 1, 1999: 38 weeks without a seizure.

The next day I got in the truck and drove up in the Buffalo Peaks through the snowmelt mud to a promontory overlooking the valley. I sat there, remembering when we—my father, my mother and I—had sat there, in the same spot, looking over at Mt. Princeton and Mt. Antero—our backyard. On that day we picnicked. When we got home, we discovered we had somehow lost a old paring knife up there, and so we called it Paring Knife Peak. I felt my mother's presence so powerfully there.

I hiked a few 14ers. That kind of hiking requires abilities and performance, but doesn't require any complicated processing of language. I got up early one morning and started the hike up one of them near to the house—in the back yard "next door." Most of the hike is actually easy, but towards the top you have to scrabble uphill through some scree—loose, sharp gravel on a steep slope down to a cul-de-sac. There were a couple of guys hiking ahead of me, but one slipped and fell and came tumbling, head over heels, down towards me. I didn't really consider that problem—I acted immediately. I stepped into his path, ground my boots into the gravel and leaned forward to try to break his fall, knowing that it would otherwise be down a couple hundred feet into that cul-de-sac. Just as I had planned, he rolled into me. He hit me just like a pool ball, and, just as I had *not* planned, I went rolling down towards the "pocket." It was a rough fall. I got very bruised up, and it hurt, and I had to work a while to get back up the slope to the trail.

Now, why am I telling you all this stuff? Here's the point. I was doing a lot of this stuff alone, knowing, as I have always known, that you shouldn't do stuff like this alone because of the danger. But I had often chosen to do it alone in the past because none of my friends wanted to or could do things like this. That was still true, but I was on the emotional edge I had actually reached years back: not even caring if it was dangerous. I would look at myself objectively, and say that what was actually scary was that I did not feel any fear. I knew that it was dangerous to do stuff like that without feeling a little careful fear, but I did it all anyway.

One morning before dawn I drove up north to hike another 14er. I did the hour-long drive to the base of the peak. I got out my backpack and my climbing stuff only to discover that I had forgotten my hat. Sunburn is a serious problem, especially in the mountains at that altitude. And furthermore, because of my medications, my danger was multiplied to the nth degree. I should have gone back for my hat, but that would take too long to head up this mountain in time that day. I should have done the smart thing, and gone back home, planning that hike for another day. But I didn't. I put on lots of sunscreen—knowing that it was not enough protection—and I climbed that mountain anyway, dangerous sunburn be damned.

That peak, Huron, has a magnificent view from the top.

You can see the Arkansas valley over to the Mosquito range on the east, and a few other 14ers to the north and south, and a big basin between Huron and the Elk range to the west. I knew that my mother would have loved this view, though she had lost the possibility of ever having it long before she died. She would have loved the fact that I loved it. On the top, I sat on the edge of the sharp cliff on one side, and remembered other peaks, in the Sierra Nevadas and in the Italian Dolomites. And I contemplated—again—whether I wanted to carry on. I contemplated the ruins of what I had lost. I contemplated my mother's sweet memories of the blue lupines at Waunita Pass.

I stood on the edge of the 1,000-foot cliff and thought about this fact: if I'm going to sail away, this would be a good, easy way to do it. To do the swan dive. I had thought about that a lot, even in the cold light of day. I had thought about it with a sense of ethics: if I did it, I wanted to do it in a way that wouldn't involve any other human being, so that nobody would ever feel that they somehow could have or should have physically stopped me from doing it. So that they wouldn't have to deal with having seen a suicide happening before them.

And then I thought about the future, about the issue of the next job. I contemplated the issues which had never faded away: what would I say about my now former job? How good would I be at not talking about any of this medical stuff? I sat there and contemplated my own detachment from the problem of the future and of the next job. I contemplated the fact that my detachment was probably a defense against having to try, again, to care enough to perform a job well. I didn't want to care about a job. I didn't want to care at all. I didn't want to feel much at all. I wanted to maintain that zen ability to withstand never-ending catastrophe. I wanted to stay numb.

I sat and contemplated the paradox, too. Whereas I had worried a lot about public knowledge of my seizures, public knowledge of my surgery was a different ballgame. The surgery had elicited sympathy. It had sparked some interest. It supported the idea that a prospective employer's knowledge of the surgery would not affect the employment question the same way as knowledge of the seizures. But it might raise the question whether I would be as good at my abilities as I had been before.

And I considered another possibility. I discovered at a certain point that some of the people who had found out, from the grapevine, that I was having brain surgery thought it was removal of a brain tumor. So I wondered a little about the irony of that. Would it be actually good that some people would not know about the epilepsy? Was a brain tumor "better" than epilepsy? And yet, would it be a background possibility to a prospective employer—having heard that—that I was a risk to employ, because I might need more surgery, and because I might die on the job? Correct knowledge of my brain surgery might raise the question as to whether I would continue to have more expensive medical treatment, but it might certainly look like it had eliminated the seizures themselves. The mistaken rumor that it was something else—a tumor—might actually be worse. And, once again, I had to deal with the fact that knowledge of my surgery was, now, public knowledge.

That fact is part of why I am writing this book. One of the main events of this book is exactly that I have done the 180 degree turn now. But wait—that's wrong. I haven't done it, it was done to me. But now, since these issues are public, I want to provide evidence to the public about all these issues. Other people with epilepsy are still in the maze. Many of them with this disorder are still in the "closet"—afraid to have to deal with the effects of public knowledge. In a certain sense, I should not say "them." I should say "us," for I feel the same way that some alcoholics feel: I will always be an epileptic. But the reason I say "them" is because I don't have to address that issue—privacy—anymore. But I'm not arguing that epileptics should go public. And I would not "out" anybody. Those who face these problems have nothing but empathy from me.

But even though I no longer have to hide all of this, I'm still an epileptic. Diagnosis and the treatment and the surgery themselves haven't "solved" the problems of the diagnosis, the treatment and the surgery. I sat and contemplated the bare facts. The last seven and a half years changed everything. I'm not saying that, had I not had that problem, I would be famous, loved, happy and rich. Who knows what that life would have been? But this life had been deeply affected by the diagnosis, the treatment and the surgery. The fact that, since the surgery—44 weeks before—I had not had a single seizure marked a kind of success, but it wasn't a cure for all the personal experiences of having had them. And it doesn't remove the possibility of ever having another seizure. And, you should remember, I was still on the same level of medication I had been on before the surgery. That—the cost of it, and the side-effects of it—had not gone away. In a certain light, what I had actually done was to trade one set of scary experiences for another.

In that sense, there is no cure. There is medication treatment, but that treatment itself has side-effects, and the side-effects can themselves be life-changing major effects. The treatment of surgery has life-changing effects. But there is no cure—not for me. Other patients might feel that it was a cure, but, I am here to tell you that some might not. Some might not ever feel that way. Those two things—treatment and cure—are different.

I climbed back down that peak.

My father came back in the middle of July, bringing some of my mother's ashes. He and I drove up to a cherished place on the other side of the valley. They had come to Colorado on vacation twenty years before, and she had loved that particular spot from Day 1. She loved to stand on that ridge, looking west over the valley, to the gorgeous Mt. Princeton, in the center of a horizon full of 14,000 ft peaks. We sprinkled her ashes there.

Then we flew back to the midwest, where my mother was born, to place a gravestone for her in the cemetery in her tiny hometown. Some old friends of theirs came, too, to have a ceremony for her. We gathered at the headstone, laid down some beautiful flowers, sat around her gravestone and had another wake for her. My father had written a memorial, and he read it for us, even though it hurt to say—again—goodbye.

I know that I've said that—saying goodbye—for several chapters now. Some people think that the word "goodbye" means you say it, turn around, and walk away. I had in the past been pretty good at that. But this time, it was different. There was no *one* goodbye. I was facing it in every direction in four dimensions. There was no place to stand, say it, and then go. I had had to live there, in the goodbye zone, for over a year—and I was still standing there. Do you remember that I had talked about my decision to do the surgery? That once I had made the decision, I wanted to get in a cab, go to the hospital, lie down and do the thing? To say the goodbye to the pre-surgery part of my life? But I couldn't. I had to grit my teeth and do the Long Goodbye. That was part of why I had gone so numb: to withstand it.

At that memorial, we told stories about my mother, about her kindness, her sense of joy in life. About the hard times, but mostly about the good times. We talked about how strong she had been, and how she gave herself to her family. We told each other about some of the times we had spent together, full of humor and pleasure and joy. We had the service she would have wanted: remember the best things in life, and cherish them.

My father and I went back to Colorado, and then made another trip back down to Tucson with some stuff from the house. We drove the Ram, full of furniture and boxes of stuff and dishes, down into the San Juans in southwest Colorado. I wanted to do a little alpine loop in those mountains, since we had the 4wd truck. It would provide us with a spectacular view of the top of the 14ers in that range. Our map told us that it was a 4wd "road." What it didn't tell us is that it was a hairy 4wd "road." I drove my father and our stuff up this hairy trail. We discovered part of the way up that there would be no easy way—in fact, in our truck it was close to impossible—to turn around and go back. The rough patches became rougher. The stuff in the back started to rattle every now and then as we bounced ourselves over larger and larger rocks. The Ram kept on climbing the narrow, twisted, and soon intermittently washed-out "road."

Once again, I felt no fear. I felt sympathy for my father, for he could clearly understand that this was a little more dangerous than we expected. We had some truly scary moments—that is, I knew they were scary, but I didn't feel fear. I drove ahead, knowing, in an abstract sense, that the truck might slide down the washed-out edge and roll headlong down a 500 ft. steep slope. I didn't feel fear for myself—I felt it for my father. But he held on. We managed to accomplish this scary trip, and to sit at the top of the pass, looking at each other, knowing that only adrenaline had gotten us up to the top. As we sat there, I remembered a similar day, long ago, when we had done another jeep trip in the San Juans. My mother had sat in the back seat of the jeep. She had literally flown around a little bit in the back seat of that jeep. And she had laughed at how crazy that trip was. She loved it. She would have loved it this time, too.

But on the way back down, I noticed this little problem. The brakes were making ominous noises, and pulling to one side. When we got back down that pass, we went immediately to the garage to discover that our right front brake had gotten jammed to the left. It would have jammed the wheel itself to the left. The mechanic smiled at us: "you're lucky that didn't happen up there on the drop-off side of the trail!" I still didn't feel fear for me—it was for my father.

In Tucson, we unloaded that pile of stuff from Colorado, amazed that none of it was damaged by that crazy mountain trip. I got in the truck, and headed back north, back to Colorado. I was already planning to hike a 14er there in the San Juans on my way back to Arizona again—we had seen the climb up the south face from the pass in our truck.

When I got back home—in Colorado—I dealt with some more paperwork on the house. I packed some more. I hiked some more. I did some more real estate stuff. And I wrote some more. The summer was coming to an end.

The last week of August I did another four 14ers. On my birthday a friend of mine—a Coloradoan and experienced hiker—hiked with me up Mt. Antero, the peak in the backyard of my mother's house, a companion to her life there. She could never climb it, but she loved it anyway. That hike was more difficult than others because the jeep trail up to the trail head was more difficult than many others. The altitude hit me more than usual, because I was on the verge of my menstrual period. It moved me to contemplate with sadness that fact that in the previous seven years the medication side-effects had eliminated the possibility—in a certain sense—for me to have any children. I was a genetic dead-end. I stopped often to rest, and to remember. I had brought with me a small handful of the rose petals we had sprinkled in the backyard, and on the top ridge, I cast them to the wind for my mother.

September 2, 1999: 47 weeks without a seizure. My mother had died on that day the year before.

The next day we did another 14er. We got a little bit of everything on that hike: rain, sleet, and snow. *Mama, here's another 14er for you.*

On the fifth of September I drove up Waunita pass. I sat there, on another gorgeous Colorado day, and thought about what my mother had said to me long ago, in this very truck, when I had simply lost my ability to carry on: *Amy, think about the beauty of nature, and remember the lupines on Waunita pass.*

My last hike in Colorado was on a clear, crisp, very cold September day. My friend and I climbed a little-known peak with a spectacular view of some of the Sawatch peaks I had done that summer. It was clearly fall. It would soon snow. I sat and contemplated the end of that period in my life and the ever-deepening sense of loss. I had to do another verse of the Long Goodbye Fugue and turn my back on that place.

My father and I settled the details of handing over the house. He came north again to sign some papers, which was, of course, another goodbye for him—this one to the house itself. Shortly before we had to leave, we sold our beloved Ram truck—the symbol of my parents'—and my own—trips high up in the Rockies. We planned the final event—we would leave the house, for the last time, the night before the new owners took possession, and meet them for breakfast in the nearby town to hand over keys. But the day before, after solving some paperwork stuff, we stood in the parking lot of the bank, and he wept. He had needed to sell the house, and he needed to say goodbye, but it hurt. He had wanted to close the door to that life in Colorado, but he stood before that door then and wept. I knew that he couldn't just stand there for the next day—for the coming night—waiting to hand over the keys. I told him how I felt: if he felt the need, he could say goodbye to his life there with my mother—and go. He did.

The next morning I met the buyers for breakfast and told them that my father had left. They were very kind—they understood how he might feel. I handed them the keys to our life in Colorado, wished them all the best, got in my car and drove away. I took my last look at that valley as I drove up Monarch pass. It began to pour. I headed south, down towards the San Juans. On the way there I went up over Wolf Creek Pass, the pass I had come down over back in June on my way to the house. At the pass it was lightly snowing again.

I went down to Ouray, in the San Juans, to case another of the 14ers down there for the last 14er hike. I stood there at the approach to the trailhead I would use the next day, and it began to snow on me. I didn't have the kind of equipment necessary to do that in the snow. The summer was over. The part of my life that Colorado symbolized was over. I had to say goodbye to the summer of living in my mother's house. I stood, there in light snow, facing the next question: what do I do now?

I drove—not home, but to Arizona—for another important reason. My father had planned a trip to see his last elderly relative the year before, but because of my mother's death and my surgery, he had not been able to do it. So I drove down to Tucson, and we went together. I watched my father return again to the last remaining member of his older family, to a home he had left long, long ago. He remembered his youth, and talked about his life with his family, and about the changes he had lived through. We both considered that that might be the last time we would visit his cousin, and that that might be yet another door closing. They both talked about the old days and about Mary, my dad's mother. I sat and communed with them. We took a little trip one day to where they had lived as boys. My dad remembered going to a spring for water, and so we went into the forest to see if we could find it. My dad didn't, but his cousin did. So we sat there awhile, them telling jokes about their lives there. My dad's cousin smiled and said he didn't think he would ever come back to that spring. My heart ached for him.

And then, after we returned, I had to go home. I took the long way home, avoiding the actual arrival back to "reality." I drove north from Tucson to the north rim of the Grand Canyon and stayed in the lodge there, the very last night of the season. I sat on the back porch at sunset, remembering my own youth. Long ago I had traveled the west in a summer. I had taken pictures of my own feet on edges of peaks and hikes and canyons to prove to myself what I had achieved, and to remind myself where I had been. But this time, I sat there on the night before the lodge would close for the winter, and remembered how I felt that time long ago. I had felt that life was all ahead of me, and that I could do whatever I wanted to do. And that I was free. And that the best was still to come.

But now I sat there, at the twilight of that summer, feeling that life was now behind me. Most of the options I had had then were no longer options. There was nothing special about that— everyone, I imagine, hits that moment in which they consider that their youth is over. But I sat there and thought about what I did not have. Many of the options I no longer had had nothing directly to do with a marriage, or children, or a career. They had everything to do with diagnosis, treatment and surgery. They had everything to do with social aspects of those factors. They had everything to do with the fact that some choices a human being must make had gotten reorganized for me. Reorganized by a medical situation, largely out of my control. I sat there, watching the sun go down over the Grand Canyon, considering—again—that my tactics of emotional detachment were self-protection against the feeling of helplessness in the face of it all.

I left before dawn the following morning and went west to Zion Canyon. It was as beautiful as always, awesome in its grandeur and at the edge of winter. The lodge there was full, and there were several big buses in the parking lot full of Japanese tourists. I stood and contemplated another hike I had done there long before—up to Angel's Landing. The hike is steep and complicated, and the last stretch is on the top of a narrow ledge out to the "landing." I had taken a picture of my boots hanging out over that landing. I took in the brisk air and the fallen leaves and contemplated heading up to that ledge one more time. "Don't do it," said the rock climber next to me who could tell what I was thinking. "There are already icy spots in the shade up there now." I flipped an emotional coin on that one, and decided that I had to face the descent down into the sea.

I drove west to Las Vegas, thinking I would stay the night there. I'm not a gambler, so Vegas is just another theme park for me. Because there were several huge conventions, there was no room at the inn, so I headed on west to Barstow. I stayed the last night there, surfing memories of moments from the past. When my parents had driven me home that January after the heart attack, we had come through Barstow. I tried hard to remember the good times, and tried hard not to think about the next few weeks.

The next morning I slid on down the Cajon pass in the brutal wind, into the huge Los Angeles metropolis, completing the return from 14,000 feet back to sea level, like a lemming to the sea.

11 The View from Sea Level

When I walked into my apartment, I didn't exactly feel home again. I felt like I was back in the box. That box had stacked inside all the *issues* of the future. My father had given me the commission on the sale of the house. Because of that, and because my mother had taught me long ago to make sure I put money in the bank, I wasn't in immediate financial need of a job. And I took a walk on the beach, thinking about whether I could seriously do this book. I knew that I wouldn't be able to do it if I got a new job and had to work, once again, at proving that I was good at my job. I considered whether doing this book was just avoidance of the whole new job issue. Maybe it is. But I decided to do it. I started the big timeline, so I had to start to actually read—again—all my old medical and insurance files. I had to start living all of this—in factual medical and financial detail—again.

November 3, 1999: One year after brain surgery.
November 4, 1999: Thirteen months without a seizure.

But I wanted this book to have some larger value. So I sat down to think about larger perspectives of disorders like the one I have. I did some research on national agencies on these issues. I read some of the more general material on epilepsy, and some of the more technical, medical material.

Here's my version of the Big Picture.

- Epilepsy is a disorder, not a disease. It is a disorder of brain function. The symptom of epilepsy is a seizure. A seizure is a storm of electrical activity in the brain.

- There are reported to be 150,000 people in the US with epilepsy, each year, for a total of maybe 2 million Americans. That comes down to something like 5 out of 1000.

- Probably more men than women have this disorder.

- Onset of the disorder can be at birth, childhood, adulthood, or late adulthood.

- A number of causes of epilepsy have been identified. Among them are development before birth, birth injury, head trauma, drugs, diseases—especially those associated with high fever. Some appear to show a genetic pattern.

- But the cause is not ever clearly identified in something like 50% of the cases.

- Late onset of epilepsy, perhaps in early or middle adulthood, is not uncommon. The reasons are unclear.

- Diagnosis of epilepsy is difficult and complicated. The diagnosis is properly made by a neurologist specializing in the disorder. Generally, the neurologist is a member of a team treating seizure disorders.

- There are no easy medical tests for epilepsy. There is no blood test for epilepsy.

- The doctor may never see you have a seizure unless it is induced under special circumstances.

- It's often very difficult to describe a seizure to a doctor or to anyone else.

- Diagnosis and treatment of epilepsy is expensive. The issues of health insurance are complicated. Whether an insurance plan will cover expensive diagnostic and treatment procedures is crucial.

- There is always concern about whether a history of epilepsy—or any kind of chronic medical condition—will affect a possible employer's consideration about hiring.

- People with epilepsy—people with any kind of chronic medical condition—who are employed on contract are at risk with respect to health insurance.

- Some people with epilepsy can control their seizures with medication, but many cannot.

- Psychologically, some people with epilepsy must deal with accepting the idea of being on drugs.

- When medical control has failed, the next step is consideration of neurosurgery, to remove the part of the brain causing the seizures.

- There continues to be unavoidable social prejudice about epilepsy.

- Everybody with epilepsy must figure out how to talk about it.

- Epilepsy changes your life forever.

@ @ @ @ @ @

And I tried for the bigger picture of the sequence of events in my story:

My Insurance Mess

The issues of health-insurance coverage of epilepsy are complicated. Indeed, whether an insurance plan will cover even diagnostic procedures—let alone various treatment procedures—is a major issue.

Diagnosis is expensive. Frequently, during diagnosis, hospitalization for several days is necessary in order to get the best picture of brain activity—an EEG—during a seizure. Use of this equipment and the necessary personnel is costly. The majority of medications for seizure control are expensive and, in my case, the prescriptions called for several doses of multiple medications each day. And then, of course, there is the matter of paying for neurosurgery, if that is indicated. Very few of us could afford to pay for all of this with our own money. Those with health insurance, with the right provisions, are lucky. Those who have no such insurance are not. Even with insurance, this is tricky business.

Currently, in general terms, there are three plans for group health insurance. One is in reality an individual plan, reimbursing costs regardless of where the service is provided, or by whom.

At the other end of the continuum is the HMO. Under an HMO contract, there are restrictions about where the service to be covered is obtained, by whom it will be provided, and how much of the cost will be reimbursed.

Somewhere in the middle is the PPO. I had chosen a PPO insurance plan—a "Preferred Provider Organization"—when I took my job, rather than an "HMO" plan. I did this *before* my diagnosis was made. Because of that, I could be referred to a specialist very soon after it became clear that I needed to see one. In fact, under my PPO, I could have chosen myself to see one, had my records sent to that chosen doctor, and gone to see that physician even without a referral. You can find out from your insurance company which doctors are "preferred providers" so that the cost of seeing them will be less than the cost of seeing a physician who is not in that group. I was extremely fortunate that the specialist to whom I was referred by Student Health, and to whom I returned after graduating, was both associated with my PPO and one of the best in his field in the United States.

I can tell you that even if my insurance had not covered specialists, I would have wanted to get a specialist's diagnosis. The effects of this kind of diagnosis are in a different category from what might be considered normal, typical diseases with normal treatment. I would have chosen to pay for their treatment myself. And again, I recommend that anyone who gets this diagnosis makes sure to see a specialist, even if you have to pay for it yourself. I don't want to be understood as saying that the average doctor who participates in an HMO is not a good doctor. But I know about some patients with complicated diseases who had enormous trouble getting referred to a specialist because of the way their HMO operated. They had to wait a long time for the general practitioner to decide to (or be able to) refer them to a specialist. And they could have no choice of specialists who might be even partially paid for—not to mention totally paid for. If a person chooses to go outside the HMO, he or she might inevitably have to pay the total price.

The specialist I was referred to was directly affiliated with a major university medical school (UCLA). I was glad to have access to the latest developments in treatment and to the results of ongoing research characteristic of a major health center. But it also meant that I got some treatment from younger doctors being trained by the highly experienced specialists. I'm from a university background, and I personally support the value of university research and training. Furthermore, my medical history has been very complicated, and has required highly expert medical treatment. So I am also grateful that my medical insurance allowed me to get that complicated and expensive treatment.

There are some large issues involved in health insurance. When I was young, one of the many things that my mother taught me had to do with what were morally and ethically the right things for human beings to do. One of those things was the issue of health insurance. It is the civilized thing to do to have all of us contribute to a pool of funds because we can't know ahead of time what will happen to any of us, or when, or in many cases what the causes will be.

For instance, no matter who you are, no matter how "healthy" you are, no matter what kind of careful and courteous driver you are, you may get T-boned in a nasty crash one morning and end up in the ER, needing all kinds of expensive equipment and three doctors and four nurses and life-saving surgery. There may not be enough money in your savings account to *begin* to cover that, and it might take the legal system a while to actually establish fault. And what if the driver at fault has nowhere near enough money to pay for your medical needs? What if that driver is "uninsured?"

And what about me?

As I have said, I was hired by a research institute in September, 1992. I had medical insurance because I was hired, and I had the kind of insurance available with my job which has been generally supportive of my medical problems over the past eight years.

My diagnosis was not made until December, 1992. Had it been made before then, the last eight years of my life would have been different. Once you have a "pre-existing condition," you may be—depending on a number of circumstances—in a situation in which you have to pay for it yourself for the rest of your life. So medical insurance which is completely organized around the details of your job career could be a catastrophe.

This problem is not new, and we know that there have been some very specific legal issues directly pertaining to this in the last few years. We need to make sure that insurance is available to people regardless of what kind of job they have and when they sign the contracts for jobs they have. My case is directly relevant: my medical problems were not the effects of any aspect of my life I could possibly have controlled. It's not related to diet, or to drugs, or even to my physical activity. It's not related to my job. No one could have known that I would have this problem in advance of my having it.

I will look for a future employer who can provide some kind of insurance for employees, but it is not necessarily the case that all health insurance would be as good as mine has been the last eight years. That will certainly mean that, in my choice of a possible job, the issue of insurance might *outrank* other considerations for possible jobs.

This fact alters your life, because you can no longer choose jobs based entirely on your strong interest in the work. I know that I am not alone in that situation either, for many people have serious health problems which will affect which jobs they would want to have—and which jobs they will get. Of course some people have other, more important priorities in their choice of jobs anyway. But for those of us who are strongly career-oriented in professional and academic research, there is already a very small market. I wouldn't have many choices anyway, and if these medical and insurance issues affect my possible employment, I may in fact be forced to radically change my career expectations. Once again, this radical life-altering effect of having complicated medical problems is not under my control.

Perhaps even more scary is the never-ending question of whether my medical history will in any way affect a possible employer's consideration about hiring. I told you that the major source I have been using for information on the aspects of epilepsy is an enormous three-volume book recently published: Jerome Engel and Timothy A. Pedley (MD), *Epilepsy: A Comprehensive Textbook,* Lippincott Williams & Williams, 1997. In fact, I have used the CD-Rom of this text, which was published in 1999 and includes revised chapters and updated information. Let me, in this case, provide you with a quotation, instead of ask you to believe that I personally know all about this problem. In the Engel and Pedley book, Chapter 212 is *Legal Concerns and Effective Advocacy Strategies.* Here's what that source says:

> "Even with the passage of laws like the ADA and its international equivalents, epilepsy raises a variety of legal concerns, including employment discrimination, driver licensing requirements, access to appropriate educational services, access to insurance, and even possible arrest for seizure-related behavior. . . . A major public policy priority for the epilepsy community in the US is comprehensive reform of the health care system. The existing mix of public and private insurance in the US has failed to provide insurance to an estimated 39 million Americans, including many individuals with chronic health conditions such as epilepsy. Private health insurance is increasingly priced beyond the reach of individuals and businesses. Benefits for individual consumers are being trimmed in an attempt to control costs, yet the costs of health care continue to skyrocket. The greatest flaw in the existing health care delivery system in the US is the fact that those individuals who most need access to health care—people with

> chronic health conditions or disabilities—are the most likely to be denied health insurance."

I understand that, technically, a prospective employer is not allowed to ask you about insurance. But I also know—from experience—that information can travel around certain professions, especially ones that are small markets. My institute, for example, indemnifies its own insurance—that means that it hires a company to process all the paperwork, but it pays all of the costs technically "covered" by the insurance company. And, of course, that situation puts employees immediately into the danger zone of information being just down the hall from your colleagues. Technically, and legally, your colleagues are not supposed to know this kind of information, but my personal experience is that this kind of information will travel.

There are two general problems here. One, then, is whether a possible employer would hesitate to hire a person with a record of needing serious, expensive, long-term medical insurance coverage. I understand why a prospective employer might need to think about that. This is one of the major aspects of the fact that the United States does not have federal or state-funded medical insurance. Indeed, my last boss was not an American, but from a European country which has federally-funded insurance. It insures all of its citizens, whether they are employed or not. In that case, no employer has to deal with these issues. My boss expressed to me his strong sympathy for that very aspect of my medical problems, but nonetheless I will have to deal with this issue.

The other problem is whether this diagnosis might personally affect a possible employer's decision. If a prospective employer were to know what the diagnosis was—epilepsy—would that employer personally be afraid of, or bothered by the idea of having an epileptic person around the office? Would that employer feel like he or she or the present employees would be negatively affected by that all by itself? Would they worry that that person would be having seizures right there in the office? And that the staff would have to do something? Would they worry that *other* employees, present or possible, might feel negatively about that environment? Or would he or she only be concerned about the financial implications for health insurance? And would the employer decide that all the other issues regarding who to select as a possible employee are important enough, and serious enough, that he or she would not want to have to consider this as yet another factor?

So will this medical condition, and its effects, seriously determine my career? This is another thing I will probably never know for sure. I lack confidence that my medical history had nothing to do with my former employer's decisions, and I lack confidence that it will have nothing to do with a future employer's decisions. But I can't control that. The lesson is that if you have any kind of serious medical problem like the one I have, it will alter your life in many, many ways.

If not covered by a group health insurance plan, then you must consider an individual plan. Recently I made a call to inquire about such a plan. I knew it was going to be rough. I had thought a lot about the problem because it had been a major factor in my decision for the surgery. It's not as though it was a total surprise. I called. I gave the shortest series of necessary medical tidbits I could manage. I felt the broker's real sympathy, but I wrote down the awesome quoted prices for the relevant category. She was very nice. She said she would send me some more information. I hung up. I got up. I went to the bathroom. For the first time in twenty years, I threw up in raw emotion, the celebration of my ability to foresee the future.

Because of my medical history, I'm in the "High Risk" category. The insurance agent—an independent one—recommended Blue Cross of California for individual health insurance. My choice would be between two kinds of policies:

$395 per month which has a $2,000 yearly deductible.

$495 per month with a regular $40 co-pay and then a 35% co-pay of up to a $4,000 yearly deductible. The bottom line, then, is that I would pay *at least* $6,000 per year.

Because of the *Health Insurance Portability and Accountability Act* (HIPAA), which went into law on August 21, 1996, I can, at least, stay insured—in some manner—for the medical situation I am in and the treatments I will need. But I was coping from 1992 to 1996 with the "pre-existing condition" nightmare. Now, I am coping with the $6,000+ a year nightmare.

Furthermore, I have to find out if my current doctors will be covered by my plan. If they are not, I will face a horrendous choice. I will pay at least 30% of their fees—and then 100% of what they charge beyond what is "Customary and Reasonable." Or I will have to find doctors covered by my plan who are capable of dealing with my complicated medical history. That itself involves some complicated issues: How do I do that? How can I find that out? Let me tell you it isn't easy. I would ask my current doctors for recommendations, but they might or might not be comfortable with making them. And even if—in the best case scenario—I can find a set of doctors who are as good as the ones I now have, I will face the problem of describing my condition and my history—going on eight years now—again.

And since I need more than one doctor, I will be doing a lot of "agains." I will get a degree in "déjà vu all over again." I will have to deal with the fact that a new doctor might very well want to retest and reconsider my present condition and appropriate treatment. And I emphasize the fact that I am not criticizing that—it can be the hallmark of truly good, careful doctors. I have already paid part of the costs of many of my highly expensive tests, but I might find myself in the position of doing some of them again, and paying part of the cost myself again.

The problem, for me and for other people in a similar position, will remain.

My Drug Wars

Here's another big, fat problem. I'm on drugs. I'm *still* on drugs. When I think about the personal cost of the surgery, I make myself remember the Drug Wars.

The drugs—the medications—I've been on are the kind that alter human brain function. They impede one of the oldest structures in your brain—the cerebellum. They affect the simplest things: your sense of balance, your ability to walk straight, to keep yourself from bumping into walls and tables and chairs. That's why they make you look like you're drunk, and, in a sense, you are. But you won't "party hearty" on this stuff. Most of them are designed to suppress higher levels of brain function, aka "cognition," aka your ability to think. These drugs are designed expressly to alter the nature—the function—of your "inside" world. They can alter the very nature of your personal experience of the "outside" world. They can alter—many of them are known to alter—your behavior. They can alter your *self*.

This stands, for me, like a painful paradox of this diagnosis and treatment. I have checked into Camp Medrugs and I can never go home again. And the realization of that was beyond depressing for me. It became despair. I had to struggle with that. I still have to struggle with that. My loved ones have struggled with that.

The diagnosis brings you treatment, but the treatment brings you trouble. And that kind of trouble is a major factor in life as an epileptic. Actually, I should say that it *can* be a major factor, because maybe some people adjust easily and well. Furthermore, some medications are known to have much milder effects on the sense of depression than others. I'm telling you about this because it's a crucial factor in my case. And it's a crucial factor in the bigger picture of the effects of having this disorder—the drugs don't *cure* you. What you end up doing is trading the effects of the seizures for the effects of the meds.

Here's another big, messy problem. How much should

you know about the side-effects? You can make the argument—I have—that your doctor should tell you what the side-effects might be so that you will be ready to deal with them. But there are multiple factors to this situation. One of them is a legal one. The physician may want to be careful to avoid being sued for not informing you of the possible consequences of the drugs. Physicians are in a complicated legal and ethical position—we want them to make decisions about how to treat us—and we want them to have access to whatever drugs (or treatments) they think will help us. We want and need their careful but caring decisions. And yet, sometimes it seems like we want to hold them legally responsible if the treatment a) doesn't work or b) is at all related to undesirable—even illegal—behaviors. And, of course, that issue is a complicated mess all by itself. How do you prove that this treatment actually caused that behavior? I'm not trying to address this set of problems—I'm only mentioning it because it is part of the larger problem. It can be a reason why the physician should tell you about the possible side-effects.

But there are also reasons why physicians might decide not to. I said before that a doctor should pay as much attention as possible to what your symptoms are. I mentioned that they need to—and mine always have—pay careful attention to what is actually happening to you, and not just decide that you have this or that syndrome, and just treat you for all the possible aspects of that. You want them to be careful to treat you as well as possible. And, in my opinion, from my background, I know that the more careful they are to pay attention to actual details, the more they can learn about the disorder itself. Furthermore, the better they will be at treating you, not just the abstract disorder.

But there's this muddy problem here, because if you are told that you might have the following three side-effects—x, y and z—does that mean that you go actually looking for those side-effects? Paying careful attention to whether you have them? Assuming, somehow, that you probably will have them, and so trying to understand the way you feel on those meds—the effects of taking them—by mixing in what you have been told you might feel? Will you end up interpreting other aspects of your life, or of how you feel, as side-effects of the medications, when they are not actually caused by the chemistry of your medications? Will we really know whether we are doing that?

So, there is also a very good reason why your neurologist might decide that it is better to not tell you lots of details about all the possible side-effects of the medications. Not telling you will increase the chances that you will tell him or her about only the side-effects you actually have. Once again, I repeat what might be the chorus of the theme song about careful medical treatment: detail, detail, detail. We all learn more, and, consequently, will be treated better, if we—and, more importantly, they—can find out what is actually happening. Another aspect of that problem has to do with how your doctor will ask you about your experiences. They have to be careful not to suggest various symptoms to you, because that might give you the suggestion that they are looking for that symptom, and that they expect that you will have it. Patients might be moved to try to interpret their own experience as a case of this or that side effect.

So here is one of the messy paradoxes: on the one hand you should know about the possible effects of your medications, but on the other hand you shouldn't know that you might have them before you try to report what you do have. I am a patient who understands this problem.

But, I am the kind of patient who wants to know what kind of chemical stuff I am taking. On the one hand, that is just the way I have always been—intellectually curious. On the other hand, it may be a defense against the sense that I would never understand what all this stuff is about—that I am a *victim*. I would swear to the fact—I am standing here swearing—that my medications have indeed had serious side-effects on me. Telling you about that is a crucial part of the story of why I did what I did. It is a major part of the importance of this story to a larger public: the consequences of both the disorder and of the treatment are life-altering.

I have—in the last eight years—been on ten major medications for seizures: Tegretol©, Dilantin©, Ativan©, Mysoline©, Neurontin©, Mesantoin©, Valium©, Lamictal©, Klonopin©, and Topomax©. They all have side-effects. I've taken another two prescription medications for problems which might be side-effects of *those* side-effects—especially my chronic low white count: Acyclovir© and Metrogel©. I am still on—I will always be on—yet another medication for the cardiac infarction: aspirin. The infarction, my doctors tell me, was probably a side-effect of the seizure medications (since there seems to be no other explanation). Aspirin is my medication number thirteen. Is thirteen a lucky number?

And I'm not counting here the vitamins and the folic acid and the antacids and the ibuprofen, even though they are related to the side-effects of the drugs.

As time went on, as I went through—as I "broke through"— that big list of medications, I started to do the following things. I started to actually read the descriptions about the medications always provided with the initial bottle of meds. They provide lots of information, much of which is incomprehensible unless you have a degree in pharmacology. I'm not complaining about that—it's probably directly related to legal issues. But some of that information is on "possible side-effects." And so I read that stuff. As time went on, I would sometimes go to the Biomedical Library at UCLA and look up information on these medications—or I would get on the web to find out any information on these medications. And I would spend some time—some serious, careful, analytic time—trying to decide whether I truly had side-effects number three, seven, eight, nine and fifteen. I would look up medical terms used in the official information. I would sit there and try to analyze whether this or that "problem" in my life might be the consequences of side-effects. But I would also sit there and wonder—seriously—about exactly what I am now talking to you about: can I truly judge this, or am I now going to reinterpret my everyday life and blame everything on drugs?

Then I would sit there, look out the window, and contemplate the fact that I would never—I could never—know that. And my depression—the futility of even knowing this stuff—would wash over me again. And then, on another good day, I would go the BioMed library and start to read about epilepsy itself. I wasn't reading personal accounts of the experience—like the one you are now reading—I was reading medical journals and textbooks on this disorder. I would sit and read medical reports on other patients' experiences, and find myself wondering whether I'm being influenced by those descriptions. But I have tried to be very careful about that.

I made a "discovery" at a certain point reading about the aspects of the kind of seizures I have—a description of a certain feeling which seems to be common in some patients. Reading about that struck me very strongly, because it provoked a kind of *sensory* memory of that feeling in my seizures. But I wondered whether I hadn't ever told Dr. D-E about that, or had but didn't remember doing so. I thought it would be wise to tell him, but I thought it would also be wise to say that I "remembered" it when I read about it. Maybe that provides some more information on my case. But then, when I did that, I felt the need to try for some evidence that I wasn't just "selecting" some more symptoms. I wrote down that I had read about other features of my own kind of epilepsy which I am confidant that I have never had. I was trying to assure him that just reading about symptoms doesn't move me to "collect" them.

And—reading these kinds of textbooks and research articles—I found out some very interesting things. It seems that some patients present "problems" which are similar to, or seem to be cases of, epileptic seizures, even though careful medical and psychological analysis may be able to determine that they are not, in fact, epileptic seizures. For example, there are patients who deliberately simulate epileptic seizures, but who are not epileptic. They are considered to have what my textbook—Engel and Pedley—calls "factitious disorder": a conscious effort to assume the role of a sick person. Some may become very clever at simulating the disorder, and deny that they are being deceptive. They may even commit considerable physical damage to themselves and check in to an emergency room to "fake" major seizures. That process is referred to as a Münchausen's syndrome.

Others who present similar aspects seem to have external incentives to get the diagnosis—with respect to insurance or employment or legal suits, among others. They are categorized as "malingering."

So here's *my* problem right here, right now. Has my education in the nature of the disorder—including the complicated issues related to deception—and in the side-effects of the drugs put me in a position where I raise doubts in the doctors' minds as to whether I am either mistakenly thinking I have x or y side-effect, or, even worse, purposely making up this or that symptom? I don't know whether they wonder about that. I don't know whether they should tell me if they do wonder about that.

So I see the problem. Should the physicians trust my account of my own experiences? Should *I* trust my account?

And yet, my neurologist needs my account of the side-effects. The obvious aspect of asking for that is to see if the treatment is actually working—to see if it outranks the side-effects. And, as I have said before, another aspect of getting that kind of information from each patient is that even if it doesn't help the patient who suffers from it, it might help the larger research and treatment problem, which will benefit other patients. So, because I know that—because of my intellectual research background and my father's direct connection with medical treatment and research—I am certainly willing to give whatever information I can.

And yet, am I giving the impression that I psychologically want to give lots of details—that I emotionally need to get attention? Even worse, do I give the impression that I trot down to the library and read up on a bunch of side-effects in order to get even more attention? And here's the Big Problem: I have trotted down to libraries to find out about side-effects. It was—and still is—part of my normal tendencies to be intellectual anyway. And it could be interpreted as a kind of logical defense against the experiences. The paradox there is that learning about epilepsy and treatment might seem to look like the exact performance of one of the syndromes of my kind of epilepsy. Can I say that that is not the case? Will the doctors believe me? Should they believe me?

11 THE VIEW FROM SEA LEVEL | 341

So what can I do about that?

And what can my physicians do about that?

I know it's a problem, and the fact *that* I know it's a problem is a problem . . . .

Here is some of the complicated and ugly truth about the side-effects of the medications I've been on. Whenever I use quotation marks I'm quoting from the comprehensive textbook: Jerome Engel and Timothy A. Pedley, eds. *Epilepsy: A Comprehensive Textbook.* 3 volumes. Lippincott Williams & Wilkins Publishers, 1997, 1999.

Drug #1. Tegretol©. Its generic name is carbamazepine. It is "the most widely prescribed antiepileptic drug for the treatment of partial and generalized tonic-clonic seizures." In the list of known side-effects: weight gain, sedation, gait problems, mood change, tremor, nausea, gas, cardiac arrhythmia.

Here are some aspects of living with these drugs. I can't blame this medication for trouble controlling my weight—I've had that problem all my life. In my case, I started to lose weight immediately after starting on this drug. But, I started taking this stuff the day after my horrendous diagnosis. In the next few weeks full of horrendous events, I was fatigued, scared, and in shock. So, I don't know, and I'll never know whether my weight loss had anything to do with the basic biochemistry of this drug. But if this drug affected the existing problems, that also is a negative side-effect. 42% of people on this medication reported "sedation"—I had that. It hit me *hard*. I had "gait problems"—I started to stumble and bump into things. 24% of the people in the study discussed in this textbook reported "mood change." I certainly had that! But, my mood had everything to do with the emotional effects of the diagnosis and all the consequences. So, can I "blame" the medication? No. But was it a factor? Maybe. It might have made my depression about everything else worse.

Other side-effects: tremor—I didn't have that. "The most common side-effect of this drug is nausea or gas." I had one of those—the stomach gas problem—but not the other.

Because of the chemical nature of this medication, cardiac arrthythmias—irregular heart beat—can occur. I have cardiac arrthythmia, but my cardiologist specialist classified it—after the infarction—as "benign"—non-threatening. But the ruling out of other possible known causes contributed to my neurologist's suspicion that it was a side-effect of Tegretol©. That arrythmia had never shown up prior to my infarction.

"The other major life-threatening complication associated with carbamazepine use is aplastic anemia or agranulocytosis. This adverse effect delayed approval of carbamazepine in the United States by the Food and Drug Administration for some years." You may recall that I told you that my blood tests taken right after I started on this drug confirmed that my white-blood cell count was consistently going down.

"Long-term surveillance of serious idiosyncratic toxicity suggests an incidence of aplastic anemia of approximately one case in 200,000 exposures to carbamazepine." So, this side-effect is very, very rare. But, because my neurologist was being very, very careful, I was tapered off Tegretol© right away, and put on the next "front line" medication.

Drug #2: Dilantin© (phenytoin). "The usual dose-dependent side effects of PHT [phenytoin] include nystagmus, ataxia, and drowsiness." "Nystagmus" has to do with uncontrolled eye-movements. I didn't have that on Dilantin©. "Ataxia" "involves station and gait more than fine motor movements." I had that, but it was minor. I don't know if anybody else noticed it. I noticed it. And I noticed it before I read about it. "Drowsiness." We all know exactly what that is. That, I had. All the time. "Nausea, vomiting, or constipation." I often felt a very slight nausea. I often had an upset stomach. I had constipation. I followed the prescriptive advice to take it with meals. I planned my meals on the schedule of the drugs.

"Enlargement of the lips and nose, coarsening of the facial features, hirsutism, chloasma-like pigmentation, and acne all have been reported to occur in patients on chronic PHT therapy." My lips aren't any larger than they were. I think my nose is thicker, but, here we are at that mess again. The only way to actually know that is to measure, precisely, the before and after condition. I didn't do that. "Hirsutisim"—hairy. I have some odd facial hairs which showed up in the last seven years, but they might have just done that anyway. I can't judge that. "Chloasma-like pigmentation"—skin pigmentation marks. Those I have. I have brown spots that showed up that first year. But, once again, it would be hard to eliminate any other possible causes. But these are in some odd places. I'm extremely careful when I go out in the sun. I gook up with sunscreen and wear hats and even gloves. But I have some odd pale brown patches on my face and neck. They might be a side-effect of this drug. "Acne." I have that. But, I have had that all my adult life, so, I'm not blaming that on this drug. The drug, though, might affect that somehow. But that does not, for me, rank as a problematic side-effect.

"Overgrowth of gums." I told my dentist about that. He knew the problem from other patients on this drug, and he watched for it. I developed that side-effect, but it wasn't terribly serious.

"Aplastic anemia and leukopenia" have been connected to Dilantin©. "Aplastic anemia" is the same dangerous decline of white blood cell count I had on Tegretol©. *No, wait*—there is an example of the problem with my doing what I'm doing—reading technical information. I need to be more precise. So: aplastic anemia is a condition related to the first drug I was on, Tegretol©. It is a possible but rare side-effect. (And by the way: there is no known antidote.) My neurologists considered that I might have that side-effect because my white cell count kept going down, or staying down. They had taken me off that first medication—Tegretol©—for that reason. This information, though, indicates that that kind of condition, aplastic anemia, may also occur in conjunction with this drug, Dilantin©.

Leukopenia is also low white count, but not as threatening as aplastic anemia.

It didn't stop the seizures.

The Big Question—on Dilantin©—was my continued low blood cell counts which might actually indicate a very rare but life-threatening response. My neurologist noted that in his files and recommended the hematology workup to try to distinguish whether I was having this more serious response. And, you may recall, he recommended that I test for HIV, since that might be related to my blood cell count. I'm not criticizing his having done that, but can you imagine what that made me feel at that point in time. Hell, at *any* point in time? (At the advice of my GP, I didn't need to do that yet.)

They decided to do the bone-marrow biopsy on me in June, 1993, while I was on this drug, to determine whether this problem was dangerous. Right after the biopsy, they started to taper me—carefully—off Dilantin©, and onto another anti-convulsant.

Drug #3: Ativan© (lorazepam). Drowsiness is the most frequently reported adverse effect. Of course, it was prescribed for me for the express purpose of making me drowsy and putting me to sleep, in particular when I was travelling. Other reported adverse effects are dizziness, weakness, fatigue and lethargy—I had those. Ataxia—difficulty speaking. I had that. Disorientation, anterograde amnesia, nausea, change in appetite, change in weight: I took it only when I traveled, or when I needed to be sure that I slept, so I don't remember having any of that. Blurred vision and diplopia, psychomotor agitation, sleep disturbance, vomiting, sexual disturbance—I don't think I had any of that. Headache—yes. Skin rashes, gastrointestinal, ear, nose and throat, musculoskeletal and respiratory disturbances—I don't think so. Mental confusion, slurred speech, oversedation—I don't exactly know how to measure "oversedation" as opposed to "normal" sedation, but I can tell you it knocked me out close to right away. Depression. Yes. Oh yes.

Drug #4: Mysoline© (primadone). Primadone is not strictly speaking a barbiturate. But, as my textbook states, it is partially transformed into one—phenobarbital—in your body. So, it shares all the side effects of phenobarbital. The side effects usually include "drowsiness, dizziness, ataxia, nausea, and vomiting." "Drowsiness" is an incredible understatement. We're talking barely awake. For me: Dizziness—yes. Ataxia (trouble speaking)—I think so. Nausea—borderline. Vomiting, no. Another source of information on Mysoline©: mental dullness and stupor. I felt those side effects so strongly. I felt like I had been hit by a train and then thrown under water.

Let me quote you some more medical research on this drug: "Before sedation is obvious to the outsider, it may slow the patient's intellectual processes and possibly cause difficulty in thinking and learning." Yes, it may. Yes it did. Yes it would never not do that. For someone with my education and my training, the side-effects of this drug were arguably the worst experiences of my life.

"Secondary behavioral disturbances may follow these difficulties, in part determined by the subject's underlying personality traits. Some patients become irritable, short-tempered, and aggressive . . . ."—I will remember all my life how I felt, and how I acted, on this drug those months before checking in for the first in-patient EEG in 1995—". . . whereas others become morose and depressed when treated with phenobarbital"—the second moment I will remember all my life is how I felt sitting in the backseat of my father's truck that day in Colorado thinking, and finally talking, about suicide. The two years I spent under this drug are neck and neck with the shock of that first six months after the diagnosis. On this drug, I felt like my brain had gone under. Despair overtook depression. And the seizures kept on breaking through.

Drug #5: Neurontin© (gabapentin). Drowsiness, dizziness, fatigue—yes. But I already had these side effects when I started on

Neurontin© in addition to my other meds. Double vision, tremor—no. Unsteadiness when walking—yes. Fluid retention (edema) in the hands, feet, or lower legs—yes. Skin rash—no. Dryness of mouth or throat, frequent urination, headache, indigestion—yes. Low blood pressure, nausea, noise in ears, runny nose, slurred speech—no. Diarrhea, vomiting, weakness or loss of strength—no. Weight gain—maybe. Trouble in thinking, trouble in sleeping—yes, *Big Time* trouble. Neurontin© didn't seem to affect my seizures at all, so my neurologist took me off it.

Drug #6: Mesantoin© (mephenytoin). The advantages of mephenytoin over phenytoin—Dilantin©—"are offset by a greater incidence of drowsiness, serious dermatitis, agranulocytosis, aplastic anemia, and hepatitis"—that is drowsiness, skin problems, blood cell anemia, and kidney damage. "The incidence of fatalities and serious side effects appears to be greater with mephenytoin than with phenobarbitol. . . . Mephenytoin is indicated only for patients with severe seizure disorders resistant to less toxic drugs." For me? Fatigue, drowsiness, very low white count, and depression. For a variation of the long series of side-effects that anti-seizure drugs had given me, Mesantoin© also gave me sore joints—arthritis. It suppressed my seizures better than the other drugs, but not entirely. The physiological risk was not worth it. When I had checked into that first EEG, I was status quo angry on the Mysoline©. When I went cold turkey on that stuff, I swam back up to the surface of my pre-diagnosed, pre-drugged life. I stayed there—chained to a bed—for a few days. When I checked out—on Mesantoin©—I dove back down to fatigue and depression and despair.

Drug #7: Valium© (diazepam). I took this stuff to sleep on my work travel trips—not continuously. Its side effects on me: ataxia, incoordination and dizziness. Drowsiness is technically a side-effect, but for me it was the main reason why I took it.

Other side-effects I did have: drooling and swallowing difficulties. Other side effects I don't think I had: vision problems and behavioral abnormalities (hyperactivity, restlessness, short attention span, irritability, disruptiveness, aggressiveness).

Drug #8: Lamictal© (lamotrigine). The most threatening side effect of this stuff is a serious skin rash. Some possible kinds of skin rash on this drug carry a high mortality rate—that is, they can be fatal. You may recall that my neurologist warned me explicitly about that, and that's why I went immediately to urgent care that one morning with what looked like a rash. It wasn't, though. The most common side-effects are: dizziness, headache, diplopia [like double vision]—I had those. Somnolence—not only did I not have that one, I had the more rare, opposite side-effect: difficulty sleeping, and constant waking episodes at night.

The major advantage of the side-effects of lamotrigine is that it seems to have a positive effect on "cognition and mood"—I swam back to the surface on lamotrigine. I felt better, but better than major-league downers doesn't mean feeling good. I felt nervous and jittery. Another noted side-effect is that lamotrigine "may produce excessive arousal, overactivity, or euphoria in some patients." Lamotrigine, for me, was an almost break-even: I was dizzy, I had a constant low-grade headache, and I had slightly blurred vision. I didn't make it all the way to euphoria, but I simply felt better. And my sexuality came back full force.

But it didn't stop my seizures.

Drug # 9: Klonopin© (clonazepam). "Clonazepam is useful in all forms of generalized seizures; however, it has a number of unpleasant side effects and also is associated with the development of tolerance, which greatly reduces its desirability." I would bruise easily on that stuff. I would slur my speech sometimes. I would be drowsy right after I took it, but then I would get *tired but wired* because I took it with the Lamotrigine. It didn't stop the seizures.

Drug #10: Topomax© (topiromate). "The most frequently reported treatment-related emergent adverse events in these trials are central nervous system-related problems, upper respiratory infection, injuries, and weight loss." For me, the worst was that this drug, even when I was still tapering up on the amount of the dosage, made me slur my speech constantly. I don't think I even arrived at the other side-effects, because I couldn't stand that one. And, of course, it didn't suppress my seizures.

The common denominator for these medications: drowsiness, aka reduced mental function. Sometimes slight, sometimes horrendous.

Can you imagine what that would be like for someone whose mental functions—and high verbal intelligence—were a central part of her job and of her very personality?

Can you imagine how knowing that—knowing that I would stay on meds the rest of my life—made me feel?

My Third Choice

From the Engel and Pedley book:

> Some patients with syndromes such as mesial temporal lobe epilepsy . . . are not helped by continued therapy with second-line drugs or combinations of drugs. If patients with evidence of these syndromes continue to have seizures after treatment with one or two major drugs, improvement is not likely to occur, even with

> promising new drugs, and surgery should be considered. . . . It is essential to keep in mind that seizures have a deleterious effect on the brain. High numbers of seizures over time can result in an irreversibly reduced mental capacity.
>
> Furthermore, the current drugs for the symptomatic suppression of seizures are effective in fewer than 65% of patients.
>
> All current antiepileptic drugs act nonspecifically to alter excitatory or inhibitory influences or reduce neuronal synchronization, processes that are critical to normal cerebral function . . . . It is not surprising, therefore, that pharmacotherapy can be associated with sedation, cognitive impairment, and more specific psychiatric disturbances.
>
> Antiepileptic drugs often alter the mood adversely, with, as already noted, PB [phenobarbital] and possibly vigabatrin specifically being implicated in depression. In addition, the longer the duration of epilepsy, the more severe the depression.
>
> Finally, temporal lobe epilepsy (TLE) and complex partial seizures (CPS) seem to be specifically implicated in depression.

I am a case of that.
Neurosurgery was the only other treatment. Period.
Because of my contract job, I had to make that choice at gunpoint.

The cost is high. It took me a while to learn more of the details of the surgery itself, in part because I couldn't process much of the explanations, but also in part because the explanations were not simple. The initial plan for the resection was to remove the smallest possible amount of tissue, but the mapping of parts of my brain which produced seizures indicated that more tissue needed to be removed. So it was. It is difficult to predict with precision what the "side-effects" of a resection will be, and I was a unique patient because of my many languages. Furthermore, it takes at least a year for the brain to "recover," and we don't truly know whether and how a brain is capable of "recovering" from this kind of experience. And yet, because of the volume of resected tissue, the "side-effects" for me probably are more than originally planned.

And so I also deal with that.

I don't know if I have anything even resembling advice for anybody else. It is certainly true that a major part of my decision was financial—directly related to the status of my job. It is certainly true that part of it was the failure of the meds to stop my seizures, and therefore to control the kind of brain damage which the seizures produce. But it is also true that part of it was a naked response to my sense of despair that things could ever change given the state I was in—and the track I was on.

I decided to go under the knife, not because I was so hopeful that it would solve all the problems, but because I was so close to the edge that I cared very little what the personal cost would be. It would, at the very least, provide the possibility that my life could somehow be different.

So, this chapter is an essay about a multiple-choice exam. My choices were:

a) life-long status quo
b) check-out
c) brain surgery

Select one—and only one—option.

12 On the Beach

So here I am, again, on the beach, looking out to sea. My companion, Depression, is not far away. Sometimes right next to me, looking out to sea. Sometimes walking down the beach, a little ways away, not talking to me, just on the borderline of my visual field.

I'm trying very, very hard to take stock of my life.

A little while ago I went to see a new personal doctor, Dr. K$_2$, who had been recommended by my surgeon. I had great anxiety about having to go through my medical history again for any new doctor. I had gotten to the point where I didn't want to talk about all this medical stuff again. And I didn't want to talk about the history of my condition—actually, conditions—again. But I eventually talked myself into going to get a doctor for the other basic medical procedures that normal people do.

When I go for appointments now with her she asks me to describe How I Am. Of course, she's seen some of my records, and had been recommended precisely because she'd be good at dealing with a complicated case like mine. And of course, she's doing exactly what good doctors—I think—should do, which is to stay close to the detail of your history and to how you feel. When I scheduled my first appointment with her, I brought a list—printed off my own computer—of major events and dates in my medical history.

There are two reasons for that. The first is that the Medical History form that a physician's staff will give you to provide helpful information is usually one double-sided sheet with tiny check-boxes and two-inch long "detail" lines. I understand why—I'm not criticizing that. But there ain't no way I can give my medical history on two-inch long lines. At least, I can't do it. Maybe that's just me, but I doubt it.

The second reason is that I could give my new physician the Big Picture a lot faster than she would get it browsing through my big fat medical file. Of course, I know that she will go through the big file. I want her to. She will see complicated details that I do not. It's just that now, when I get asked any medical question at all I hesitate to answer. And I don't mean by that that I am considering not answering, or that I don't like the question. I mean that I sit there trying to think of whether I should try for a yes or no, or "give a provisional answer based on the fact that I might have some complicated issues directly related to the importance of that question . . . ." and blather on. I wonder if I'm giving the impression that I have "created"—on my computer!—my "condition." It's another *deer in the headlights* moment for me. But that's a paradox: it isn't that I'm afraid of the physician or the treatment.

When she did the first physical exam for me, she looked at my inner elbows and smiled, and said: "Needle tracks!" I smiled back, considering the irony of it all. Yes, I had had lots of needles stuck in my arms over the years, but it wasn't—with a few exceptions—to pump stuff in, it was to draw blood out! Quarts of blood, by now. I sat there, remembering that question in the cardiology ward long ago: "Did you take cocaine?" I was hoping that my doctor here didn't think she was looking at a junkie.

But she listened to my not-entirely-clear answers to her questions, and gave me confidence that she can see the bigger picture. And she gives me confidence that she can understand some aspects of how difficult those moments can be for me. Furthermore, she assures me that she will try to be an advocate for me with respect to medical issues and treatment. I have confidence in her, and I'm very grateful that she agreed to take me as a patient.

I have the sense that I should give as much information as I can because I now feel that any aspect of my physical life might be directly related to some kind of medical cause or effect. I have the sense that my disorder is related to lots of other factors. And for the general internal medicine physician to have the Big Picture means that she should be able to look at everything. And for her to know everything requires that I try to mention every little thing that might be conceivably wrong with me. Her specialty is to see that larger picture which my other specialists don't look for. But I'm not criticizing them, either, for their specialty concentration is why you need them. And, knowing that I should give all the information that I can, I make myself a list of "items" to mention when I see her.

So, I find myself sitting there in this doctor's office rattling off this list of probably unrelated details of How I Am. And then I rattle off the list of unimportant, innocuous details of my physical life. If I'm really on the ball, I can achieve The List. If I'm not, items on the list start to get footnotes, as it were. I start to core-dump details. I start to explain *why* I am core-dumping, and I sail away into a spider-web of multiplex conditional assertions.

And so I feel silly. I sit there and consider the paradox of it all: I'm acting like a hypochondriac, who enjoys thinking that she has forty-seven serious medical conditions, or who is telling her doctors about fictitious stuff for the express purpose of getting their medical sympathy. But my more-or-less-detached-intellectual-presentation of all of that is in part a technique of my personal, analytical response to all of that.

And there's another factor here. Some medical studies of the kind of epilepsy I have seem to indicate that some people with left temporal lobe epilepsy typically give very lengthy responses to questions, with many unnecessary details and asides. So sometimes I sit there wondering if the fact that I'm sitting there wondering is the symptom itself. So I ask myself whether I am performing this disorder. But then I answer to myself: I'm not just making this stuff up! My life is complicated and has been full of lots of problems. And then I ask myself again: is the fact that I'm sitting here having this discussion with myself a symptom? And, on a difficult day, I'm thinking this stuff while I'm trying to answer a question.

And there's yet another factor. I'm not as good at presentation of details as I was before my surgery. I have to go looking for words. I have to stall my sentences sometimes hoping for the arrival of the noun I'm trying for. And sometimes, when I can't get it "on time," I have to try to go around that noun—to explain what I would mean by the noun if I could produce it—or reorganize the sentence I started with. I sit there making complicated sentences which seem to indicate that I don't know what I mean. I blather on wondering if I look like I want to blather.

The actual truth—for me—is that I would give my life to go back to the point where I had none of these problems. But there's no going back. And going forward—for me—is trying to find out more about what my body is doing. My curiosity about that might be interpreted as another known side-effect of my disorder. I'm not saying that all the patients with this disorder will have this particular problem, but I've got it in spades. For I can emotionally deal better with the scientifically interesting aspects of this problem or that problem, but I seem close to unable to give a general description of how I am. How I—my self—am. My crazy response to this question won't be a surprise to you, for you are now in Chapter 12 of *How I Am*.

Dr. F and Dr. D-E had told me that recovery from the cognitive effects of the surgery might take a year. But, they said, whatever changes you have in your mental functions after a year will, in all probability, be permanent.

I had recovered from the surgery, but I had not entirely returned to my pre-surgery thought patterns or verbal abilities—I know that I will never return to them. In fact, I don't think—simply think—the way I formerly thought. I have to stop and think about—even search for—which word to use, and whether, even, that word is correct. I can just make random lists of words easily and quickly. But when I "search" for a word to use for a particular expression, several will "pop up." But, not only are they not the word I need, sometimes they are constructions of some of the syllables of the word I am looking for. For example: once I was trying to remember a word about mental processes from an article I had read. I started with "gameme." No, that's not it. "Genome?" Nope. Then I went from "genome" somehow to "endgame"—still not the word I'm trying to remember. But from "endgame" I got to the one I wanted: "engram."

One day I was talking to a friend in the hallway, but had to blow my nose. I started to say to him, "just because I'm blowing my nose, doesn't mean that I'm . . . . ??" I stopped cold. That I'm what? I knew the content of what I wanted to say: don't worry, this isn't the kind of nose problem which might give you a cold. I knew there was a word which named that problem. But what was it? I stood there stunned. Various words would occur to me: congested, computer, comissure. But I couldn't get to what I meant: contagious.

I would see a drawn figure on an advertisement—a figure playing a kind of flute, looking as though he were dancing. I tried to name it. I would think of "copacetic," but I knew instantly that that was the wrong word. I went to "Cotopaxi "—the name of a small town in Colorado. I knew that was wrong. It was close, but it was wrong. I couldn't arrive at the name for that figure—I had to look it up: "Kokopelli." But then a few minutes later, I couldn't remember what I had just looked up. So I had to actually construct a verbal clue for myself—that the name starts with "cocoa"—in order to remember it later. Now it's easier, but it doesn't always work.

And it uses up a little of my time.

Here's a more complicated example. I'm trying to think of the name of a medication prescribed for some people suffering from depression. The word "quantum" pops up. I know that it's not the right word. I get to the word "qualude." I know that's not the one either. But I what I'm looking for is "close" to "qualude"—which is a drug—by meaning and by alphabet. So I sort of shove "qualude" aside and move to the "P's". I get the sense that it involves a "pro-" syllable. Protocol? No. Proquel? No. the "que" sound is from "qualude." It seems to need a "z" sound. Prosody? No. Close, though. Do I need a "k" too? Maybe it's not the letter, just the sound . . . Aha: Prozac!

Doing this uses up a little of my time.

That experience shows two aspects of this problem. I might have thought of the word "qualude" because it was also a drug (though it does the opposite of Prozac). But maybe I thought of that drug because it started with a "q" which is close, in the alphabet, to the "p" I was looking for. Was my brain trying to run two parallel tracks? 1) this word names something like that one and 2) this word is located down the hall from that one.

Here's another example. Someone told me about an achievement he had just accomplished. I was congratulating him for doing something I couldn't do. I said: "I was never in your . . ." and then I stopped dead. In your what? I reasoned with myself: it's like a category. It rhymes with "teal." . . . . Aha! "league." But this time, the word I wanted was not alphabetically close to the word which gave the clue. But it was phonetically close.

I have a lot more trouble spelling correctly, since I don't immediately remember how to spell a word. I had very few problems spelling before brain surgery. Now, I have to think about it. And, of course, it isn't always the case that that process of spelling is "logical." Problems with spelling might be normal for you, but it wasn't normal for me. If I ask you a question, and you give me the answer, I might forget your answer immediately, and have to ask you again. If I search for a word, and then remember it, I might forget that search itself a minute later. Sometimes, when I can't immediately think of the name of something, I can immediately think of it in a foreign language. When that happens, sometimes I can consider whether the English word I'm trying to think of is also related to Latin origins— think back from the foreign language to the root and then out from the root to English—but that takes a little while.

And my Russian seems to have come back to the surface! Maybe my neurons, avoiding the Big Scramble in my brain, paved the old road to a stash of *po-russki* nouns and suffixes. I don't mean that I am all of a sudden as good in Russian as I was long ago. I'm definitely not. But Russian words and Russian syllables pop up sometimes now. Do my neurons just open the wrong dresser drawers? I have always used nicknames for files on my computer, and the important feature is that the names have memorable cues (one of the advantages of foreign languages is that you can have more than one stack of drawers!). Some of the nicknames which simply occur to me have English roots with Russian suffixes: that would be a *fileski*. But some of them have full names in Russian. One of my storage files for writing this book is a big collection of diverse "items" all temporarily clumped together—I named it *krasnaya ploshad*: Red Square (that's the Times Square of the city of Moscow). But then I shortened the name to *krasnaya* (because I don't, at the moment, have any other files having to do with the Russian color of red with which it might be confused).

I think I am more visually oriented than I was before, and I think sometimes I have to be to remember some little things. When I work out at the gym, I have to take my heart rate to see what level I'm at. I put my fingers to my pulse and watch the digital calculator on the machine I'm on. I wait for the moment in which a pulse beat and the beginning of a measured second coincide exactly. Then I count pulses until the digital display counts 10 seconds. Sometimes I would start at "7," and sometimes "3"—whenever the pulse and the digital second begin at exactly the same moment. I never had a problem with that. Now, I do the same procedure. But if I start counting at "6" (for example), and I start to count my pulse, a few seconds later I won't remember where I started. So I won't know where the "10-second" deadline actually is. It took me a while, but I changed my approach. If I start to count at "6," I'll work at imagining the image of the number 6 while I count my pulse. That works better.

It takes me longer to express myself than before because I have to search for words. But I should put "search" in quote marks, because research shows us that the ways in which our brain produces language is much more complicated than just looking through stacks of words. I sometimes have to literally construct—not just find—words, and from several sets of different syllables. It takes me longer to write than it did before. Sometimes much longer. Most of the time the people I'm talking to don't see that as any kind of abnormality. They might have to do similar things to find the appropriate words. This process may not be new to human behavior, but it's new for me.

Other people can't actually perceive what happens in my brain, but I can perceive it. I will feel the loss, even if no one else notices that. This was one of the tragic features of my particular kind of epilepsy. Its location was in the part of my brain where I was the best—language. If it had been anywhere else—my right temporal lobe, for example—this would have been a very different experience. If you are in this position, you have to consider what the trade-off will be.

So: I've recovered from the physical trauma of the surgery. That is, my body has. But my brain hasn't "recovered," it has just "regrouped." My view of all of this: you can't win. Wait, let me start over: I can't win. I can maybe break even.

As I write this book, I have dealt with, again and again, the question of how to talk about the problems of depression with the disorder, the diagnosis, the drugs, the effects . . . . Depression is a constant companion. I would start to give some details, but then I would defer talking about the depression itself to just continue to give the story. I would write notes to myself in my own text saying—*Depression. Where to put this?*

Then I would try to decide how and where to talk about the bigger issues of the effects of the drugs. I would give some details when I wrote about starting this or that drug, or with discussions about major issues, such as my constantly low white blood cell count. But then I would think about where to put the information on the depressant effects of the medications. I would start into a description, and then I would think to myself that that would be too distracting from the main story, so I would scribble an editorial note to myself: *dep from the drugs—where?*

As I wrote my own story, I was facing the past again, and reliving how I had felt in the past, but one of my techniques for surviving all of this had been to close the door on many of the worst experiences in my life. In some cases, I would simply stop typing in the middle of a sentence, feeling the wave of despair hitting me again. In some cases I got up, walked out the door and went to do something else to try to pull away from the pain. Sometimes I would go to the gym and do a lengthy, exhausting work-out with a sense of running away from the past. Sometimes I would go to the grocery store and find myself just wandering up and down aisles, not even looking for anything. Sometimes I would drive up the coast and look out to sea and try for some kind of zen acceptance of it all.

Then I would come back and write some more story. When I hit another factor having to do with the depression itself—not just as a response to all the other factors—I would write that little note to myself: dep. where? Then I would sit and say to myself: this isn't really relevant here—I'll stick it in another chapter. Or I would say to myself: I don't want to stick all of this in here now, because the issue of depression itself will disrupt the narrative. So I'll do a separate chapter on this issue somewhere. As I was drafting various chapters, I would put a note to myself at the top of the first page: *In dep chap? Where?* I actually started a timeline on depression—not a description—with notes on "events." I kept that file on a back burner, and I kept writing the basic narrative. I would put in some of the bigger issues, and try to talk about them in the course of my narrative. And I would say, okay, while I'm talking about the bigger issues themselves I can mention that it is depressing to think about them. I would hit a certain point in the story and say: aha! I should put the issue of job insurance here! And then: aha! Here's where I'll put in this official stuff from my medical records. Aha! I'll put in some of my friends' reactions here.

I didn't hit that aha! point with Depression. I kept writing, though. At a certain point in my narrative, I started to make some references to that description of depression that I would have already done somewhere in an earlier chapter. And then I got to the end of the story. But I hadn't done the chapter about Depression itself.

This is a very hard thing to talk about. I knew that it would be. I knew that I was trying to solve the intellectual problem about where to put and how to describe those details, but I knew I was also trying to push away the frightening task of talking about it. I felt that I ought to talk about it, but I didn't want to talk about it.

Why?

Have you ever felt serious, major depression?

Of course you will very likely say "yes." I don't know anybody who has never felt depressed. But have you felt it for longer than a week? Have you felt it for longer than a month? A year? Three years? Seven and a half?

I sit here trying to write this without giving the impression that I think that it's some kind of contest. That I'm telling you that *you* think you were depressed, but you've got no idea what depression really is. That I am so egotistical that I simply assume no one else could ever possibly know how I feel. I know better than that. It's hard to judge what other people have felt in their lives. It's sometimes hard to judge what people are feeling standing right there looking at you.

I have had lots of moments of depression in my pre-diagnosis life, and they probably have a multitude of causes and aspects and effects. They are not the topic here.

This diagnosis moved that experience—depression—to entirely new levels. I had never felt before the way I have felt since.

I have tried for a little intellectual distraction from my depression by . . . .

Now, I stopped dead here while I was writing this. I got up to go for a glass of water. I briefly wondered if I should go get the mail. I looked to see if I have any more nectarines. And then I said to myself: you are chickening out. Strap yourself back down and write this thing!

. . . considering what we know about it. We know that it is certainly a common problem for people in my medical condition—left temporal lobe epilepsy. We know, also, that a number of the medications either cause it or exacerbate it. You may recall that depression was the hallmark of one of the meds I was on for a long time: Mysoline© (generic name: primadone). It is closely associated with most of the other meds I have been on, especially the one which seemed to be the most successful at suppressing seizures, Mesantoin©. Once again, Dr. D-E was the first to warn me that it is extremely difficult to distinguish chemical depression on the meds from personal, psychological depression for the seizures and the diagnosis. But it is sometimes the case that you'll be taken off a seizure medication if your depression while on it is severe. It's probably true that the strongest weapon against depression an epileptic can get is the sense of personal support. And yet . . .

My parents never wavered, neither did my closest friends (with the one big exception). I knew all along that any of them would listen to me talk about it and try to do the very best they could to give me comfort. But sometimes that "comfort" strongly resembled "correction" of how I felt by telling me how I should feel. (I'm sure I have done that in my life as well.) But I know that my response to that now might be one of the aspects of depression itself. It might also be considered one of the aspects of my kind of epilepsy.

So let me try for the intellectual analysis again. If part of your depression is the social consequences of the disorder and the diagnosis, then you won't be able to get rid of that problem. Some environments may be much better than others, but it's out there. If you get enough support and comfort from your friends and family, then maybe you can defend against that, or manage to not let it bother you. Bravo. And when I say "enough support," I am not in any way measuring the amount of support from other people. The measure is how you feel about it.

If you can actually feel some anger at the public response, then maybe the anger will supplant the depression. That might be good. It might be a weapon in the battle to change the way the public thinks about this disorder, because it highlights the effects of public response on you. But it might be considered—it is considered by some doctors—one of the hallmark psychological features of some kinds of epilepsy. And if people respond to your anger as though it were just a biochemical outburst, they may forgive you, but they probably won't listen to you. That will piss you off sometimes. Sometimes, though, they will forgive but still listen.

If part of your depression has to do with the nature of the treatment, you can do your best—that is, your neurologist can do his or her best—to alter the amounts of or the combinations of the medicine. But, you may be facing that problem as well, as I did.

If part of your depression has to do with the forceful and then reactive reorganization of your life, all you can do is try to keep as much control as possible, and try to "see the bright side"—or try to invent a bright side. In my opinion—but I'm depressed by all of this—there is no bright side. Not for me. You get to decide your own case. The question is coping with both the consequences and the depression.

And now let me try to get more personal.

People will tell you that it's good for you to express it, to let it out. But when you get to the point where you don't think that expressing it will make it better—on the contrary, it will make you even more depressed to think about it—you end up wanting to suppress the fact that you are depressed. Some people will tell you—and you might agree—that not talking about it makes it worse. But does talking about it make it feel better? Sometimes I would try to talk about it. Sometimes my friends would tell me that things weren't that bad. Sometimes I would sit there knowing that some part of me wanted to say, *"how the hell could you possibly know whether this is that bad?"* But the other part of me knew that their intent was comfort, and so I would suppress my depressing response to a depressing experience. It would make me feel more alone, but not because they had not tried to reach me.

Sometimes you want to close the door on being depressed, so that you can turn your back and carry on with life. You don't want to open that door and have to stand there and take it while "carrying on." You have the gnawing sense that you aren't going to actually feel better, but you might make it through a day.

For me, sitting here writing this book requires that I strap myself in. I have to look at it and think about it and explain it.

You know that maybe you are getting more depressed by thinking about your depression. Psychologists may tell you: you need to refocus. On a good day, you might be a little pissed off by that. On a really good day, you might be able to distract yourself from the sense of despair by staying angry. I have done that. On a bad day, though, you will just sit there and feel more despair that it will ever change. I have been there. I've also been to the edge of the galaxy: I have just sat there and felt nothing at all.

Now look at that. I started trying to talk about me, but I seem to be talking about "you." Let me try to correct that.

On a good day—better, in some sense, than a day of despair—I might be pissed off. Looking back, I know that I was angry about almost everything having to do with that first in-patient EEG. I think it was part of my defense against the futility of it all. But it was also related to the known side effects of the medication I was on—Mysoline©. So I'm not telling you that you will feel that way. Maybe you will feel better seeing a psychologist.

I don't want to talk about depression. I don't want to feel it, either, but talking about it doesn't help. It doesn't help me. It makes me talk about how I feel, and that makes me—literally—make up some stories about How I Feel. To give some reasons and to identify some causes. To *blame* something. But maybe there is no blame. Maybe some substantial part of depression is just the biochemical nature of my brain. Maybe trying to blame something or someone is an example of—on a good day—personal defense, or—on a bad day—psychological paranoia.

I have faced suicide. I have thought about it. Often. According to my textbook, people with left temporal lobe epilepsy have a higher rate of suicidal feelings—and of actual suicide. I know that. People who had the kind of brain surgery I had have an even higher rate of suicidal feelings. I know that, too. I have reasoned with myself about it. I have considered all of the stuff that was happening to me, not just the seizures themselves, and considered whether there was any way to recover from all of that. I have stood on ocean beaches and on 14,000 peaks facing the situation: *here are the facts—do you want to carry on?*

I have had some moments—not many—when I felt the need to say that to somebody else, and to have another human being hold me close so that I did not feel so alone. I sometimes need that simple thing: physical touch.

I have had a few moments where I was very, very close to sailing away. I haven't talked to anybody about that. Why? Because I know what they will say. I know that they will try for comfort, for help. But I stand there, looking out to sea, thinking: there is nothing that anybody else can do to help this. There's no fault here. There's no blame here. We all want to argue that there are causes and reasons for suicide, and I won't argue with that. I will be told to "look at the bright side," and I will have to choose a response to that. But I stand now, most of the time, at the point where I have no response to give. For I don't want to argue about this. There's no point in arguing about this. And I know that that person will start to feel anxiety that something bad might happen, and fear that there is something he or she should do about it. My deep depression will cause deep anxiety—maybe panic—in others. I don't want to do that.

There seem to be some biochemical realities about depression, too. The effects of drugs are proof of that. I can literally "testify" to the fact that getting off that major-league depressant—Mysoline©—changed me radically. It changed my depression—and my anger—even while I was sitting there in the hospital, sleep-deprived and strapped in for that first in-patient EEG. I had come back to the possibilities of pre-drug life. But, then they put me on the next set of drugs—an even more toxic downer—and back down I went, to new variations of the depressing side effects. There is some scientific research on the chemical nature of emotional depression, and so some drugs are for treatment of depression itself. That has been presented to me, but all I can do is stand there and think about taking another handful of drugs. I find that depressing. But maybe another handful of drugs would make me feel better—biochemically feel differently than I do now. But would it solve any of this network of huge, life-altering factors? No. They will remain. So what exactly will it change?

More *me*. Seizures changed the way my brain works. The diagnosis changed the way my life was going and would go, medications changed the way I literally biologically felt 24 hours a day. The way I felt changed my intentions and my abilities to live up to them. The realities of my life forced me to decide about surgery. The surgery changed—again, like the seizures themselves—how my brain worked and would ever again work. Brain surgery like mine produces documented changes in the emotions and behavior—the very personality—of patients. There's not a hell of a lot of the original, pre-diagnosis me left.

I go back and forth sometimes. I think: okay. There's not much of the original me left. What are you still gripped onto? Take some more drugs—why not? It will be another *investigation*. It will be the sardonic paradox to the fact that you never experimentally tried drugs for fun. And then I think: it will be another metamorphosis of the mutant me. I feel nostalgia for the drug-free me. But is there some kind of actual logic, now, for the way I feel about more drugs? Maybe I just feel nostalgia in some biochemical way. Should I go get a bottle of prescription Feelgoodzapam©?

And I can't blame everything on drugs. I spend time thinking about that, too. I chastise myself: that would be a chickening-out of responsibility for what I do and why. I spend some time wondering how we—the Big We—can ever truly distinguish between the ethical and the biochemical causes of why we do what we do. And I wonder if the biochemical ability to see the dark side—to feel the dark side—is part of our sense of individuality itself. It's part of mine. If we can make everybody chemically happy, then what would civilization become? A biochemical toga party?

I don't want to do that. Some people do—some people feel that drug-happy would be the best possible way they might be able to feel. And I know that the fact that I don't want to do it is considered evidence that I somehow want to stay depressed. It prompts in me the urge to say: *okay, you try this—my last eight years—and then we'll talk*. We'll see if you want to talk. Here's the scientific pragmatic locution, which, for me, is relevant to my epileptic condition: You can't win, you can't break even, and you can't get out of the game. It's all a question of how *you* play. It's all a question of how you play. Now, here's the main point: can *you* break even? Can you feel like your treatment breaks even? I don't know. I lack confidence here. I certainly don't know whether you can do it—that's not my call. But part of my experience with all of this is an increased sensitivity to what other people in this situation—in this condition or in others like it—have to personally deal with, every day. Part of the reason I am writing this book is to say to others: I know how you might feel. I'm not telling you that you should just be happy.

And then people tell me that I should join a group of people who suffer from depression, so that I can talk about this and learn how other people have dealt with it. My father has felt that way all along the way. But my mother never said that to me. I would bet that she never felt that way, and understood from the start why I didn't feel that way. I will always remember many things about my mother, but one of the strongest and deepest will be that day on Waunita Pass.

I know that I'm not alone. I know a few other people who have dealt with the same level—if not kind—of horrendous, life-altering and frightening medical problems as have I. We have talked a little about it. We know that we can talk about it. But depression isn't the reason that we like each other, and it isn't the main content of what we say to each other. That fact is the heart and soul of its comfort to me.

If the intention of another is to give support and kindness, I have respect for that, even when the conversation annoys me, or provokes a self-defense mechanism in me.

But if the intention of another is to tell me why I feel this way, and that I should change the way I feel, and how I should change it, I begin to feel disdain. If I'm sitting in a psychiatrist's office, I may be told—I have been told—that that is my defense against change. I know that it's an emotional response on my part, but I feel it anyway. That can be a kind of Mexican Stand-off—at $200 an hour.

And I sit at an appointment like that thinking about the multiplex mess of my answer to questions about Why I Feel This Way. My answers to those questions involve—for me—a long and constant series of events and circumstances—some of which you have now read about. My answers are complicated, loquacious, and detailed. Highly complicated, loquacious, detailed answers to questions—and arguments about answers—are often considered "evidence" of the psychological and biochemical effects of left temporal lobe epilepsy. I know that. And my resistance against that diagnosis and treatment—the psychological one—is considered a symptom of the emotional nature (the "affect") of patients with my kind of epilepsy. I know that. But we don't need evidence that I have left temporal lobe epilepsy. And I don't need an explanation as to why I somehow feel this way. Is my sense of personal ethics just a symptom of epileptic "affect" disorder?

So what's the point? I sit in an appointment like that, reluctant—sometimes close to unable—to talk at all. I sit there and think: do I need some more argument here? do we need some more blather here, in which I explain all the aspects of my life that make me depressed?

Are there drugs—"medications"—for blather? Can we do a blather-ectomy?

Is my disdain for this experience a defense against treatment? Can we do a disdain-ectomy?

Is my defense against treatment itself a symptom of this disorder? Can this treatment do a symptom-ectomy?

Will removing the symptoms cure the disorder?

No, it won't. And that's not an emotional response. There is no known cure.

There is a consideration whether seizures are, indeed, epileptic, or are considered "non-epileptic" ones. If mine are "non-epileptic," then maybe they can be "cured"—I don't know anything about that. I don't think my seizures were non-epileptic. I don't think that my doctors think they are. Am I making up new ones? I don't think so. Does a psychiatrist think I might be doing that? I don't know. What would a psychiatrist say to me about that? "Let's try to understand why you are making them up, and encourage you to stop it"? I don't know.

Here's my opinion, if it's worth anything to you: if you feel the need to get prescriptions to make you chemically feel better, then do it—that is, if your doctors support it. If you feel the need to have a psychologist or a psychiatrist try to make you feel better, then do it. Maybe it will work—I'm not telling you that it won't.

But get out your piggy-bank. And find out in advance how much treatment will be covered by your insurance. My tally—what I personally paid—on "psychological" procedures is over $1000.

Me? I feel that there is no need to pay for feeling this way. That's a depressing experience. I don't want to do that one. This kind of depression is—textbooks tell us—directly connected with this kind of epilepsy. But this kind of epilepsy is, for me, directly connected with lots of real pain and real loss in my life. Both Dr. D-E and Dr. K$_2$ have known that all along. And that isn't over. The past will remain the same. I paid the price I paid.

And, of course, for me, there is another way—always available—to get rid of depression . . . .

So. Back to suicide. Have I thought about it? Yes. Do I want to talk about it? No. Why? Because I will be told that I shouldn't feel that way. That I am not looking at the bright side. That I should go right down the stairs to stand in line at the pharmacy. Do I have any actual advice about this? No.

If you feel the need, then talk. If your friends are anything like mine, they will try to understand. But even if your friends and your family don't understand, they will try to give you comfort and encouragement. And if they know about your emotional states, they will watch for signs. And then you can all cope with the Cry Wolf scenario. Am I making fun of this situation, or of anybody who is in it? No. I'm telling you how I feel about the ethics of it all—for me.

But is there any defensible reason for suicide? Let me tell you, that's a big, deep, historical, ethical and biochemical question. I could give big, deep, historical and ethical answers. (They will probably be interpreted as a classic symptom of left temporal lobe epilepsy.) But I'm not arguing about this. And I'm not crying out for help. Help is right there—I know it. I know the people who would give it without question. But I also know some who understand.

And I'm still here.

13 The First Draft...

Thirteen is a lucky number

The first draft of the last chapter started out like this:

> My last—no, I shouldn't say that word—my "most recent" appointment with Dr. D-E was on November 15, 1999. He was sensitive to my current life problems, but pleased that I had had no seizures since the surgery a year before—the surgery was "successful." I exhibited a few verbal problems, though. He did that typical test: showed me five little flash cards of pictures and asked me to remember them, and then told me five words and asked me to remember them. Before the surgery, I could almost always do all five in both categories very easily. But this time I could remember only three images myself. He gave me a clue, and I got number four. But I couldn't get number five. And I could remember only two out of the five words. He told me that I noticed that more than other people because I was so verbal.
>
> He agreed that I could start down on my medications, very slowly, so that I wouldn't have reactions to withdrawal. I'll see him again in six months, and if I have had no reactions to the reduction

of the drugs, he'll consider reducing the dosage even more. However, as he had told me before the surgery, it wasn't a guarantee that I could stop the medications altogether. But the goal was to start to take me off all of the medication, so that I could return to that state I had been over seven years ago—free of the medications—but also live without seizures. I sat there and tried to remember how I felt then. I'm not sure that I can actually remember that.

He ended up talking about the fact that if all went well, I wouldn't have to come back and see him in the future. I felt the paradox of that: it would be the symbol of successful treatment, but it would also be the loss of one relationship—a professional but a long-standing one, fully honest about the disorder and the treatment and the consequences. I knew that it would be a good sign, and I knew that therapists would tell me that it would be a good transition to the next part of my life. I didn't argue with that, but I knew that my doctors knew more—in a professional and in a personal sense—about this part of my life than anyone else ever would. I knew that it would be the paradoxical case: a loss of them means a gain of ground. But to me, that is one of the many complicated aspects of a problem like this: my personal response to what is—and what, in fact, should be—a non-personal relationship. I imagine that that happens for a lot of patients with any kind of complicated problems.

I went home, trying to remember what "looking forward" to the future was. I went home thinking about the fact that, in a certain sense, I had returned to my life before the onset of seizures, but in another sense, there was no going back to that life. "You can never go home again"—that's a quotation from a very sensitive American author, Thomas Wolfe. I have talked about the fact that if my diagnosis had been made—and I had started my medications—before I had done my Ph.D. exams, I don't think I would have passed them. And if I had gotten a university teaching and research job while on those medications, I wouldn't have been able to do what is necessary to succeed at that. If I had had my brain surgery before those exams or after I got a job like that, I wouldn't have made it then, either. So, truth to tell, I'm glad I did not choose to see a specialist, and get that diagnosis, before I had finished my degree, and before I got that job. But I sit here and wonder whether anybody should think of that as advice.

The razor's edge remains: the longer you wait to get the diagnosis and the treatment, the more likely you are to suffer brain damage from the seizures, or to have the seizures get worse. The sooner you get that diagnosis, the longer you will have to cope with the consequences and the side effects. I'm not trying to tell anybody how to cope with this.

So: am I glad that I don't have seizures anymore? Yes. Do I feel "cured"? No. Do I feel like I have gained some ground? Yes. Did I lose some ground? Yes.

Is the war over? No. I feel like I struggled for many years—many of the most important years of my adult life. My seizures—the "cause" of my disorder—are gone now. But many of the "side effects" of this disorder—the personal and professional and life-controlling ones—are irreversible. The future may be different, but the past remains the same. I feel like—I know—that I made a deal and I paid the price—part of my brain itself is gone. I can tell the difference between myself—my language abilities—before the surgery and after the surgery, whether other people perceive it or not. I will remember all my life that night before I went in for the surgery. I laid in bed, thinking in as many languages as I knew, about everything about language that I knew, listing the quotations I knew by heart. I was witnessing

> my own linguistic abilities. I was trying to forge a memory of that life, hoping that the memory of it would survive the surgery, even if—especially if—my ability to perform it did not.
>
> Psychologists would tell me—some have—that that feeling is an emotional fear to let go of the past, to face the future, and to take control again. They would say that bracing yourself for more anticipated pain is self-defeating. I know—or at least I think I might know—why they think that way. But I wonder if they, personally, have any bloody idea what this life is really like. My impulse, of course, is to say that studying something isn't the same as knowing what it actually is. But maybe they do personally know. I will say again something that my mother taught me: you can't judge the inner life of other people. I try to keep that in mind.
>
> I try to move on. I need to say that the changes in my life because of this disorder and its treatment will always remain. But I need to finish this—this account—and look towards the future.

So, I finished that chapter. And then I spent some time editing what I had written planning how to try to publish this book. My dad and I were trying to decide if the last chapter should actually be a kind of summary of the major issues and the Bigger Picture so that you could decide how much of this story might affect you or someone you care about. We spent some time considering that tactic.

And then something happened.

From my diary:

> 12/5/99. 5:02 woke up—foreboding sense that it would happen. I felt that strange feeling coming on—epigastric wave from lower belly—racing heart rate,

fear. Wave moved through me. I started to swallow.
I knew—I knew—what was happening. It's back.

A seizure.

I laid there in the dark for a while, stunned. I wasn't exactly shocked. I think I was trying for numb again, but I couldn't suppress that *gripping* feeling of dread.

The Revised Draft of the Last Chapter

This time around I will give you the radically abbreviated story. From my notes:

12/20/99	4:08—one full but mild. Back up to 400mg // 15 days later
1/7/00	5:00—very mild aura alone // 10 days after med change; 18 days after 12/20/99 seizure
1/28/00	5:02—one full but mild // at 21 days

I spent some time walking along the beach again, looking out to sea and coming to grips with the fact that surgery had not succeeded in stopping the seizures. They were truly back in town. It ain't over.

It will never be over.

I stalled at finishing this book.

I sat there and thought about *Numb: the Next Generation*. My emotional responses to the surgery, and to the fact—up until that last December—that I hadn't had any seizures—had stayed messy and uneasy. I never felt elation that it was all over. I never felt that it was all over. As I said in the first draft, ending your seizures doesn't change your history. And, as I said, some psychological interpretations would be that you were afraid of changing your life. I think I might have been nervous about taking the bait—letting myself think that everything was now better. Because—it was clear—not everything was better. Lots of grim facts were still as grim as they ever were. So, emotionally, I hadn't loosened my belt. I think I had moved a lot of emotional items around. I think I stuffed my fear under some intellectual shrubbery. So what I mostly felt—again—was a case of dull ache.

2/8/00	5:14—one mild // at 11 days
2/29/00	4:00—one full but mild // at 21 days

I sat and looked out to sea sometimes, and thought about the astonishing fact that I didn't seem to feel a sense of horrendous tragedy. I didn't seem to feel angry at the failure of the surgery. I didn't seem to feel much at all. Just some gut-level wavering dread. I wondered if I would ever be able to feel very much again.

3/15/00	5:45—"// at 15 days
4/12/00	3:57—"// at 28 days

I knew I needed to end this book. Or, technically, I need to stop writing this book. Either that, or keep on writing and never publish it. Or try for something really weird: publish a cliff-hanging Volume One now and then write "the sequel." But let me assure you, I wasn't sitting there thinking that everybody would be eager to get serial installments of my ongoing life story. What I did was to go back to the earlier chapters and "edit" some more, saying to myself: *maybe I'll get some inspiration as to how to finish this.*

I would lay awake at night and think: *I'll need to do an addendum to the depression chapter.*

Every now and then I would wake up at about 5 am, feel the epigastric wave, and do it all again. My seizures had almost always produced in me—biologically produced—the feeling of *déjà vu*. But now I would lie there having a truly, madly, deeply complicated biological and intellectual experience of *déjà vu* all over again.

On April 8, 2000 I went back to my follow-up appointment with Dr. D-E, and told him the awful truth. He was sympathetic, but he didn't seem exactly surprised. I sat there wondering if I was giving the impression that I psychologically wanted to return to the position of a person with epilepsy needing complicated medical treatment, or, even worse, that I was making this up. I've read about that. But I had been clearly a patient with "intractable" seizures, and it was now clear—to me—that even brain surgery couldn't defeat mine. He said we might be able to suppress the "embers" of former, pre-surgery seizure locations, and increased my medications. I started to take more medication than I had taken *before* the surgery. (Lamictal© 100mg and 200mg: $222.69 per month [averaging $2.40 per pill], plus Diazepam [at $2.16 per pill].)

I went home that afternoon and went to bed with an eerie sense of gnawing depression. I woke up early the next morning:

5/9/00   4:58—one partial but mild // at 27 days

I hadn't told many people—in fact I hadn't chosen to tell anybody. But, as before, I was virtually unable to tell the "Lie Direct"—if I was directly asked whether I had had any seizures, I would tell the truth. I tried not to break down when I said it— just another variation of the Stay Numb Fugue—but I failed one time, with my good friend, R. She did all she could to comfort me. One day the inevitable happened. My dad said to me, "You haven't had any seizures for over a year, right?" I paused. I gritted my teeth and told him the truth. He fell silent. Stunned. Again. *God.* What was there to say?

My dad and my nephew and I went to visit some friends in Japan. Planning for that trip gave me a reason why I wasn't finishing this book. My dad and I held each other's hands and remembered those times, long ago, when we had visited Japan with my mother. I spent some time remembering how easily I had learned some

Japanese, but how little of it I remembered. I remembered some fragments, though. They had stayed with me all those years, stuffed in a back drawer (two drawers down from the Russian). I had trouble, though, remembering Japanese words I was working on "now." I didn't get them into a drawer. I threw them out the window. Sometimes, when I remembered an expression from the past, the powerful image of my mother would come to me, and make me cry. Sometimes, when we visited a place we had never seen before, I would feel her presence there, and be moved, and cry.

We visited Hiroshima and I spent a lot of time thinking about the awesome human experiences there. Hiroshima moved me to suppress my own mess and contemplate some larger perspectives on bottomless human suffering.

We came home through Hawaii. I hiked out to the ocean, on the rough black waves of a recent, cooled lava flow, and stood there, in that desert, thinking about things again.

> 6/12/00   5:23—one partial but mild (in Hilo, Hawaii) // 34 days

I didn't tell my dad or my nephew.

I flew home from Hawaii, unpacked and said, *Okay Amy. What's it gonna be?*

I drafted an "Epigraph" for this book, which was that citation from my diary of that first post-op seizure. And then I considered that that might be a nice "literary" end, but it would be the right thing to do to say, briefly, what the next episode of this saga will inevitably be—for me. So I started to redo this last chapter.

> 6/27/00   5:32—one partial but mild // 15 days

In July I got the chance to go back to Colorado for a short vacation. I slid down into one of the worst waffles of my life, floundering back and forth between making myself stay home to finish this book and going back to my beloved Colorado to hike some more 14ers for my mother. I flipped a metaphorical quarter and headed up north. I hiked some more. I *stalled* some more. I thought about the past and the future. I cried for my mother. I hugged myself.

> 7/19/00   5:27—**First set of 2**—both mild. Does this mean I'll start to have more and more and more?

I came back home. I went for a check-up with Dr. K$_2$—my personal doctor—and blathered some more. Halfway into my blather, she asked me a simple, straightforward question about how I felt, and for once a simple answer popped out: *angst*. A feeling of dread. And then I sat there, remembering a book I had read: anxiety is one of the two main psychotic symptoms of my kind of epilepsy. Depression is the other one. But, on the other hand, there is a reason why I have both of those feelings . . . . Welcome back to the *Other Hand Bar and Grill*.

We scheduled another appointment in a month to try to get a handle on my overall condition. I think she's starting to get a handle on the overall me.

I went to an 18-month follow-up with my surgeon, and told him the story. Not this story! The very short, abbreviated version of the seizures themselves. We talked a little bit about what it would now be wise to do. He wanted careful descriptions—again—to consider where, exactly, they might be happening. We talked a little bit about this book—he was interested in the idea of my writing an account like this. We talked about considering doing another in-patient EEG in order to map exactly where these seizures are originating. A main factor, now, is whether my insurance would support any further EEGs.

I talked about being willing, now, to be an "experimental rat"—to do any kind of research needed to get more information on this kind of problem—not just my problem. But I sat there wondering if I was giving him the impression that I psychologically wanted to return to the position of a person with epilepsy needing complicated medical treatment. That I wanted to go get strapped in and wired up. Do I truly think that he was feeling that way? If I thought he thought I was making this up, would that be interpreted as paranoia in me? I don't know.

I remain uneasy. I don't know how to keep from giving that impression. It is one of the supreme paradoxes for me now: is the fact that I wonder if I seem paranoid itself a sign of paranoia?

What I intellectually wanted (and still want) to do was provide data. What I emotionally wanted (and still want) to do was to go camp out, not in the Deep Suffering from Epilepsy Camp, but in the Detached Intellectual Neutral Zone. Again.

I went to see Dr. D-E again and gave him the list of post-op seizures. I sat there while he read that, and then he looked through my huge, heavy file of blood tests and reports and PET scans and MRIs and notes and scribbles. Then he looked at me. Then he looked at his notes. Then he looked at me.

And then he asked me to *describe* the seizures I was now having . . . .

I did. I was trying for detachment. Again. He knew that. He could see that.

We talked about the possibility of some new drugs—only just approved—he could start me on to suppress the seizures. He went to get a sample packet to give me. That way I could try out a new medication before I went to the pharmacy to start to pay for the years of biochemical research which produced it. He warned me about the known but rare dangerous side-effect of this drug: kidney stones. (Ah! Something new and different!) We talked about the common side-effects of this drug: dizziness, sore throat, physical weakness, mental slowing, fatigue.

Fatigue.

He filled out the blood-test form and said: come back in 10 days.

Déjà-voodoo seizing fandango all over again . . . .

I will grit my teeth some more. I will do the Numbdango.

Okay. I am going to stop the story, *right here*.

The Moral of the Story

Some people tell me that they expect—or want—a happy ending here. Can I give one? I don't think so. Can I say to you that I am a stronger person for all of this? I don't think so. Can I tell you that there is a silver linings to the storm clouds? I don't see it. Can I tell you that *any* aspect of my life is somehow better for this 10-year odyssey? I don't feel that way.

Then why tell it?

What's the *moral* of this long, complicated, never-ending story? Morals need to be short and pithy.

Here's the big one: a biological anomaly can radically change everything about your life. It might be this anomaly—epilepsy—but this is not the only one. You might end up having it. Or it might be your mother, or your brother. It might be your best friend. You can't know ahead of time. You can't prevent it. You might have very few choices because of it. That is a fact we can know ahead of time. I am evidence of that.

So: will we try to change the way we—all of us—might think about these kinds of medical problems? About the nature of their treatment? About the cost of their treatment?

Will you try to change the stigma of public knowledge, even if you don't have this disorder? Will we consider what other kinds of stigma there are for other disorders—and consider that maybe we should try hard at resisting that kind of ignorant response?

And when I say "we," I mean all of us. I include those of us who have the disorders—for we are also part of the problem. Our fear of what others think is also part of the problem. Let's not forget that. Let's not ignore that.

While writing this book, I started to get interested in research at UCLA in the disciplines of Neuroscience and Neurobiology. I started to try to get that kind of scientific handle on my own epileptic brain. And I began to comprehend the enormous system of basic scientific and medical research, extensive treatment, and million-dollar technologies necessary for a case like mine, or, indeed, for any kind of complicated brain disorders.

Will we support the kind of medical research which develops treatments—*especially* medications—for this disorder and other disorders like it? Indeed, basic research on pharmaceuticals has been invaluable for epilepsy medications—and several of those drugs have been discovered to be, in addition, very effective as treatment of other medical problems, including intractable pain. That kind of research is complicated and can be what most people would consider "outrageously" expensive. It sometimes takes years for useful results, but useful—sometimes life-saving—results will show up. And we won't know in advance who will need them. We have to face that problem head on: we want those scientists and those doctors to keep doing that kind of medical research so that they will have the best possible treatment for us, but we don't want to pay the price. What's the solution?

And here is, in a sense, the Big Kicker: will we all try to change the present policies, and consequently the life-altering effects, of private medical insurance? Private medical insurance in the United States is in direct connection with all of the various aspects of employment. It is certainly true that the extremely high costs of some medications—and some diagnostic tools—have to do with the private companies who produced them. That is because private companies need to recoup the high cost of developing them. And, of course, they want to "recoup" those costs in order to produce a profit for the company at large.

Will we consider whether to do this kind of research and development—somehow—as a national system? This is in no way a simple problem. Will we consider how to reorganize the financial structure and operation of medical efforts so that you—or your loved ones—won't have to make these kinds of life-altering decisions based *solely* on the dollar amount on the bottom line of the bill?

@ @ @ @ @

So I stand here again, on my metaphorical beach, trying to decide what is the best way to end this book (for the "story," of course, goes on and on and on). I've been standing here a long time—it feels like years now. It has been a painfully difficult decision. In a way, I would like to give you a personal "happy ending," because I know that people like happy endings. I know that we all hope for happy endings. But I wanted to try to tell my true story, because I believe that the value of an account like this—if there is any value—is to try for the truth. And if you want reality—not just how you feel—to get any better for you, or for your loved ones, some of us have to face its dark side.

But I'm not standing here telling you that your life will be like mine, either. A complicated and life-altering medical history doesn't always turn out this way. Your doctor will tell you—and I am evidence of the fact—that depression itself can pull you under. Don't let mine pull you under. If you can find a way to stay afloat and stay above water, use it.

As for me, I carry on, dealing the best I can with all of the consequences known and yet to come.

And I carry with me the image of the lupines on Waunita pass.

Resources

Here is a listing of resources I have used during the writing of this book. Mainly they provided me with technical information about the disorder, diagnosis and treatment.

Books

There are two books which are outstanding in their usefulness to the lay person in helping to better understand epilepsy, its diagnosis, and its treatment. Both are written by physicians who are obviously well experienced as clinicians with patients. Both are well written and easy to read. In both, the author makes every attempt, whenever possible, to avoid highly technical vocabulary. Dr. Devinsky also includes an excellent glossary of terms. Dr. Wilner uses the question-answer format.

I recommend them both.

A Guide To Understanding and Living with Epilepsy. 1994. Authored by Orrin Devinsky. F. A. Davis Co., Philadelphia.

Epilepsy: 199 Answers. 1996. Authored by Andrew N. Wilner. Demos Vermande, New York.

There is a very recent book with more information on "partial" disorders—as distinct from *gran mal* seizures.

> *Partial Seizure Disorders. Help for Patients and Families.* 2001. Authored by Mitzi Waltz. Patient-Centered Guides. A division of O'Reilly & Associates, Inc.

And there is also a new general review of aspects of epilepsy and treatment options.

> *Epilepsy and Seizures. Everything You Need to Know.* 2001. Authored by Dr. Donald Weaver. A Firefly Book.

Next is the book that appears to be the current leader in describing the many aspects of epilepsy. This is the reference I have used—and referred to—whenever I talk about technical issues either in my personal account or in my references to epilepsy in general. Without any doubt, this is the major publication now available. As the title indicates, the coverage of the disorder is indeed comprehensive. It is a massive work, with some 3000 pages—in three volumes—written by nearly 400 authors. For the most part, the material is highly technical and not easily read by a lay person. But there is a wealth of information here for the reader able to follow the discussions.

I recommend it highly.

> *Epilepsy: A Comprehensive Textbook.* 1997. Edited by Jerome Engel, Jr., and Timothy A. Pedley. Lippincott-Raven, Philadelphia. In three volumes. A CD-Rom version with updated material, published in 1999, is also available

Next are two books written specifically for physicians and others who attend patients with epilepsy. Both are relatively easy to read, but some medical background is very useful.

> *Handbook of Epilepsy Treatment.* 2000. Authored by S. D. Shorvon. Blackwell, Oxford, Madden MA.
>
> *The Comprehensive Evaluation and Treatment of Epilepsy: A Practical Guide.* 1997. Edited by Steven C. Schachter and David L. Schomer. Academic Press, San Diego.

There is also a kind of dictionary of medications that might be useful. It is a general source which includes information on many of the medications used for epilepsy.

> *Johns Hopkins Complete Home Encyclopedia of Drugs.* 1998. The medical editor is Simeon Margolis (M.D. and Ph.D). Rebus, New York.

Dr. Steven C. Schachter and several colleagues have written a series of books on various kinds of cases of epilepsy written for a more general audience. Many of them have a series title of *Brainstorms*.... They are published by Lippincott-Raven.

The anesthesiologist for my surgery, Dr. Van de Wiele, invited me to submit a brief account of my own experiences in the surgery for a publication on this particular kind of neurosurgery. It is:

> "My Experience of the Asleep-Awake-Asleep Procedure," *UCLA Department of Anesthesiology News,* Winter 2001, UCLA School of Medicine, p. 3.

Scientific and professional journals

I spent some time at the Biomedical Research Library at UCLA looking up information on epilepsy and my medications.

That library also gave me access to medical journals. Two are devoted entirely to epilepsy and, as expected, contain articles that are for the most part highly technical. However, an occasional article is informative about general aspects of the disorder. Examples are reports of recent studies about the prevalence of epilepsy.

Epilepsia is the official journal of the International League Against Epilepsy. Published in it are original articles on all clinical and experimental aspects of epilepsy.

Epilepsy Research provides for the rapid publication of high-quality articles in both experimental and clinical epileptology, where the principal emphasis of the research is concerned with brain mechanisms in epilepsy.

I also found some informative articles in *Neurology,* the official journal of the American Academy of Neurology; *Neurosurgery,* the official journal of the Congress of Neurological Surgeons; *Neurosurgery Clinics Of North America;* the well known *New England Journal of Medicine; Pharmacotherapy;* and *Neuroscience.*

The Epilepsy Foundation of America

The EFA and its local affiliates around the country support programs of information, referral, public and professional education, employment assistance, advocacy, and self help. Write to the Foundation at 4351 Garden City Drive, Landover MD 20786, or call 800/ 213-5821. You can also visit their website at www.efa.org.

The National Institute of Neurological Diseases and Stroke (NINDS)

NINDS is one of the National Institutes of Health (NIH), with the purpose of providing support for research about diseases that are neurologic, including epilepsy. Information about NINDS programs and activities is available, at no charge, to the public. Call 800/ 352-9424, or visit their web page at www.ninds.nih.gov.